ANIMAL PROBLEM SOLVING

Selected Readings

Edited by A. J. Riopelle

Penguin Books

Penguin Books Ltd, Harmondsworth,
Middlesex, England
Penguin Books Inc., 3300 Clipper Mill Road,
Baltimore, Md 21211, U.S.A.
Penguin Books Australia Ltd, Ringwood,
Victoria, Australia

First published by Penguin Books 1967

This selection © A. J. Riopelle, 1967
Introduction and Notes © A. J. Riopelle, 1967

Made and printed in Great Britain by
Richard Clay (The Chaucer Press), Ltd,
Bungay, Suffolk
Set in Monotype Times Roman

Contents

Introduction   9

Part One   HISTORICAL AND SYSTEMATIC BACKGROUND   13

1   H. W. Nissen (1954)
Problems of mental evolution in the primates   15

2   M. Scheerer (1963)
Problem-solving   26

3   G. J. Romanes (1888)
Animal intelligence   43

4   C. Lloyd Morgan (1909)
Introduction to comparative psychology   54

5   E. L. Thorndike (1898)
Animal intelligence; an experimental study of the associative processes in animals   62

6   W. T. Shepherd (1923)
Some observations and experiments of the intelligence of the chimpanzee and ourang   70

Part Two   DELAYED RESPONSE   75

7   O. L. Tinklepaugh (1928)
An experimental study of representative factors in monkeys   77

Part Three   TOOL USING   83

8   K. R. L. Hall (1965)
Animals that use tools   85

9   M. R. A. Chance (1960)
Kohler's chimpanzees – how did they perform?   91

10   P. H. Schiller (1952)
Innate constituents of complex responses in primates   103

11 H. G. Birch (1945)
The relation of previous experience to insightful
problem solving 116

12 K. R. L. Hall (1963)
Tool-using performances as indicators of behavioral
adaptability 137

Part Four   GESTURES 177

13 M. P. Crawford (1936)
Further study of coöperative behavior in chimpanzee 179

Part Five   LEARNING AND PROBLEM
SOLVING 181

14 I. Krechevsky (1932)
'Hypothesis' versus 'chance' in the pre-solution period
in sensory discrimination-learning 183

15 K. W. Spence (1938)
Gradual versus sudden solution of discrimination
problems by chimpanzees 198

16 H. F. Harlow (1949)
The formation of learning sets 209

17 K. J. Hayes, R. Thompson and C. Hayes (1953)
Concurrent discrimination learning in chimpanzees 227

18 M. Levine (1959)
A model of hypothesis behavior in discrimination
learning set 233

Part Six   FLEXIBILITY OF RESPONSE 253

19 G. V. Hamilton (1911)
A study of trial and error reactions in mammals 255

20 N. R. F. Maier (1931)
Reasoning and learning 287

21 J. Cole (1951)
A study of discrimination reversal learning in monkeys 297

22 H. W. Nissen (1951)
Analysis of a complex conditional reaction in chimpanzee 305

Part Seven   MATCHING   315

23   B. Weinstein (1941)
     Matching-from-sample by rhesus monkeys and by
     children   317

24   H. W. Nissen, J. S. Blum and R. A. Blum (1948)
     Analysis of matching behavior in chimpanzee   334

     Part Eight   OBSERVATIONAL LEARNING
                  AND IMITATION   351

25   C. Lloyd Morgan (1896)
     Habit and instinct   353

26   E. L. Thorndike (1898)
     Animal intelligence; an experimental study of associ-
     ative processes in animals   363

27   C. L. Darby and A. J. Riopelle (1959)
     Observational learning in the rhesus monkey   370

28   K. J. Hayes and C. Hayes (1952)
     Imitation in a home-raised chimpanzee   378

29   K. R. L. Hall (1963)
     Observational learning in monkeys and apes   390

     Further Reading   425

     Acknowledgements   427

     Author Index   429

     Subject   435

Introduction

Man has been curious about the behaviour of animals for centuries, as archaeological findings have shown. Modern interest began with Darwin, for with the spread of his theory of adaptive evolution, which postulated the affinity of man and animals, the study of the adaptive capabilities of animals accelerated immensely.

The theory of evolution raised a tempest of controversy. It would perhaps have been quite peacefully accepted, had it applied only to man's physical nature; but when it was proposed that man's emotions, his thoughts and his sensibilities were also products of evolution, and were therefore shared with lower animals, the very uniqueness of man as proclaimed by established authority was challenged.

This challenge to the dogma of special creation was accompanied by intensive collection of data on the adaptive behaviour of animals, particularly in its highest forms. Reports of remarkable and often amazing powers possessed by lower animals appeared in the scientific and popular press like a tidal wave after the storm. What the adherents of the new theory lacked in experience and trained objectivity, they made up for in enthusiasm. Furthermore, the best scientific psychology available at the time was based on the introspective method and its subject matter was the contents of consciousness. Accordingly, each person was his own model, against which the animal mind was to be judged. It is therefore not surprising that complex mental functions were readily ascribed to lower animals, and that examples of behaviour which could be interpreted as demonstrating rational action were easily found.

It seems likely that when this flood of information appeared in the scientific and popular press there was much duplication in the content of the reports, and this would add to their apparent objectivity and credibility. It is also likely that later investigators, if they were to get their findings into print, had to make them rather more dramatic than any previously published. There was thus a tendency towards exaggeration and few checks on the interpretation of the data gathered.

It was in the face of these excesses that C. Lloyd Morgan warned against the absolute acceptance of purely anecdotal reports of the astonishing feats of animals. And in the form of the now famous 'canon', he urged that the principle of parsimony be adopted in the interpretation of animal behaviour.

The intense popular interest in animal behaviour stimulated the more thoughtful to explore new objective methods. Among these the method of experiment, in which situations were contrived specifically to test the capabilities of animals, was especially important. Revolutions were going on simultaneously in all branches of biological science, with strong emphasis on comparative and experimental studies, and these developments were particularly influential. Thus the study of animal behaviour, which early became a battlefield for a philosophical and religious controversy, was later to become a part of the general stream of contemporary science. In so doing, it utilized the methods and the explanatory concepts of current science and in turn itself helped to shape the growth of that science, especially of the new science of psychology.

There followed the development of many objective behavioural measures. Scientists of the time became concerned to analyse behaviour as well as to describe it. Characteristically, the attempts at analysis were based on developments in the theory of learning and motivation. Loeb, for example, described the tropisms of lower animals, and Jennings noted the trial and error behaviour of protozoa.

One tradition approached the study of complex behaviour from the standpoint of associationism in its current modified form. The other tradition regarded complex problem solving as demonstrating the inadequacy of associationistic concepts. This simple statement fails to take into account the complexity of the concepts involved and the wide theoretical differences which existed among the variants of the two traditions; nor does it indicate the remarkable methodological advances that were resulting from the pursuit of new knowledge within the two frameworks. It does, however, give some indication of the theoretical frameworks in which the studies assembled here are embedded.

This collection of papers covers a span of three-quarters of a century; thus different articles are products of different historical stages in the development of the study of complex processes in lower animals.

Thus far we have been talking about problem solving as though it were a unitary process; but this is not so. Specific research problems vary widely, as do the experimental approaches employed. This collection aims to provide a glimpse of the diversity of approaches that have been made to a variety of experimental problems.

Since the historical trend is cumulative, and concepts were borrowed and incorporated from different problems and disciplines, these articles are interrelated, but probably no two are related in precisely the same way.

Numerous factors entered into the decision to include a particular paper in this collection. Since my purpose was to give a survey of the field, I was sometimes forced to lay aside some of the 'important' papers in favour of one which to me seemed to represent best either a technique or an idea. Some papers were excessively long and their inclusion would have given disproportionate weight to the topic they discussed. If a shorter one served our purpose equally well and allowed me to print it with the minimum amount of cutting and editing, it was chosen. Other papers, though important or relevant to our purpose, were excluded here because they were likely to be included in one of the other compilations in this series.

The selection is not meant to be representative of the orders and species of animals that have served as experimental subjects; that is the province of comparative psychology. Rather more weight than might be expected has been given to papers on primate behaviour. Primates, especially the higher primates, have the most complex behavioural repertoire and are capable of engaging in activity that is more complicated than that of nonprimate orders. Consequently, experiments with primates can often illustrate most clearly the problems at issue with a minimum of time and experimental effort.

One further reason for selecting many of these papers should be mentioned. And that is sheer enjoyment. Many of these articles I have read and re-read, and they have lost none of their interest for me. I hope that the reader too will share some of this pleasure in them.

Part One HISTORICAL AND SYSTEMATIC BACKGROUND

Students of complex animal behaviour work in diverse contexts. Some investigators, particularly those with training in classical zoological disciplines, concern themselves particularly with the role of evolution in determining the trends which culminate in the remarkable capabilities of man. For them the emphasis is on broad multiphyletic similarities and differences. Other scientists, principally those with training in the psychological or medical sciences, approach problem solving primarily from the standpoint of understanding human behaviour. For them animals serve as experimental models with which to study critical variables which apply both to the species under study and to man. Both of these groups reflect changes occurring in their own basic disciplines. Despite obvious differences in theoretical and experimental approach, interchange of ideas and data occur frequently between workers in these two camps. Representatives of the two groups often appear together in symposia, and their papers may be published in the same scientific journal.

It will be helpful for an appreciation of the later papers to look at some of the earlier approaches to the study of problem solving and to get some idea of the methods and the psychological concepts, for the two are mutually related, employed by scientists of the period. Morgan's famous canon, although still honoured today in a new and modern context, really represents a reaction to the theory and methods of his own particular period. In their turn, modern students of problem solving still depend, to some extent, upon methods and concepts outlined in the early experimental and theoretical papers.

1   H. W. Nissen

Problems of Mental Evolution in the Primates

H. W. Nissen, 'Problems of mental evolution in the primates', *Human Biology*, vol. 26 (1954), pp. 277–87.

The inclusion in this symposium of four papers dealing with behavior is a measure of the increasing importance assigned to behavioral phenomena in their relevance for the general problem of evolution. This relevance, recognized since even before Darwin, still needs to be underscored. The fact that the theory of evolution as we know it today is founded primarily on structural evidence is understandable enough, since structures leave a record whereas physiological processes and behavior for the most part do not. It might well be that if we had a record of behavior as complete as the fossil record of structures, this would yield as convincing a body of evidence for evolution as does the latter. As a matter of fact, a study of the behaviors of living species alone – together with the paleontological evidence regarding the order in which these forms appeared – provides in itself a substantial basis for postulating a process of evolution. It is true, also, that here and there behavioral criteria have been found useful in supplementing structural evidence in problems of taxonomic classification (e.g., Lorenz, 1937).

In the hierarchy of life sciences, psychology or the study of behavior occupies a rather unique position. On the one hand, it represents the most complex unit, the highest level of organization, dealt with by any of the so-called biological sciences. On the other hand, it represents the unit from which all the social sciences take their start. Among the sciences, therefore, psychology is a sort of two-way funnel into which the biological sciences converge and from which the social sciences diverge. It happens, also, that scientists – all scientists – are individuals and primates. This makes it not only natural but inevitable that we should be egocentric and anthropocentric in our interests. The essence of the individual is his behavior, including his feelings, attitudes and strivings. His bones, muscles and blood chemistry are in this respect secondary, being the conditions necessary for behavior. Psychology thus represents the most direct approach to what is of most immediate interest to man. And comparative psychology is concerned with the phylogenetic or historical basis of man's behavior.

More to the point in the present connection is this: that if we think of evolution as having a direction – this direction being a *post hoc* inference from observation and thus implying no guiding purpose – then this direction is most readily defined in terms of a trend in behavior. As we shall see, behavioral differences are especially striking within the order of primates. We of course assume that a trend in structural change – specifically change in the nervous system – underlies the behavioral trend, but as of now the former is even less clearly defined than is the latter. This statement is not necessarily inconsistent with one of the main points I wish to make today: that one of the weakest links in the sciences dealing with evolution, the one most needing to strengthen its facts and theoretical framework, is that dealing with behavior. I should also introduce here a word of explanation about what follows in this discussion. Of the 50-odd living genera of primates (Simpson, 1945) only a very few have been studied to any extent in regard to behavior: man, chimpanzee, the macaques and cebus monkeys. Our discussion of behavior, therefore, cannot give anything like the extensive comparisons within the order as did some of the previous papers. We shall have to content ourselves with the grosser distinctions between the few aforementioned primates.

In a survey of behavior from amoeba to man we find both similarities and differences, depending largely on the scale of observation used. In general, the similarities are expressed in terms of function or adaptive outcome. The differences are quantitative or refer to details of mechanisms which have more or less the same results. That is to say, the evolutionary development of behavior shows a continuity which parallels that of physical structures. There is, however, one possible exception. Whereas the physical differences between man and some of the other primates are no greater than those found at many points along the phylogenetic scale, the behavioral differences between *Homo sapiens* and the living nonhuman primates exceed those found anywhere else. They are so striking that the possibility of a break in the continuum, of a qualitatively new emergent, may be and is widely entertained. Simpson (1949, p. 286) for instance, characterizes man as 'fundamentally a new sort of animal' with a 'new sort of evolution'. The 'new sort of evolution' refers, of course, to culture, or, as he puts it, 'the inheritance of learning'. The importance of culture as an offshoot of organic evolution, and with almost limitless possibilities of development, has been stressed by many writers. Few would deny that it is an almost uniquely human achievement. It is a social phenomenon in that we are all affected by culture and in varying degrees contribute to it. Nevertheless it is, in the last analysis, a product of the human individual; it has to be 'invented' as well as used. It is in the characteristics of the individual, therefore, that we must seek its explanation. Simpson (1949, pp. 291–2) goes on to say that the human species 'has properties unique to itself among all forms of life'. These properties of the individual include especially 'the accumulation of knowledge, . . . a sense of values, and the possibility of conscious choice' (1949, p. 290). As I shall try to show later, the differences in knowledge and in 'a sense of values' are basically quantitative.

Let us consider first the chronically vexatious problem of consciousness. Is man the only conscious animal, or is he merely more conscious than others? Or could it be that some animals are more conscious than man? These are obviously hopeless questions. The only consciousness that we can observe directly is our own, personal awareness. And especially since Freud, we know that conscious content gives only a partial and highly prejudiced account of the factors actually determining behavior. In comparative psychology, certainly, we cannot use conscious processes as data. This fact has no implication for the question of whether animals are, or are not, conscious. Our best guess may be that consciousness is a quantitative rather than all-or-none phenomenon and that it appears in some degree in animals other than man. Having worked with chimpanzees for a number of years, I have no doubt that these animals are sometimes angry, resentful, jealous, remorseful, affectionate, happy or sad; that they have intentions and expectations which may be frustrated or satisfied. This conviction probably influences the design of my experiments but is almost worthless in reporting my results. Mentalistic terms are a convenient, short-hand way of designating and classifying various sorts of behavior, but they do not furnish any usable data. The term 'mental evolution' in the title of this paper was intended to convey the idea that most or all of those forms of behavior, which in us are accompanied by awareness, can be seen also in the higher nonhuman primates. Whether in them those behaviors are accompanied by awareness is irrelevant; the behaviors themselves, and their mechanisms, are legitimate material for comparative psychology and are pertinent to the general problem of evolution.

The phenomena to be considered in a phyletic comparison of behavior may be grouped into three classes: (1) the realm of cognitive or intellective functions – all those problem-solving capacities which we often lump under the term 'intelligence'; (2) the emotional and motivational aspects of behavior; and (3) these first two classes in their social–cultural manifestations. In each of these fields evolutionary progression (or succession) has been characterized in various ill-defined ways. It is said that as we 'go up' in the phyletic scale we find a greater range, diversity, and complexity of intelligent behavior; more flexibility or plasticity versus rigidity; increased learning capacity. Some intellectual functions such as abstraction and symbolism, are usually ascribed only to the 'highest' animals. The needs of the organism increase in number and complexity. Play, exploration and curiosity become more prominent as motivators of behavior. The forward reference of striving and planning encompasses longer periods of time. There is, in general, greater socialization, specialization and division of labor among individuals; and social organization becomes increasingly independent of genetic determination. This list could be greatly extended but is long enough to illustrate how vaguely phylogenetic differences in behavior are usually formulated. The first need, obviously, is the analysis of these gross descriptions into their components. To say that man differs from other primates in his capacity for tool-making and language is not very useful until we have identified the mechanisms or processes which produce these complex end-results.

Our problem is one of measurement: to measure the differences and similarities of behaviors exhibited at various phylogenetic levels. Before we can measure we need, first, axes or continua of variation, and second, units in terms of which differences along the axes may be described. In the physical world we have such axes as length and such units as inches. In psychology we have good measures of certain basic functions but as yet relatively few clearly defined dimensions of variation and units of measurement for the higher levels of behavior. In respect to the basic or relatively simple functions, the measures indicate very little difference between the primate species which have been tested. Visual acuity, for instance, is almost the same in man and chimpanzee (Spence, 1934); color vision is slightly better in man than in chimpanzee and rhesus monkeys (Grether, 1939, 1940). Simple reaction time – the speed with which an organism can respond to a signal – is the same for young chimpanzees and human children of comparable age (Forster, 1935). In the speed of forming those uncomplicated associations known as classical conditioning, there appear to be no differences between the most primitive and the most highly developed animals (Razran, 1933). In remembering a well-practiced task or association over long periods of time, the available data show no differences among the primates which have been tested (Nissen, 1951a). Phylogenetic differences, and especially those critical for a comparison of the lower and higher primates, are evidently to be sought in what we loosely refer to as the 'higher mental functions'. And these functions, as I have indicated, are as yet imperfectly defined. I might say, parenthetically, that the same difficulty confronts the testers of human intelligence. For the most part their measures of mental age and IQ are based on unanalyzed end-products, with little knowledge of the functions which entered into the test-performances.

The difficulties of measurement, and also our earlier rough survey of phylogenetic differences, suggest a phrase which characterizes these changes: increasing complexity. This term is obviously descriptive rather than explanatory and is too broad to be useful unless the complexity is further specified. I suggest that complexity be defined in terms of the sheer number of factors which determine behavior. The number of determinants may increase both spatially and temporally. In the lowest organisms the most intense stimulus of the moment tends to govern the reaction. Later, the reaction is increasingly determined by a number of concomitant stimuli that influence each other by summation, inhibition and so on. In vision, for instance, light intensity and direction govern the responses of the protista. In higher invertebrates, light distribution or patterning also becomes effective. The cumulative effects of previous experience become major factors in governing response to present stimulation, and this influence extends to more remote time. This temporal integration, I should point out, is a function of the individual. It is tempting to analogize and to say that the time-binding capacity of man extends to the race, via culture. But this is only an analogy. Education, imitation and so on are special ways of having experience; the integration of those experiences is still a function of the individual.

A formal experiment may serve to illustrate the proposed dimension of increasing behavior determinants (Nissen, 1951b). A chimpanzee is trained that choice of the larger of two square white plaques is rewarded, whereas choice of the smaller one is not rewarded. He then learns that if the two squares are black, the smaller one is correct. After these two habits are learned, he finds out that if the plaques are triangular instead of square, the previous relations are reversed; the smaller of the white triangles and the larger of the black triangles are positive. The problem is further complicated until the chimpanzee has to take into account 5 different factors or cues in order to make the right choice. This problem, which puts some strain on a human subject, was mastered by the chimpanzee. A similar experiment conducted by Noer and Harlow (1946) indicates that rhesus monkeys can respond to at least 4 cues. Rodents and carnivores have great difficulty when the number of essential cues exceeds two.

Since behavioral complexity is roughly correlated with phylogenetic level, we may ask whether, in back of this correlation, there is a more fundamental difference in cognitive mechanisms. The relative importance of genetic versus experiential determination would seem to constitute such a difference. This distinction, often referred to as 'instinct versus intelligence', is especially clear if we compare, say, the insects and man. In the former, behavior seems to be largely a function of inherited mechanisms, whereas in the latter it is determined more by individual experience. The distinction is usually interpreted as a difference in the rigidity of stimulus–response connections; in the one case a certain response is innately elicited by a certain stimulus or situation, whereas in the other S-R connections are learned. This may constitute one of the differences but, I believe, only a minor one. More important is that in the 'lower' animal the repertoire of perceptions is for the most part genetically fixed, whereas in the 'higher' animals that repertoire is built up by or in experience. The instinct-guided animal is ready for its species-characteristic behavior almost as soon as it is born; the primate passes through an extended period of helpless infancy and childhood before it is ready for self-sufficient adult behavior. Evidence is accumulating that in chimpanzee as in man the principal learning going on during this time is the formation of perceptions that is to say, the building up of a knowledge of the world, making sense out of what at first is an undifferentiated confusion. I have suggested elsewhere (Nissen, 1951a) that so-called play behavior provides the experience which leads to perceptions and knowledge, and that this is why we see so much more play in the primates than in those animals which come equipped with ready made perceptions, and more in young than in old animals. Experiments conducted at the Yerkes Laboratories with dark-reared infant chimpanzees indicate that the art of seeing, of perceiving contours and patterns, recognizing a milk bottle and the familiar attendant, is the result of prolonged learning or experience. The distinction between acquiring perceptions as contrasted with forming habits or S–R connections is important. The child has the perception of a door when he knows that it is a means of entrance and exit, a way to let in fresh air or to keep out the cold, and so on. He has a door-habit when he always slams the door shut. Perceptions are knowledge which can be used in forming habits or in acquiring other higher-order perceptions. Having learned to perceive squares, circles, triangles and so on, we may then, if we are one of the higher primates, acquire the perception – or as it is more commonly called, the concept – of form. The learning animals, therefore, can multiply their perceptions enormously, and this increase in the number of behavior determinants correspondingly increases the complexity of behavior. The instinct-guided animals, on the other hand, are stuck with their limited number of innately provided perceptions, which increase little with experience and which thus limit behavior to a lower degree of complexity.

In case there are any extreme environmentalists present today, it may be in order to point out here that man and the other learning animals have not actually escaped genetic determination. The potentialities for perception and conceptualization are inherited just as much as is eye-color, and those potentialities are limited in kind and number. With the right inheritance an individual may, under favorable conditions, acquire a great deal of knowledge, but, by definition, he will not become Superman. We are thus assured that experience will not make a man out of a monkey, although the opposite is alleged to occur sometimes.

In respect to innateness of behavior-determination, it is clear that the higher monkeys and apes stand a great deal closer to man than to most other mammals. The chimpanzee seems to have hardly any more instinctive modes of response than does man. Wild chimpanzees regularly build tree nests to sleep in at night, and these nests have a fairly uniform structure. There is pretty good evidence, however, that this nest building is not instinctive, as in birds, but is, rather, transmitted by imitation or tuition from one generation to the next; it is, therefore, one of the very few items of behavior seen in these animals which may be classified as cultural. Mating behavior, which is highly instinctive in most mammals, is for the most part a matter of trial-and-error learning in the chimpanzee. One of the few behaviors of this ape which may be designated instinctive is grooming, or as it is often called, flea-picking. This appears in the captive-born chimpanzee when there has been no opportunity for imitation or tuition. The stimulus is a shiny object or small irregularity in any surface. In general, however, the perceptions of chimpanzees appear to be as much a product of experience as are those of man; the ape's potentialities are more limited, but certainly much greater than those of nonprimate mammals.

Limitation in respect to the kind of perceptions which an organism can learn is related to the amount of temporal integration involved. The perception of relations such as larger–smaller, lighter–heavier and so on are immediately given in a single experience. Other relations, such as 'the middle one of 3, 5, or 7', 'the odd one', or 'the one which matches the sample' cannot be perceived in a single experience but come from observing the common element in a number of successive experiences. This is true likewise of concepts like 'color' and 'form'. In the conditional matching problem (Nissen, Blum and Blum, 1949) the animal must choose the color-matching object when sign A is present, but must choose the form-matching object in the presence of sign B. Mastery of this problem clearly involves the percepts or concepts of form and color. Although nonhuman primates do solve this problem, it takes them a long time. A human subject can solve it much faster. This difference may be in part a function of the backlog of experience and education, relevant to the problem, which most nonhuman primates do not have when first confronted by the situation. In much larger part, I believe, the difference is a function of a hypothetical mechanism which increases enormously the capacity for temporal integration.

The facts which compel us to infer such a mechanism are the radical increase (*a*) in the speed with which associations are formed and reformed, especially those involving higher level relations or concepts, (*b*) in the facility with which general principles or laws are used as short-cuts to problem solution, and (*c*) in the number of factors or items which can be utilized in determining response. This mechanism, therefore, does not introduce a new or higher kind of mental functioning, but it does increase greatly the efficiency with which certain functions, already present in nonhuman primates, are performed. That greater efficiency permits a pyramiding of percepts and concepts, each level building on top of that of lower complexity. Each level operates in two ways: (1) it makes possible the formation of concepts of still higher complexity, and (2) it facilitates the handling of lower level percepts. Problems which the chimpanzee solves by slow and laborious memorization, the human solves easily and quickly by applying a higher level formula or principle. Mathematics furnishes many good examples of this pyramiding process. The name we give to our inferred mechanism is unimportant; if the term had not been so uncritically misapplied in the past I should be inclined to call it a symbolic process. Certainly it is associated with and, in us finds its major expression in, language. It should be emphasized, however, that 'language' is two separable things: (a) a method of communication, and (b) a tool or instrument of thinking. If one of these functions has developmental priority over the other, it would seem reasonable to suppose that the use of symbolic processes as an aid to the individual in thinking and problem solving preceded language as a means of communication in social intercourse. At any rate, according to this schema of cumulative pyramiding increasing complexity of behavior determination is in the first place a function of quantitative increase, but this involves new kinds, i.e., higher level, concepts.

If we analyze the process of logical thought, including the formation of concepts, we find that it reduces to three processes: the recognition of differences, the recognition of similarities or identities, and most important, a proper balance between these two. To take a simple example: in the conditional matching problem already referred to, the subject must respond to the differences among colors *or* among forms, but must also respond to the similarity of various colors as contrasted to forms. Overemphasis on either similarity or difference interferes with solution. In respect to this balance or, as we may call it, sagacity,[1] the nonhuman primate tends to err on the side of over-responding to difference. In general, the chimpanzee classifies as a scatterbrained individual, very sensitive to difference or change, and unlike the obsessed individual who responds to the similarities between widely divergent phenomena. This ape is therefore the 'scientific' rather than the 'philosophical' type. The species difference in sagacity is, of course, a quantitative one.

I have taken so much time in discussing the cognitive side of behavior that the perhaps more spectacular differences in motivational–emotional aspects, and their expression in social phenomena, will have to be neglected. I shall have to content myself

1. This meaning of 'sagacity' is consistent with, but more restricted and specific than, that found in the writings of William James (1890) and Hollingworth (1928).

with a bald statement of the thesis that there are no fundamental or qualitative differences between the emotions and motivations of man and the other primates; that the very large and dramatic differences in the expression of emotions and in the organization of motivational hierarchies are secondary, deriving from the cognitive differences already discussed. What especially characterizes human motivation is not its initiating goals, but rather the indirection and complexity of its approach to those goals. With our superior capacity for temporal integration and our higher level concepts which enable us to foresee a series of causes and consequences, we can make long-range plans by which our ultimate goals are more efficiently approached. We are not restricted to an immediate striving towards the advantages of the moment.

Through complications introduced by social interaction and culture, most of our activities may appear unrelated to primary drives, but our more obvious goals are merely way-stations on the road to satisfying a relatively few simple but universal needs. As to Simpson's criterion of a 'sense of values' for differentiating between man and the lower animals, I believe that no one who has had intimate acquaintance with the higher nonhuman primates will question that their actions are also guided by a delicately balanced system of values. The larger and stronger male chimpanzee deferring to his female companion in the division of food, even after the female is pregnant and no longer suitable as a sex partner – the animal 'punishing' the misbehavior of his cagemate and in position to inflict serious injury, but contenting himself with merely nipping him painfully – the chimpanzee refusing to expose himself to the frustration of occasional failure in a difficult problem, although he could get a desirable tidbit 50% of the time by merely continuing to make a simple and easy response – these are but a few of many instances of a finely adjusted hierarchy of values. Like man, the chimpanzee has many values only indirectly related to primary needs, as for food, sex and knowledge. But man recognizes in almost everything some relevance, however farfetched, to his basic needs, and his system of values therefore has a greater numerical range and thus a greater complexity of interrelationships. Activities motivated by the primary drives involve the whole intricate organization of human economic and cultural life with the many subgoals which occupy most of our attention. Even the motives of altruism, ethical conduct and the like, are the expression of basic motivations, in us guided by superior intelligence, which we share with the other primates.

References

FORSTER, M. C. 1935. Temporal relations of behavior in chimpanzee and man as measured by reaction time. I. Simple reaction time. J. Comp. Psychol., *20*:361–383.

GRETHER, W. F. 1939. Color vision and color blindness in monkeys. Comp. Psychol. Monogr., *15* (4):1–38.

——1940. A comparison of human and chimpanzee spectral hue discrimination curves. J. Exp. Psychol., *26*:394–403.

HOLLINGWORTH, H. L. 1928. Psychology; Its Facts and Principles. D. Appleton and Co., New York.

JAMES, W. 1890. The Principles of Psychology. Henry Holt and Co., New York.

LORENZ, K. 1937. Ueber die Bildung des Instinktbegriffs. Naturwissenschaften, *25*:289–300, 307–318, 324–331.

NISSEN, H. W. 1951a. Phylogenetic comparison, in Handbook of Experimental Psychology (Ed. S. S. Stevens), John Wiley and Sons, New York.

—— 1951b. Analysis of a complex conditional reaction in chimpanzee. J. Comp. Physiol. Psychol., *44*:9–16.

NISSEN, H. W., JOSEPHINE S. BLUM, AND R. A. BLUM. 1949. Conditional matching behavior in chimpanzee. J. Comp. Physiol. Psychol., *42*:339–356.

NOER, MARY C., AND H. F. HARLOW. 1946. Discrimination of ambivalent cue stimuli by macaque monkeys. J. General Psychol., *34*:165–177.

RAZRAN, G. H. S. 1933. Conditioned responses in animals other than dogs. Psychol. Bull., *30*:261–324.

SIMPSON, G. G. 1945. The principles of classification and a classification of mammals. Bull. American Museum of Natural History, *85*, page 35.

—— 1949. The Meaning of Evolution. Yale University Press, New Haven, Conn.

SPENCE, K. W. 1934. Visual acuity and its relation to brightness in chimpanzee and man. J. Comp. Psychol., *18*:333–361.

2 M. Scheerer

Problem-Solving

M. Scheerer, 'Problem-solving', *Scientific American*, vol. 208 (1963), pp. 118–28.

A cat is penned in a wooden cage, the door of which can be released by a tug on a latchstring. The cat has never seen a latchstring. In an effort to get out it tries to squeeze between the bars and claws and bites at them in a random fashion until, by pure chance, it happens to claw at a loop in the string and pull. After gaining its freedom the cat is put back in the cage. Again it squeezes and claws and bites and finally happens to pull the string. On repeated trials the cat gets to the string a little sooner each time, and eventually it pulls the loop as soon as it is placed in the cage.

A hungry chimpanzee confined in a cage sees a banana outside the bars just beyond its reach. After some futile attempts to get the banana by reaching through the bars the chimpanzee discovers a stick lying on the floor of the cage. In one swift action the ape picks up the stick and with it retrieves the banana.

The cat and the chimpanzee each faced a problem and solved it in a very different way. The manner in which a cat or a chimpanzee – or a human being – solves a problem is a fundamental characteristic of the animal or person. The behavior manifested in solving a problem, moreover, provides a convenient window through which to observe mental processes. Since the turn of the century the experimental investigation of problem-solving has been a fruitful source of information on how animals and men think and learn.

The course of this experimentation has been heavily influenced by a canon laid down by the British zoologist and comparative psychologist, C. Lloyd Morgan: Never attribute behavior in an animal to a high level of thinking or knowing if the behavior can be explained in terms of lower processes; in other words, always explain behavior in terms of the simplest possible mechanism.

In 1898 the U.S. psychologist Edward Lee Thorndike undertook to apply this principle of psychological parsimony in a comprehensive study of problem-solving in the cat and other animals. Thorndike's definition of 'problem' is still widely

26

accepted: A problem exists when the goal that is sought is not directly attainable by the performance of a simple act available in the animal's repertory; the solution calls for either a novel action or a new integration of available actions. It was Thorndike who performed the cat-in-the-cage experiment described at the beginning of this article. He posed these questions: Is it necessary to assume that the cat has intelligence in the human meaning of the term? Does the solution – pulling the string – require any understanding or insight or can it be achieved quite mechanically?

Thorndike noted that the cat pulled the string by chance and that the time it required to trip the latch declined gradually in successive trials. He concluded that the solution behavior could be explained quite simply: The string was a stimulus and the tugging was a response. The tugging was rewarded by escape. From this and similar experiments Thorndike derived his principle of learning: Whatever behavior is rewarded is 'stamped in' and whatever behavior is not rewarded or is punished is 'stamped out'. This principle is at the heart of contemporary stimulus-response psychology, which was shaped not only by Thorndike but also by I. P. Pavlov, John B. Watson, Clark Hull and many others. In this view the tugging behavior is a learned habit, acquired through repeated 'reinforcement', or reward. There is no need to assume that the cat has any understanding of why the tugging leads to escape; there is no need to assume any kind of intelligence other than a plasticity that allows the learning of new habits.

Then the Gestalt psychologists came on the scene. They emphasized the tendency of the mind to organize and integrate and to perceive situations, including problems, as total structures. They argued that more is involved in problem-solving than a sequence of stimuli and responses. One of the founders of Gestalt psychology, Wolfgang Köhler, objected specifically to Thorndike's test situations. The cat, he maintained, cannot possibly behave intelligently in the cage because the release mechanism is hidden and therefore not part of the perceived situation, and because its functioning is too complicated for an animal to unravel. Isolated on Tenerife in the Canary Islands during World War I, Köhler carried out a classic series of experiments with chimpanzees. One of his problem situations was the one involving the banana and the stick. In this case the chimpanzee's solution did not come gradually and was not the result of trial and error. It was intelligent behavior, Köhler said, based on a perception of what was required to solve the problem: some way of overcoming the distance barrier.

The insight that leads to a solution, in the Gestalt view, stems from this perception of the requirements of a problem. Max Wertheimer, another founder of Gestalt psychology, pro-

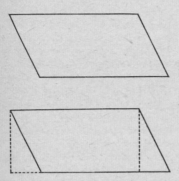

Figure 1 Parallelogram (top) is equal in area to a rectangle of the same base and altitude because the 'protuberance' at one end is equal to the 'gap' at the other (bottom).

vided a good example to support this point of view. Suppose a child who already knows how to get the area of a rectangle is asked to find the formula for the area of a parallelogram. If the child thinks about it, Wertheimer said, he will be struck by the fact that a parallelogram would look like a rectangle were it not for the fact that one side has a 'protuberance' and the other side has a 'gap' [*see figure 1*]. He formulates the hypothesis: 'Get rid of the protuberance and fill in the gap.' Then he realizes that the protuberance is equivalent to the gap; if he moves the protruding corner to the indented side, the figure is converted into a rectangle of the same base and altitude. Hence the formula is the same as it is for a rectangle.

With Morgan's warning in mind one can ask at this point if it is necessary to assume that the child has done more than go through a process of trial and error and call on previously learned habits. The Gestalt answer is that although there may be trial and error it is not a blind, or random, sequence as Thorndike believed. Productive thinking is not accidental success or the mere application of bits of past experience. The problem has a structure of its own that points the way to its solution. Only within this total framework, or context, does the problem-solver draw selectively on relevant knowledge.

This view of problem-solving has direct implications for theories of learning and teaching. It is interesting, in passing, to consider how the thought process outlined above differs from the way the formula for the area of a parallelogram is usually taught. A geometry teacher would probably give the formula $b \times a$ (base times altitude) and offer the following proof. He would extend the base line and drop perpendiculars to construct two triangles and then demonstrate that the triangles are congruent. But he would probably not have pointed out in advance the simple reason why one should want to prove the congruence of the triangles. A bright student might grasp the reason but others would never attain that insight. Fortunately, insight achieved in the solving of a problem can be explained to others, who should then have precisely the same understanding attained by the original problem-solver. This true understanding has two major advantages beyond the intrinsic pleasure of grasping something: it can be retained easily and it can be transferred to other, similar problems. Once a student understands the reason the area of a parallelogram is given by $b \times a$, he can figure out how to get the area of a triangle or a trapezoid.

Wertheimer and Karl Duncker, who was then at the University of Berlin, explored the nature of the process by which people gain or fail to gain insight into problems. They found that although men have the capacity for genuine insight and often attain it, not everyone gains insight into a problem in the same way or at the same stage – or ever. Insight is often delayed or thwarted by 'fixation' on an inappropriate solution. If the chimpanzee fails to realize that it simply cannot get the banana without a tool and keeps reaching through the bars, it will not notice the stick; the fixation stands in the way of a correct solution.

The author's own work in problem-solving has been centered on this phenomenon of fixation. He found that it operates in many ways. Sometimes a person clings misguidedly to a false premise or assumption concerning the task before him. Consider two simple problems that are made difficult by this fixation [*see figure 2*]. The first requires that nine dots be connected by four straight lines drawn without lifting the pencil from the paper. This cannot be done unless one extends the lines beyond the dots [*see figure 3*]. But almost everyone assumes – although it is

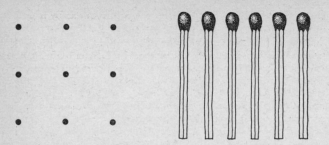

Figure 2 Nine dots are arranged in a square. The problem is to connect them by drawing four continuous straight lines without lifting pencil from paper. Solution is in figure 3.
Six matches must be assembled to form four congruent equilateral triangles each side of which is equal to the length of the matches. The solution is in figure 3.

not stated as a condition of the problem – that he must stay within the group of dots. The second problem, assembling six matches of equal length to form four equilateral triangles with sides equal to the length of the matches, cannot be solved as long as one assumes that the matches must lie on one plane, and virtually everyone who tries it assumes just that. The assumption is implicit; most people do not even know they have made it. The way to the correct solution – an equilateral tetrahedron, or pyramid – is opened as soon as one realizes that the matches need not lie flat. This shift from one premise to a new one is what Gestalt psychologists call a 'reformulation', or 'recentering', of one's thoughts.

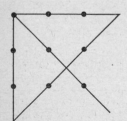 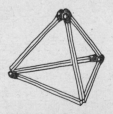

Figure 3 Dot problem is solved by extending the lines beyond the dots. But most people assume incorrectly that they may not do this.
Match problem is solved by building a three-dimensional pyramid. Most people wrongly assume that matches must lie flat.

The power of fixation and recentering is illustrated by a problem the author developed in collaboration with the neuropsychiatrist Kurt Goldstein and Edwin G. Boring of Harvard University. The puzzle, which the author first came upon in an advertisement, involves a drawing of two misshapen horses and a drawing of two riders [*see figure 4*]. The problem is to place the drawing of the riders (*B*) on the other drawing (*A*) in such a way that the riders are properly astride the horses. (The reader can try

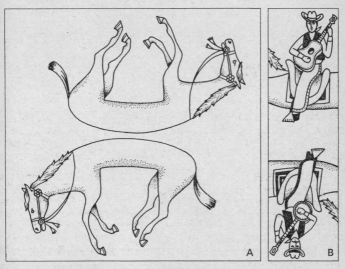

Figure 4 Horse-and-rider puzzle illustrates the power of fixation. The problem is to place drawing B on drawing A in such a way that the riders are properly astride the horses. This drawing is adapted from the original version. The correct solution is in figure 5.

this himself by tracing the two drawings on two strips of paper.) The overwhelming tendency is to try to place each rider on one of the horses drawn in *A*. It is quite clear that this will not work (the horses are back-to-back in *A* and belly-to-belly in *B*, and the space between the horses is much less than the distance between the two riders) but most people keep trying. The correct solution requires a complete recentering of one's perception of the elements of the puzzle. The two horses in *A* must be broken into parts, so to speak, after which the head and the hindquarters of one combine respectively with the hindquarters and the head

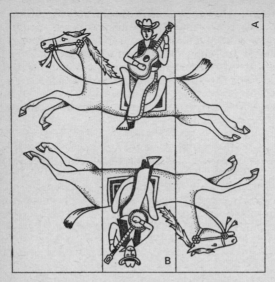

Figure 5 Solution of the horse-and-rider puzzle requires a 'recentering'. The horses cannot be used as they are drawn in A but must be abstracted into their component parts and recombined into two new horses. Then, if drawing A is rotated 90 degrees, the riders fit properly.

of the other to form two new horses. Then, when one of the strips is turned 90 degrees with respect to the other, the riders fit nicely on the newly created horses [*see figure 5*]. In this case a solution is inhibited by a fixation that arises from the perceptual make-up of the puzzle. Another puzzle presents a similar problem with more abstract shapes [*see figures 6 and 7*].

Duncker discovered that fixation often interferes when the solution of a test problem requires the use of a familiar object in a novel way. Suppose someone needs a screw driver and one is not available. He could make do with any thin and sufficiently hard object – a coin, for example. But to see this possibility he must shift from his usual idea of 'coin as money' to the new functional concept of 'coin as screw driver', and this is a difficult kind of shift for many people to make. (Substitution of a coin, to be sure, seems rather obvious because it is a familiar expedient, but a person who thinks of it independently should be credited with a truly creative insight.) Duncker found that it was particularly hard for a person to think of an object as adaptable for a novel function if he had just put it to its conventional use. In one experiment the task was to suspend a piece of string from a wooden ledge. The subject had no hooks but he did have a gimlet; the solution was to screw the gimlet into the wood, leave it there and hang the string on it. Subjects given a preliminary task

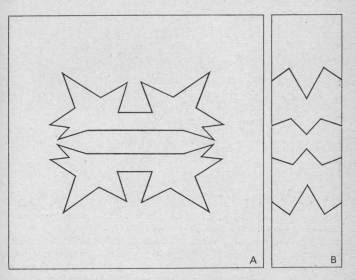

Figure 6 Perceptual fixation demonstrated by the horse-and-rider puzzle operates also with these abstract shapes. The problem here is to place element B on element A in such a way that two closed figures are formed. The solution to this problem appears in figure 7

in which they employed the gimlet to make holes were less likely than others to think of using it as a peg.

The author sought to extend Duncker's investigation of 'functional fixedness' in a series of experiments conducted with Maurice Huling of the University of Kansas. The problem, originally developed with Zelda S. Klapper and Herman Witkin of the State University of New York College of Medicine in Brooklyn, required the subject to put two rings on a peg from a position six feet from the rings and the peg. He could not do it without a tool to extend his reach. Except when he was picking up the rings and putting them on the peg, he was allowed to move about the room,

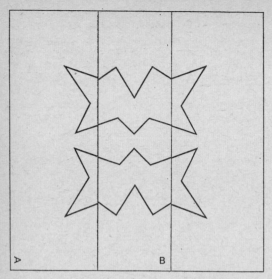

Figure 7 Recentering also solves this problem. The abstract shapes of A are broken up and rotated 90 degrees. B then fits properly.

and he could use anything he saw. There were two sticks in the room, but neither was long enough to bridge the gap alone; they had to be joined together. The only piece of string in the room was one by which an object hung from a nail on the wall [*see figure 8*]. This string was in clear view but it was embedded in a meaningful context. It was predicted that it might not be seen as an available piece of string; although not hidden perceptually, it would prove to be psychologically inaccessible for anything but its present function.

At first 16 volunteers were given the problem with a piece of string hanging alone on the nail. All of them took down the string, tied the sticks together and with them placed the rings on the peg. The experimental series was then begun with the string holding things that had no real function: a piece of blank cardboard, an old calendar and a cloudy mirror. It was predicted that the string would still be psychologically available, and virtually everyone tested in these situations did indeed solve the problem. In the next phase the objects hung on the wall had definite functions: a current calendar, a clear mirror and a 'No Smoking' sign. These could be expected to have a 'stay put' quality. Fifty-six per cent of the subjects failed with the current calendar, 69 per cent with the intact mirror and 53 per cent with the 'No Smoking' sign.

In each case the string had been tied with a square knot, which was placed in plain sight above the nail and looked eminently untieable. The subjects who failed to take down the string did not think they were forbidden to make use of it; they simply did not think to do so, as could be ascertained from their comments (they had been encouraged to think aloud) and follow-up interviews. Moreover, almost everyone decided quickly that he needed

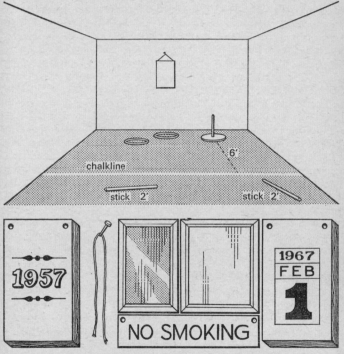

Figure 8 Ring-and-peg problem could be solved with a piece of string with which to tie the two sticks together. The only string in the room hung on a nail on the wall. When it hung there alone, every subject solved the problem. When it was used to suspend a cardboard, an old calendar or a cloudy mirror, some people failed. When the string was a hanger for functional things such as a sign, a clear mirror or a current calendar, more than half failed.

a string. This means that in this phase of the experiment more than half of the individuals sought a string for nearly the entire 20-minute test period but did not think of using for their purpose a string that was one of the most prominent things in their field of view.

In one situation the subject himself was asked to hang the object on the wall. While he was occupied with some unrelated written problems the departmental secretary came into the room, apologized for intruding and left a mirror on the table, explaining that mirrors were being put in all the laboratory cubicles 'for an experiment next week'. The experimenter said casually: 'I suppose this should be hung up. Would you do it for me?' The subject hung the mirror on the nail (the only one in the room) and went back to his paper work. Fifteen minutes later he was given the ring-and-peg problem. In spite of the direct experience with the piece of string, the failure rate in this situation was 50 per cent.

The results were quite different when the string was handled ahead of time but was handled as 'string'. In what was called a 'test of manual dexterity' we had a group of volunteers hang up the old calendar, the cardboard or the clear mirror using tweezers to tie the string. The object was left on the wall. When these subjects undertook the ring-and-peg problem after a 15-minute interval, only one out of 36 failed. Apparently even a functional mirror, if hung on the wall in the course of a 'dexterity test', did not later take on the coloration of something that belonged on the wall. Instead the mirror and the string were perceived as two things left on the wall after fulfilling a specific but transient purpose. The string remained a string, not just a means of hanging things.

The follow-up interviews with people who had failed showed how persistent a fixation can be. The experimenter began by pointing in the general direction of the object on the wall and asking: 'What about that?' The hint was enough for only five out of 47 people. When the experimenter then asked, 'What about that mirror [or calendar and so on]?' only four more saw the solution. Many of the others responded: 'What about it?' Still others suggested making the sign or mirror into a shovel-like tool with one of the sticks, wrapping the sticks in the sign or somehow employing the screw eyes in the back of the mirror. When the experimenter finally asked directly, 'What about the tring?' all 8 of the remaining subjects expressed surprise, chagrin and self-reproach as they admitted this was indeed a olution.

Fixation had been reported to be a function of involvement n a situation. To see if an increase in 'psychological distance' vould help to overcome it, some observers were allowed to watch is a 'subject' ran through the motions of trying to solve the pro-blem. The subject was excused when he reached the point of verbalizing the need for something with which to fasten the two ticks together. The observers were then asked to work out the problem in their minds. Only one out of seven of these observers ailed, compared with the more than half of the deeply involved subjects who had tried to solve the same problem in action.

One of the difficulties in the study of problem-solving is that he experimenter can never be sure just what is going on in the ubject's mind. He can ask after the experiment is over, but the ubject may forget details or may reconstruct his thought pro-esses incorrectly. Even when the person being tested thinks aloud n the course of the solution, he may not mention everything that ccurs to him. It is desirable, therefore, to construct a problem hat invites and encourages a running translation of thought into isible action. James M. Elliott and the author worked out such situation in another experiment at the University of Kansas.

The problem chosen was essentially the familiar one of the iver crossing. Eight soldiers have to cross a river. The only neans of transportation is a small boat in which two little boys re playing: the boat can carry at most two boys or one soldier. Iow do the soldiers get across? If the reader will try to solve this roblem before reading on, he will understand the difficulties ur subjects faced.

The river puzzle was converted into one involving physical ob-ects and requiring a sequence of discrete moves on the part of the erson attempting it. A crude wagon was substituted for the boat, nd eight large weights and two small ones for the soldiers and ne boys [see figure 9]. The wagon wheels locked if no weights ere placed in it and also if more than one large weight or two nall ones were loaded. Each subject was told that his task was to ansport all the weights in the wagon from one side of a table Lawrence') to the other side ('Topeka'), that the wheels must oll freely, that he could make as many trips as he wished and hat there were no hidden tricks or gadgets on the wagon – that s rolling was a function of the amount of weight in it.

37

Figure 9 Wagon and weights were used in the author's analogue of the river-crossing problem. The wagon was constructed on a double-seesaw principle. Flanges at the ends locked the front wheels if no weight was placed in the container (top) and the rear wheels if too much weight was loaded (second from top). The wheels turned and the wagon rolled only when either one large weight or one or two small ones were loaded (two lower pictures).

The solution consists in realizing that a precondition for getting the large weights across is to have one small weight on each side. The way to achieve this is to begin by taking both small weights across to Topeka. After one of them has returned the wagon to Lawrence the first large one can make the trip to Topeka. Then the small weight originally left in Topeka serves its purpose, getting the wagon back to Lawrence. Now the entire cycle must be repeated, and so on until all the weights are across.

Two experiments were performed. In the first the problem was simply given to 49 individuals. In the second the subjects were divided into groups and interrupted at certain points in order to know what they were thinking or planning. In both cases the participants were asked to think aloud and were observed as their thoughts took the form of concrete behavior, recording each loading of a weight and each abortive or successful movement of the wagon.

No two individuals proceeded in exactly the same way but there were some striking similarities in the behavior of the volunteers. They began by exploring the various weight loadings that would allow the wagon to roll. They soon discovered that it would carry either one large weight or one or two small ones. After this discovery most of them formulated a hypothesis: 'Take one weight over at a time, thus transporting them all in repeated trips.' This hypothesis led 40 of the 49 into the error of promptly loading one large weight and taking it to Topeka – only to realize when they got there that it was impossible to get the wagon back without taking the weight back again.

Once they realized it did no good to start by transporting a large weight alone, most of the subjects decided: 'Take at least two weights over in order to return the wagon with one.' This 'rider' hypothesis, combined with the knowledge that the wagon would not roll with too much weight, usually led to the idea of transporting one large and one small weight – a combination that accounted for 52 per cent of the trial loadings at this stage. Virtually all the subjects who made that attempt said they intended to get the wagon back from Topeka with the small weight – that it seemed the best 'rider' for the purpose. And although the wagon would clearly not roll with a large and small weight aboard, they returned again and again to that combination. For 30 of the subjects who persevered at it, the mean number of repetitions was 6.1. Many of them tried to rationalize the fixation as an attempt to find some special way of placing the weights so that the wagon would roll.

The reason for the fixation is fairly clear. These subjects had decided that they needed to carry a rider, and that the small weight was a logical one because it was less of an extra load than a second large weight. Even the few subjects who considered taking the two small weights across together saw one as a rider for the other only on a preliminary trip; thereafter, they thought, it would be a rider for a large one – so they might as well face the small-plus-large problem at the outset. Some went so far as to load the two small weights and still failed to see that it was the essence of the solution. All of these subjects were fixating on what appeared to them to be the goal: transporting the large weights to Topeka. For them the small weights had lost the quality of weights to be transported and were seen as riders only. It was therefore a detour from the major goal to transport two small weights first to Topeka merely in order to leave one there. The solution required them to shift to the perception of both small weights as tools to be taken across on a preliminary trip.

When individuals loading a large and a small weight were interrupted and asked, as the experimenter pointed to the other small weight, 'What about this one? Have you ever thought of using them together?' a few were able to solve the problem. But most of them said something like: 'It looks the same . . . I could take these two [small ones] over, but after one trip I couldn't do any more . . . I'd still be faced with the problem of getting the large ones over.'

Even as they finally hit on the correct first step of transporting the two small weights, many subjects failed to see the point. Some got back to Lawrence with a small weight and then tried once again to load a large and a small weight together. Even more of them got safely through the next steps of sending over one large weight and returning the waiting small one but failed to see that they had to start all over again at that point with the two small weights. In other words, they had not yet attained the second major insight: the cyclical nature of the solution.

Eventually all the subjects did solve the problem and all but two of them understood the solution. On questioning later, 36 per cent of them expressed the underlying principle in spatial terms: 'You need a small one on each side at all times.' Another 41 per cent expressed it in temporal terms, reciting the required sequence of events in the cycle. The remaining 23 per cent were unable to verbalize the principle clearly.

The various problems discussed here illustrate several causes of fixation in problem-solving. A person may start with an implicit but incorrect premise. He may fail to perceive an object's suitability for a solution because it must be used in a novel way or because it is embedded in a conventional context. Or he may be unwilling to accept a detour that delays the achievement of his goal. Any type of fixation can be strengthened by too much motivation. Herbert D. Birch, now at the Albert Einstein College of Medicine, found that if a chimpanzee is too hungry it will not do as well at a problem requiring a detour – the Köhler banana problem, for example – as an animal that is only moderately hungry. The overly hungry chimpanzee fixates rigidly on the goal, striving to no avail to reach the banana. On the human level there is some evidence that strong ego-involvement in a problem makes for overmotivation and is detrimental to a solution.

One final factor affecting fixation is habituation. There is truth in William James's statement that habit is the 'flywheel of society', but one might add that habit can also be the flypaper of society. The direct availability of a habitual mode of response may make it much harder to break with habit and approach a problem afresh. This effect was beautifully illustrated some years ago by Abraham S. Luchins, who was then associated with Wertheimer at the New School for Social Research. The subject is asked to measure out mentally a given quantity of water; the tools available to him are three pitchers of specified sizes [*see figure 10*]. Take the first problem: With three pitchers that hold three, 21 and 127 quarts, and with an unlimited supply of water, measure out 100 quarts. The solution is to fill the 127-quart vessel (b), pour off enough to fill the 21-quart pitcher (a) and then enough to fill the three-quart pitcher (c) twice. This leaves the desired 100 quarts in the big pitcher (b). The reader is invited to do the whole series.

Most people solve Problem 6 by pouring water from the filled 49-quart vessel into the 23-quart vessel and then twice into the three-quart pitcher, and they follow the same routine in Problem 7. But both problems have much simpler solutions. Problem 6 can be solved by filling a and pouring from it into c once; Problem 7 can be solved by filling a and c and pouring them into an empty b. But because Problems 1 through 5 all call for the $b - a - 2c$ solution the subject becomes habituated to it, consciously or not, and holds to the same pattern even when it is inappropriate. This fixation is exploited in the traditional childhood game in which one child is called on to pronounce as the other spells out:

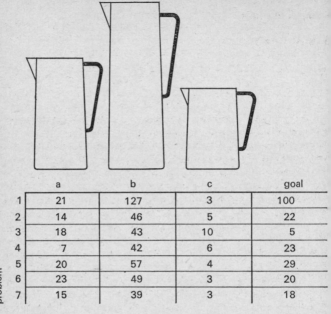

problem	a	b	c	goal
1	21	127	3	100
2	14	46	5	22
3	18	43	10	5
4	7	42	6	23
5	20	57	4	29
6	23	49	3	20
7	15	39	3	18

Figure 10 Fixation because of habit is illustrated by this series of problems. In each a quantity of water (right) must be measured out; there is an unlimited supply of water but the only tools available are three pitchers, a, b and c, the volumes of which are specified for each problem. Once the subject hits on a successful pattern of filling and pouring (b−a−2c) he tends to follow the pattern even when, in Problems 6 and 7, there is an easier solution.

'MACDONALD .... MACHENRY .... MACMAHON ... MAC-HINERY.' The victim is trapped into pronouncing the last 'name' as 'Mac Hinery' instead of 'machinery'.

If insight is the essential element in intelligent problem-solving, fixation is its arch-enemy. Fixation is overcome and insight attained by a sudden shift in the way the problem or the objects involved in it are viewed. The work described in this article has pointed to some of the factors that necessitate this sudden shift, but precisely what brings it about is still unknown. It remains the central problem of problem-solving.

G. J. Romanes

Animal Intelligence

Excerpt from G. J. Romanes, *Animal intelligence*, D. Appleton, 1888.

. . . .] It remains to add a few words on the principles which I have laid down for my own guidance in the selection and arrangement of facts. Considering it desirable to cast as wide a net as possible, I have fished the seas of popular literature as well as the rivers of scientific writing. The endless multitude of alleged facts which I have thus been obliged to read, I have found, as may well be imagined, excessively tedious; and as they are for the most part recorded by wholly unknown observers, the labour of reading them would have been useless without some trustworthy principles of selection. The first and most obvious principle that occurred to me was to regard only those facts which stood upon the authority of observers well known as competent; but I soon found that this principle constituted much too close a mesh. Where one of my objects was to determine the upper limit of intelligence reached by this and that class, order, or species of animals, I usually found that the most remarkable instances of the display of intelligence were recorded by persons bearing names more or less unknown to fame. This, of course, is what we might antecedently expect, as it is obvious that the chances must always be greatly against the more intelligent individuals among animals happening to fall under the observation of the more intelligent individuals among men. Therefore I soon found that I had to choose between neglecting all the more important part of the evidence – and consequently in most cases feeling sure that I had fixed the upper limit of intelligence too low – or supplementing the principle of looking to authority alone with some other principles of selection, which, while embracing the enormous class of alleged facts recorded by unknown observers, might be felt to meet the requirements of a reasonably critical method. I therefore adopted the following principles as a filter to this class of facts. First, never to accept an alleged fact without the authority of some name. Second, in the case of the name being unknown, and the alleged fact of sufficient importance to be entertained, carefully to consider whether, from all the circumstances of the case

as recorded, there was any considerable opportunity for mal
observation; this principle generally demanded that the alleged
fact, or action on the part of the animal, should be of a par
ticularly marked and unmistakable kind, looking to the end which
the action is said to have accomplished. Third, to tabulate all
important observations recorded by unknown observers, with the
view of ascertaining whether they have ever been corroborated by
similar or analogous observations made by other and inde
pendent observers. This principle I have found to be of great use
in guiding my selection of instances, for where statements of fact
which present nothing intrinsically improbable are found to be
unconsciously confirmed by different observers, they have as
good a right to be deemed trustworthy as statements which stand
on the single authority of a known observer, and I have found the
former to be at least as abundant as the latter. Moreover, by
getting into the habit of always seeking for corroborative cases, I
have frequently been able to substantiate the assertions of known
observers by those of other observers as well or better known
[. . . .]

Introduction

Before we begin to consider the phenomena of mind throughout
the animal kingdom it is desirable that we should understand, as
far as possible, what it is that we exactly mean by mind. Now, by
mind we may mean two very different things, according as we
contemplate it in our own individual selves, or in other organisms.
For if we contemplate our own mind, we have an immediate
cognizance of a certain flow of thoughts or feelings, which are the
most ultimate things, and indeed the only things, of which we are
cognizant. But if we contemplate mind in other persons or
organisms, we have no such immediate cognizance of thoughts or
feelings. In such cases we can only *infer* the existence and the
nature of thoughts and feelings from the activities of the organ
isms which appear to exhibit them. Thus it is that we may have a
subjective analysis of mind and an objective analysis of mind,
the difference between the two consisting in this, that in our sub
jective analysis we are restricted to the limits of a single isolated
mind which we call our own, and within the territory of which we
have immediate cognizance of all the processes that are going on,
or at any rate of all the processes that fall within the scope of our
introspection. But in our objective analysis of other or foreign
minds we have no such immediate cognizance; all our knowledge
of their operations is derived, as it were, through the medium of

ambassadors – these ambassadors being the activities of the organism. Hence it is evident that in our study of animal intelligence we are wholly restricted to the objective method. Starting from what I know subjectively of the operations of my own individual mind, and the activities which in my own organism they prompt, I proceed by analogy to infer from the observable activities of other organisms what are the mental operations that underlie them.

Now, in this mode of procedure what is the kind of activities which may be regarded as indicative of mind? I certainly do not so regard the flowing of a river or the blowing of the wind. Why? First, because the objects are too remote in kind from my own organism to admit of my drawing any reasonable analogy between them and it; and, secondly, because the activities which they present are of invariably the same kind under the same circumstances; they afford no evidence of feeling or purpose. In other words, two conditions require to be satisfied before we even begin to imagine that observable activities are indicative of mind: first, the activities must be displayed by a living organism; and secondly, they must be of a kind to suggest the presence of two elements which we recognise as the distinctive characteristics of mind as such – consciousness and choice. [. . . .]

On this whole subject of mind-like and yet not truly mental action I shall have much to say in my subsequent treatise, where I shall be concerned among other things with tracing the probable genesis of mind from non-mental antecedents. But here it is sufficient merely to make this general statement of the fact, that even within the experience supplied by our own organisms adaptive movements of a highly complex and therefore apparently purposive character may be performed without any real purpose, or even consciousness of their performance. It thus becomes evident that before we can predicate the bare existence of mind in the lower animals, we need some yet more definite criterion of mind than that which is supplied by the adaptive actions of a living organism, howsoever apparently intentional such actions may be. Such a criterion I have now to lay down, and I think it is one that is as practically adequate as it is theoretically legitimate.

Objectively considered, the only distinction between adaptive movements due to reflex action and adaptive movements due to mental perception, consists in the former depending on inherited mechanisms within the nervous system being so constructed as to effect *particular* adaptive movements in response to *particular* stimulations, while the latter are independent of any such inherited adjustment of special mechanisms to the exigencies of special circumstances. Reflex actions under the influence of their appropriate stimuli may be compared to the actions of a machine under the manipulations of an operator; when certain springs of action are touched by certain stimuli, the whole machine is thrown into appropriate movement; there is no room for choice there is no room for uncertainty; but as surely as any of these inherited mechanisms are affected by the stimulus with reference to which it has been constructed to act, so surely will it act in precisely the same way as it always has acted. But the case with conscious mental adjustment is quite different. For, without at present going into the question concerning the relation of body and mind, or waiting to ask whether cases of mental adjustmen are not really quite as *mechanical* in the sense of being the necessary result or correlative of a chain of physical sequences due to a physical stimulation, it is enough to point to the variable and incalculable character of mental adjustments as distinguished from the constant and foreseeable character of reflex adjustments All, in fact, that in an objective sense we can mean by a mental adjustment is an adjustment of a kind that has not been definitely fixed by heredity as the only adjustment possible in the given circumstances of stimulation. For were there no alternative of adjustment, the case, in an animal at least, would be indistinguishable from one of reflex action.

It is, then, adaptive action by a living organism in cases where the inherited machinery of the nervous system does not furnish data for our prevision of what the adaptive action must necessarily be – it is only here that we recognise the objective evidence of mind. The criterion of mind, therefore, which I propose, and to which I shall adhere throughout the present volume, is as follows: – Does the organism learn to make new adjustments, or to modify old ones, in accordance with the results of its own individual experience? If it does so, the fact cannot be due merely to reflex action in the sense above described, for it is impossible that heredity can have provided in advance for innovations upon, or alterations of, its machinery during the lifetime of a particular individual. [. . . .]

It is quite true, however, that since the days of Descartes – or rather, we might say, since the days of Joule – the question of animal automatism has assumed a new or more defined aspect seeing that it now runs straight into the most profound and insoluble problem that has ever been presented to human thought viz. the relation of body to mind in view of the doctrine of the conservation of energy. I shall subsequently have occasion to consider this problem with the close attention that it demands; but in the present volume, which has to deal only with the phenomena of mind as such, I expressly pass the problem aside as one reserved for separate treatment. Here I desire only to make it plain that the mind of animals must be placed in the same category, with reference to this problem, as the mind of man; and that we cannot without gross inconsistency ignore or question the evidence of mind in the former, while we accept precisely the same kind of evidence as sufficient proof of mind in the latter.

And this proof, as I have endeavoured to show, is in all cases and in its last analysis the fact of a living organism showing itself able to learn by its own individual experience. Wherever we find an animal able to do this, we have the same right to predicate mind as existing in such an animal that we have to predicate it as existing in any human being other than ourselves. For instance, a dog has always been accustomed to eat a piece of meat when his organism requires nourishment, and when his olfactory nerves respond to the particular stimulus occasioned by the proximity of the food. So far, it may be said, there is no evidence of mind; the whole series of events comprised in the stimulations and muscular movements may be due to reflex action alone. But now suppose that by a number of lessons the dog has been taught not to eat the meat when he is hungry until he receives a certain verbal signal: then we have exactly the same kind of evidence that the dog's actions are prompted by mind as we have that the actions of a man are so prompted.[1] Now we find that the lower down we go in the animal kingdom, the more we observe reflex action, or non-mental adjustment, to predominate over volitional action, or mental adjustment. That is to say, the lower down we go in the animal kingdom, the less capacity do we find for changing adjustive movements in correspondence with changed conditions; it becomes more and more hopeless to *teach* animals – that is, to establish associations of ideas; and the reason of this, of course, is that ideas or mental units become fewer and less definite the lower we descend through the structure of mind.

It is not my object in the present work to enter upon any analysis of the operations of mind, as this will require to be done

1. Of course it may be said that we have no evidence of *prompting* in either case; but this is the side issue which concerns the general relation of body and mind, and has nothing to do with the guarantee of inferring the presence of mind in particular cases.

as fully as possible in my next work. Nevertheless, a few words must here be said with regard to the main divisions of mental operation, in order to define closely the meanings which I shall attach to certain terms relating to these divisions, and the use of which I cannot avoid.

The terms sensation, perception, emotion, and volition need not here be considered. I shall use them in their ordinary psychological significations; and although I shall subsequently have to analyse each of the organic or mental states which they respectively denote, there will be no occasion in the present volume to enter upon this subject. I may, however, point out one general consideration to which I shall throughout adhere. Taking it for granted that the external indications of mental processes which we observe in animals are trustworthy, so that we are justified in inferring particular mental states from particular bodily actions, it follows that in consistency we must everywhere apply the same criteria.

For instance, if we find a dog or a monkey exhibiting marked expressions of affection, sympathy, jealousy, rage, &c., few persons are sceptical enough to doubt that the complete analogy which these expressions afford with those which are manifested by man, sufficiently prove the existence of mental states analogous to those in man of which these expressions are the outward and visible signs. But when we find an ant or a bee apparently exhibiting by its actions these same emotions, few persons are sufficiently non-sceptical not to doubt whether the outward and visible signs are here trustworthy as evidence of analogous or corresponding inward and mental states. The whole organisation of such a creature is so different from that of a man that it becomes questionable how far analogy drawn from the activities of the insect is a safe guide to the inferring of mental states – particularly in view of the fact that in many respects, such as in the great preponderance of 'instinct' over 'reason', the psychology of an insect is demonstrably a widely different thing from that of a man. Now it is, of course, perfectly true that the less the resemblance the less is the value of any analogy built upon the resemblance, and therefore that the inference of an ant or a bee feeling sympathy or rage is not so valid, as is the similar inference in the case of a dog or a monkey. Still it *is* an inference, and, so far as it goes, a valid one – being, in fact, the only inference available. That is to say, if we observe an ant or a bee apparently exhibiting sympathy or rage, we must either conclude that some psychological state resembling that of sympathy or rage is present, or else refuse to think about the subject at all; from the observable facts there is no other inference open. Therefore, having full regard to the progressive weakening of the analogy from human to brute psychology as we recede through the animal kingdom downwards from man, still, as it is the only analogy available, I shall follow it throughout the animal series. [. . . .]

The term 'reason' is used in significations almost as various as those which are applied to 'instinct'. Sometimes it stands for all the distinctively human faculties taken collectively, and in antithesis to the mental faculties of the brute; while at other times it is taken to mean the distinctively human faculties of intellect.

Dr Johnson defines it as 'the power by which man deduces one proposition from another, and proceeds from premises to consequences'. This definition presupposes language, and therefore ignores all cases of inference not thrown into the formal shape of predication. Yet even in man the majority of inferences drawn by the mind never emerge as articulate propositions; so that although, as we shall have occasion fully to observe in my subsequent work, there is much profound philosophy in identifying reason with speech as they were identified in the term Logos, yet for purposes of careful definition so to identify intellect with language is clearly a mistake.

More correctly, the word reason is used to signify the power of perceiving analogies or ratios, and is in this sense equivalent to the term 'ratiocination', or the faculty of deducing inferences from a perceived equivalency of relations. Such is the only use of the word that is strictly legitimate, and it is thus that I shall use it throughout the present treatise. This faculty, however, of balancing relations, drawing inferences, and so of forecasting probabilities, admits of numberless degrees; and as in the designation of its lower manifestations it sounds somewhat unusual to employ the word reason, I shall in these cases frequently substitute the word intelligence. Where we find, for instance, that an oyster profits by individual experience, or is able to perceive new relations and suitably to act upon the result of its perceptions, I think it sounds less unusual to speak of the oyster as displaying intelligence than as displaying reason. On this account I shall use the former term to signify the lower degrees of the ratiocinative faculty; and thus in my usage it will be opposed to such terms as instinct, reflex action, &c., in the same manner as the term reason is so opposed. This is a point which, for the sake of clearness, I desire the reader to retain in his memory. I shall always speak of intelligence and intellect in antithesis to instinct, emotion, and the rest, as implying mental faculties the same in kind as those which in ourselves we call rational. [. . . .]

General Intelligence

Coming now to the higher powers, I shall give a few cases to show that monkeys certainly surpass all other animals in the scope of their rational faculty. Professor Croora Robertson writes me: –

I witnessed the following incident in the Jardin des Plantes, now many years ago; but it struck me greatly at the time, and I have narrated it repeatedly in the interval. A large ape – I believe anthropoid, but cannot tell the species – was in the great iron cage with a number of smaller monkeys, and was lording it over them with many wild gambols, to the amusement of a crowd of spectators. Many things – fruits and the like – had been thrown between the bars into the cage, which the ape was always forward to seize. At last some one threw in a small hand looking-glass, with a strongly made frame of wood. This the ape at once laid hold of, and began to brandish like a hammer. Suddenly he was arrested by the reflection of himself in the glass, and looked puzzled for a moment; then he darted his head behind the glass to find the other of his kind that he evidently supposed to be there. Astonished to find nothing, he apparently bethought himself that he had not been quick enough with his movement. He now proceeded to raise and draw the glass nearer to him with great caution, and then with a swifter dart looked behind. Again finding nothing, he repeated the attempt once more. He now passed from astonishment to anger, and began to beat with the frame violently on the floor of the cage. Soon the glass was shattered, and pieces fell out. Continuing to beat, he was in the course of one blow again arrested by his image in the piece of glass still remaining in the frame. Then, as it seemed, he determined to make one trial more. More circumspectly than ever the whole first part of the process was gone through with; more violently than ever the final dart made. His fury over this last failure knew no bounds. He crunched the frame and glass together with his teeth, he beat on the floor, he crunched again, till nothing but splinters was left.

Mr Darwin writes: 'Rengger, a most careful observer, states that when first he gave eggs to his monkeys in Paraguay, they smashed them, and thus lost much of their contents; afterwards they generally hit one end against some hard body, and picked off the bits with their fingers. After cutting themselves only *once* with any sharp tool, they would not touch it again, or would handle it with the greatest caution. Lumps of sugar were often given them wrapped up in paper; and Rengger sometimes put a live wasp in the paper, so that in hastily unfolding it they got stung; after this had *once* happened, they always first held the packet to their ears to detect any movement within.'[2]

The powers of observation and readiness to establish new associations thus rendered apparent, display a high level of general intelligence. Mr Darwin further observes that Mr Belt 'likewise describes various actions of a tamed cebus, which, I think, clearly show that this animal possessed some reasoning power'. The following is the account to which Mr Darwin here refers, and I quote it *in extenso*, because, as I shall presently show, I have myself been able to confirm most of the observations on another monkey of the same genus: –

It would sometimes entangle itself round a pole to which it was fastened, and then unwind the coils again with the greatest discernment. Its chain allowed it to swing down below the verandah, but it could not reach to the ground. Sometimes, when there were broods of young ducks about, it would hold out a piece of bread in one hand, and when it had tempted a duckling within reach, seize it by the other, and kill it with a bite in the breast. There was such an uproar amongst the fowls on these occasions, that we soon knew what was the matter, and would rush out and punish Mickey (as we called him) with a switch; so that he was ultimately cured of his poultry-killing propensities. One day, when whipping him, I held up the dead duckling in front of him, and at each blow of the light switch told him to take hold of it, and at last, much to my surprise, he did so, taking it and holding it tremblingly in one hand. He would draw things towards him with a stick, and even used a swing for the same purpose. It had been put up for the children, and could be reached by Mickey, who now and then indulged himself in a swing on it. One day I had put down some bird-skins on a chair to dry, far beyond, as I thought, Mickey's reach; but, fertile in expedients, he took the swing and launched it towards the chair, and actually managed to knock the skins off in the return of the swing, so as to bring them within his reach. He also procured some jelly that was set out to cool in the same way. Mickey's actions were very human-like. When any one came near to fondle him, he never neglected the opportunity of pocket-picking. He would pull out letters, and quickly take them from their envelopes.[3]

I shall now proceed to state some further facts, showing the high level of intelligence to which monkeys of various kinds attain.

The orang which Cuvier had used to draw a chair from one end to the other of a room, in order to stand upon it so as to reach a latch which it desired to open; and in this we have a display of

2. *Descent of Man*, pp. 77–8.
3. *Naturalist in Nicaragua*, p. 119.

rationally adaptive action which no dog has equalled, although, as in the case before given of the dog dragging the mat, it has been closely approached. Again, Rengger describes a monkey employing a stick wherewith to prise up the lid of a chest, which was too heavy for the animal to raise otherwise. This use of a lever as a mechanical instrument is an action to which no animal other than a monkey has ever been known to attain; and, as we shall subsequently see, my own observation has fully corroborated that of Rengger in this respect. More remarkable still, as we shall also subsequently see, the monkey to which I allude as having myself observed, succeeded also by methodical investigation, and without any assistance, in discovering for himself the mechanical principle of the screw; and that monkeys well understand how to use stones as hammers is a matter of common observation since Dampier and Wafer first described this action as practised by these animals in the breaking open of oyster-shells. The additional observation of Gernelli Carreri of monkeys thrusting stones into the open valves of oysters so as to save themselves the trouble of smashing the shells, though not incredible, requires confirmation. But Mr Haden, of Dundee, has communicated to me the following very remarkable appreciation of mechanical principles which he himself observed in a monkey (species not noted), and which would certainly be beyond the mental powers of any other animal: –

'A large monkey, confined alone in a large cage, had its sleeping-place in the form of a kind of hut in the centre of the cage. Springing near the hut was a tree, or imitation tree, the main branch of which ascended over the top of the hut, and then came forwards away from it. Whether the roof of the hut enabled this animal to gain any part of this branch, I did not observe, but only remarked its method at the time of gaining the part of the branch which led frontwards, and away from the hut. This could be done by means of the hut door, which, when opened, swung beneath this part of the branch. The door, either by accident or by the design of its construction, *swung to* each time the animal opened it to mount upon its top edge. After one or two efforts to mount by it in spite of its immediate swinging to, the creature procured a thick blanket which lay in the cage, and threw it over the door, having opened the same, so that its complete swinging to was prevented sufficiently for the creature to mount upon its free edge, and so gain that part of the branch which ran above it.'

The following, which I quote from 'Nature' (vol. xxiii, p. 533), also displays high intelligence: –

One of the large monkeys at the Alexandra Palace had been for some time suffering from the decay of the right lower canine, and an abscess, forming a large protuberance on the jaw, had resulted. The pain seemed so great, it was decided to consult a dentist as to what should be done; and, as the poor creature was at times very savage, it was thought that if the tooth had to be extracted, gas should be used for the safety of the operation. Preparations were made accordingly, but the behaviour of the monkey was quite a surprise to all who were concerned. He showed great fight on being taken out of the cage, and not only struggled against being put into a sack prepared with a hole cut for his head, but forced one of his hands out, and snapped and screamed, and gave promise of being very troublesome. Directly, however, Mr Lewin Moseley, who had undertaken the operation, managed to get his hand on the abscess and gave relief, the monkey's demeanour changed entirely. He laid his head down quietly for examination, and, without the use of the gas, submitted to the removal of a stump of a tooth as quietly as possible.

According to D'Osbonville, certain monkeys that he observed in the wild state were in the habit of administering corporal chastisement to their young. After suckling and cleansing them, the mothers used to sit down and watch the youngsters play. These would wrestle, throw and chase each other, &c.; but if any of them grew malicious, the dams would spring up, and, seizing their offspring by the tail with one hand, correct them severely with the other.

We have already seen that dogs and cats display the idea of maintaining discipline among their progeny.

According to Houzeau the sacred monkey of India (*Semnopithecus entellus*) is very clever in catching snakes, and in the case of poisonous species destroys the fangs by breaking them against stones.

Of the fact that monkeys act in co-operation, many proofs might be given, but one will suffice.

Lieutenant Schipp, in his Memoirs, says: –

A Cape baboon having taken off some clothes from the barracks, I formed a party to recover them. With twenty men I made a circuit to cut them off from the caverns, to which they always fled for shelter. They observed my movements, and detaching about fifty to guard the entrance, the others kept their post. We could see them collecting large stones and other missiles. One old grey-headed one, who had often paid us a visit at the barracks, was seen distributing his orders, as if a general. We rushed on to the attack, when, at a scream from him, they rolled down enormous stones on us, so that we were forced to give up the contest. [. . . .]

4 C. Lloyd Morgan

Introduction to Comparative Psychology

Excerpt from C. Lloyd Morgan, *Introduction to comparative psychology*, Scribners, 2nd edition, 1909.

[. . . .] Now it is idle to assert that one set of inductions is more important than the other, since both are essential. But there can be no question that the subjective inductions are in some respect more subtle and difficult and delicate than the inductions concerning objective phenomena. There can be no question that false assumptions and vague generalizations more commonly pass muster with regard to mental processes than with regard to their physical manifestations. And there can be no question that in the systematic training of the comparative psychologist the subjective aspect is not *less* important than the objective aspect.

The question now arises whether in passing from human to animal psychology any other method of interpretation is possible than that which holds good for the former. Can the zoological psychologist afford to dispense with that systematic training in introspective or subjective analysis and induction which is absolutely essential for the student of human psychology? I venture to contend that he cannot. The scheme of interpretation [. . . .] holds good I maintain as well for animal psychology as for the psychology of man. There are, I am well aware, many people who fancy that by the objective study of animal life they can pass by direct induction to conclusions concerning the psychical faculties of animals. But this is, I think, through ignorance of the methods of psychology, or perhaps one may say, without injustice, through ignorance of the method that they themselves unconsciously adopt. All that is necessary, these people will tell you, is to observe carefully, and to explain the actions you observe in the most natural manner. 'In the most natural manner', here means and is equivalent to, in just the same way as you explain the actions of your human neighbours and acquaintances. And these human actions are explained on the assumption that your neighbour is actuated by motives and impulses similar to your own. Thus these observers who think that their explanations are reached by direct induction are really proceeding unconsciously on the method they affect to disregard. Reduced to its logical basis their contention is that the thorough and systematic study of that mind in terms of which they unconsciously interpret all other minds is unnecessary if not misleading.

Now it appears to me that the foundation of this erroneous view, for as such I must regard it, is the tacit assumption that what suffices for practical purposes suffices also for scientific purposes. All fairly successful men and women acquire, and must acquire, a knowledge of human nature sufficient for the practical needs of everyday life under social conditions. Over-subtlety and refinement of analysis, too great nicety of interpretation, are rather disadvantageous than otherwise in the practical conduct of affairs. Hence practical men are wont to look with some suspicion at the psychologist as one who is prone to be a mere theorist. In the same way practical politicians not uncommonly look with suspicion on sociologists and political economists, practical engineers regard with similar eyes the subtler theories of the physicist, practical metallurgists look askance on the more delicate methods and more advanced hypotheses of the chemist, and in general the practical man is inclined to utilize the results of the man of science but to regard his more refined interpretations of natural phenomena as mere theory.

There can be no question that the interpretation of the actions of animals as the outcome of mental processes essentially similar to those of man amply suffices for practical needs. The farmer, the keeper of a kennel, the cattlebreeder, the gamekeeper, the breaker-in of horses, all the practical men who are employed in the breeding, rearing, and training of animals, and the great number of people who keep animals as pets or in domestic service find a somewhat rough and ready interpretation amply sufficient for their purposes in hand. And not unnaturally they are surprised that the explanation which suffices for them with their wide practical experience is found by the man of science to need serious revision and correction. Often unacquainted with the methods and aims of science in its intellectual aspect as endeavouring to interpret the phenomena of nature, often regarding science as the generally unpaid servant of practical utility, they smile if they do not sneer, at the arrogance of the man of science who tells them that the explanation which is good enough for the practical purposes of daily life is not sufficient for the more subtle and refined purposes of scientific interpretation. Be this as it may, I venture to affirm that whereas the man who has to deal with animals for practical purposes can afford to be ignorant of psychological methods and results, the man who would deal scientifically with the psychical faculties of animals cannot afford to be thus ignorant. For the practical man accuracy of observation and careful induction therefrom are of primary importance, validity of psychological interpretation being for him altogether subsidiary. But for the scientific investigator thorough and accurate knowledge of and training in psychology is of at least co-ordinate importance with accuracy of objective observation.

Unfortunately many able men who are eminently fitted to make and record exact observations on the habits and activities of animals have not undergone the training necessary to enable them to deal with the psychological aspect of the question. The skilled naturalist or biologist is seldom also skilled in psychological analysis. Nothwithstanding therefore the admirable and invaluable observations of our great naturalists, we cannot help feeling that their psychological conclusions are hardly on the same level as that reached by their conclusions in the purely biological field.

For in the study of animal psychology as a branch of scientific inquiry, it is necessary that accurate observation, and a sound knowledge of the biological relationships of animals, should go hand in hand with a thorough appreciation of the methods and results of modern psychology. The only fruitful method of procedure is the interpretation of facts observed with due care in the light of sound psychological principles.

What some of these principles are we have considered, or shall consider, in this work. There is one basal principle, however, the brief exposition of which may fitly bring to a close this chapter. It may be thus stated: – *In no case may we interpret an action as the outcome of the exercise of a higher psychical faculty, if it can be interpreted as the outcome of the exercise of one which stands lower in the psychological scale.* [. . . .]

Do Animals Perceive Relations?

When I take a walk across the downs with Tony, a fox-terrier pup, I carry with me a stick; for it is his delight to race after it and bound back with it in his mouth. The other day I took with me a heavy-knobbed stick, a Kaffir knob-kerrie. At first he seized this by the middle; but to carry it thus was an awkward, lop-sided, unbalanced operation, and by the close of the afternoon he had profited by an hour or two of experience, and seized the stick near the knob end. Now such a proceeding can be completely explained in terms of sense-experience. The process was throughout one of trial and error; gradually he found the most comfortable way of carrying that stick, and adopted it. Incidentally he was solving in a practical way a problem in mechanics; he was finding the centre of gravity of the stick. Incidentally, too, he gave me an opportunity of perceiving that the centre of gravity had certain space-relations. It lay within about seven inches of the knob-end of the stick. But is there any reason to suppose that Tony perceived this relationship in even a rudimentary and indefinite way? I could see none. Through sense-experience he became aware in a practical way of how best to deal with the stick. There is no necessity for the adequate explanation of all that I observed to suppose that the pup perceived the relations as such; the relations at most may be regarded as implicit in practical performance by certain activities, not as explicit in focal perception. If therefore the canon we have already laid down is to be adopted, namely, that in no case is an animal activity to be interpreted as the outcome of a higher psychical faculty, if it can be fairly interpreted as the outcome of one which stands lower in the psychological scale, – if, I say, this canon is to be adopted, then we are bound to interpret the action of the dog as performed through sense-experience alone. And it will conduce to clearness if I here distinctly state that in *sense-experience* and in *intelligent* adaptation to circumstances, there is no perception of relations. This absence of perception is part of the connotation of these terms as I employ them in this work. That is to say, if the dog does perceive relations, then he displays something more than sense-experience and intelligence. [. . . .]

Do Animals Reason?

We are now in a position to consider the question which I have prefixed as a heading to this chapter. It is obvious that, as we attempt to answer the question, we must steadily bear in mind the sense in which the term 'reasoning' is employed. If we apply this term to the process by which an animal, profiting by experience, adapts his actions to somewhat varying circumstances, there can be no hesitation whatever in giving an affirmative answer to the question. There is no doubt that animals not only profit by past experience, but that they can apply this experience to concrete situations as they severally arise. So much is implied by the attribution to them of intelligence. Where a situation is assimilated with those in which experience has already been gained, expectations arise which are a sufficient guide to practical behaviour. As we have seen, such expectations are sometimes called practical inferences: if the word is to be used with a wide meaning, we may regard them as intelligent inferences. Mr L. T. Hobhouse calls them, in a recent work on *Mind in Evolution*, practical judgments as contrasted with the universal judgments of conceptual thought. It is true that his 'practical judgment' may seem to imply more than I am disposed to allow to animal psychology. It is true that he credits the animal with a power of perceiving relations which appears to be more than I am myself prepared to grant. But then he says: 'In such a perception, the relations contained contribute to the character of the whole as much as the elements that are related, and in that sense the relations may be said to be perceived. It does not follow that the character of any of the relations concerned is analysed out and distinguished from the terms which compose it.' This distinguishing of the relation from its terms, which is just what I mean by the perception of relations as considered in the thirteenth chapter, he does not claim for the animal. As the outcome of a very careful consideration of the whole question, supplemented by a number of interesting and valuable experimental observations, he concludes that 'the highest animals have as much capacity for dealing with the practical exigencies of their surroundings as can be attained by an intelligence limited in its scope to the concrete and the practical. Intelligence as we conceive it in this stage is capable of forming what we have called practical judgments.'

If then behaviour which is the outcome of concrete sense-experience, is placed in the same category as rational conduct based on the conceptual thought which results from the analysis of experience and the synthesis of ideal construction, we must freely admit that animals can and do reason. But I have used the term reason in a more restricted sense. Mr Hobhouse regards such restriction as arbitrary. The whole question, in his view, is a matter of degree. 'It is not that new faculties are introduced, but that old faculties receive a fresh development.' 'A chicken avoids a caterpillar because he dislikes the taste. We perhaps refuse to allow that the chicken reasons because he does not know what it is that makes the caterpillar taste bad. After the chicken follows the chemist, who finds that the caterpillar secretes a certain acid. But will the chemist explain why a given acid has an acrid taste, or show how the experience of unpleasantness should modify subsequent action? A horse learns to lift a latch. We do not think he reasons. He merely has found out how it is done, and does it. A man explains to a child the action of the latch, and shows how by pressing it at one point you lift it out of a catch at another. He, we say, reasons because he analyses the process and how it is done. But a physicist might point out that the man knows nothing whatever about it unless he sees that the principle of the lever is involved in a simple form; and a metaphysician might add that the physicist cannot be said to understand the principle of the lever unless he is prepared to decide whether it is a principle which holds true of reality, and if so, on what epistemological grounds. If we allow reason to the human species in general, and yet restrict it to that species, it must be by identifying the term reason arbitrarily with a certain grade in the development of analysis.'

But there are no grounds for supposing that in the chicken or the horse there is any development of analysis. It is not a question of a certain grade but of *any* grade. I may call Mr Hobhouse himself as a witness. Under the heading *Absence of Analysis*, he says: 'At the same time it must be understood that, if we attribute ideas to an animal, they are not ideas arrived at by any breaking-up, analysis, or other elaboration of what is given in perception [*i.e.*, concrete experience]. None of my animals (with the possible exception now and again of the monkeys) showed the least understanding of the how or why of their actions, as distinct from the crude fact that to do such and such a thing produced the result they required. It is the want of what we may call analysis that made, for example, the push-back bolt [in certain experiments] such a difficulty. What Jack [a dog] and the elephant knew was, crudely, that they had to push this bolt. That the reason why they had to push it was to get it clear of the staple they obviously never grasped.' Such is Mr Hobhouse's testimony. Of course all definition and restriction of terms is arbitrary. The object is to attain such clearness of thought as will enable us to understand exactly what we are discussing. To this end I have restricted the term 'reason', not indeed so as to identify it with a certain grade of analysis, but rather to that process which, as the result of analysis and re-synthesis, affords a scheme in the light of which action is taken. The process which I have described in an earlier chapter under the heading *The Perception of Relations* is the avenue to analysis; and this process, as we have seen, is closely bound up with the beginnings of conceptual thought. Mr Hobhouse, indeed, says that when, by an act of analysis, we make the relation a distinct object of thought, independent of the terms which it connects in a particular case, we pass from perception to conception, and this passage takes place in such close connection with the focusing of the relation in the particular case, that the question whether animals reason, in the restricted sense of the term, and the question whether they are capable of analysis are very closely related. I have already recorded my opinion that animals do not focally perceive relations: from this it follows that they do not utilize conceptions so as to reason. But it will be well to discuss the question further from the somewhat different standpoint which we have now reached.

Tony, the fox-terrier pup already introduced to my readers, when he wanted to go out into the road, used to put his head under the latch of the gate, lift it, and wait for the gate to swing open. Now an observer of the dog's intelligent action might well suppose that he clearly perceived how the end in view was to be gained, and the most appropriate means for effecting his purpose. But here much depends on the sense in which this statement is understood. It may be understood in the sense that the situation had acquired what Dr Stout calls 'meaning', so that certain concrete surroundings suggested directly, and without analysis, a given mode of practical behaviour. Or it may be understood in the sense that the dog formed a general conception of means such as could be profitably applied to this particular end. If the former interpretation be correct, I should say that Tony acted intelligently as the result of sense-experience; if the latter, I should regard his conduct as rational. And it may be said that it is quite impossible to decide between the two views, since we cannot ascertain what passed through the dog's mind. Once more, therefore, I must draw attention to the canon of interpretation adopted at the outset of our inquiries concerning other minds than ours, namely, that in no case is an animal activity to be interpreted in terms of higher psychological processes, if it can be fairly interpreted in terms of processes which stand lower in the scale of psychological evolution and development. The question is therefore whether Tony's behaviour can be fairly explained without his forming any conception of the relation of the means employed to the end attained. It appears to me that it can. I watched the development of the habit. The gate is of iron and has iron bars running vertically with interspaces of five or six inches between. On either side is a wall or low parapet, on which are similar vertical rails. The latch of the gate is at a level of about a foot above that of the top of the low wall. When it is lifted, the gate swings open by its own weight. When the dog was put out of the front door he naturally wanted to get out into the road, where there was often much to interest him; cats to be worried, other dogs with whom to establish a sniffing acquaintance, and so forth. I watched the dog at a very early stage of the development of the habit. He then ran up and down the low wall, and put his head out between the iron bars, now here, now there, now elsewhere, keenly gazing into the road. This he did for quite three or four minutes. Although he had gone out of that gate many times, although he had opportunities for seeing me lift the latch (a matter that probably had no interest whatever for him, following me out being a matter of course in his experience), he did not specially look out at or near the gate. He certainly did not seem to have any notion of means to attain an end; nor indeed did he seem to be trying to get out. He appeared only to be looking restlessly and wistfully at the familiar road. At length it so happened that he put out his head beneath the latch, which, as I have said, is at a convenient height for his doing so, being about a foot above the level of the wall. The latch was thus lifted. He withdrew his head and began to look out elsewhere, when he noticed that the gate was swinging open, and out he bolted. After that, whenever I took him out, instead of opening the gate for him, I waited until he lifted the latch. Gradually he went, after less frequent poking of his head in the wrong place, to the one opening from which the latch could be lifted. But it was nearly three weeks, during which I took him out about a dozen times, before he went at once and without hesitation to the right place and put his head without any ineffectual fumbling beneath the latch. Why did he take so long? I think partly because there was so little connection between gazing out into the road and getting out into the road. He did not, at first at any rate, seem to do the former in order to effect the latter. The relation between means and end did not appear to take form in his mind, even subconsciously as means to the end. And I take it that he never had the faintest notion of how or why looking out just there came to mean walking forth into the road.

With regard to this particular trick, then, I venture to affirm that, *when we know the whole history of it*, Tony's action is quite similar in kind to that of my little chick, Blackie, which, profiting by a chance experience, pulled down the corner of the newspaper and escaped from my experimental poultry-yard. As it stands, it is quite within the range of sense-experience [. . . .]

5 E. L. Thorndike

Animal Intelligence; an Experimental Study of the Associative Processes in Animals

Excerpt from E. L. Thorndike, 'Animal intelligence; an experimental study of the associative processes in animals', *Psych. Rev. Monogr. Suppl.* vol. 2 (1898), pp. 1–9.

This monograph is an attempt at an explanation of the nature of the process of association in the animal mind. Inasmuch as there have been no extended researches of a character similar to the present one either in subject-matter or experimental method, it is necessary to explain briefly its standpoint.

Our knowledge of the mental life of animals equals in the main our knowledge of their sense-powers, of their instincts or re-actions performed without experience, and of their reactions which are built up by experience. Confining our attention to the latter we find it the opinion of the better observers and analysts that these reactions can all be explained by the ordinary associa-tive processes without aid from abstract, conceptual, inferential thinking. These associative processes then, as present in animals' minds and as displayed in their acts, are my subject-matter. Any one familiar in even a general way with the literature of com-parative psychology will recall that this part of the field has re-ceived faulty and unsuccessful treatment. The careful, minute, and solid knowledge of the sense-organs of animals finds no counterpart in the realm of associations and habits. We do not know how delicate or how complex or how permanent are the possible associations of any given group of animals. And al-though one would be rash who said that our present equipment of facts about instincts was sufficient or that our theories about it were surely sound, yet our notions of what occurs when a chick grabs a worm are luminous and infallible compared to our notions of what happens when a kitten runs into the house at the familiar call. The reason that they have satisfied us as well as they have is just that they are so vague. We say that the kitten associates the sound 'kitty kitty' with the experience of nice milk to drink, which does very well for a commonsense answer. It also suffices as a rebuke to those who would have the kitten ratiocinate about the matter, but it fails to tell what real mental content is present. Does the kitten feel '*sound of call, memory-image of milk in a saucer in the kitchen, thought of running into the house, a feeling, finally, of " I will run in"* ? Does he perhaps feel only the sound of the bell and an impulse to run in, similar in quality to the impulses which make a tennis player run to and fro when playing? The word association may cover a multitude of essentially different processes, and when a writer attributes anything that an animal may do to association his statement has only the negative value of eliminating reasoning on the one hand and instinct on the other. His position is like that of a zoologist who should to-day class an animal among the 'worms'. To give to the word a positive value and several definite possibilities of meaning is one aim of this investigation.

The importance to comparative psychology in general of a more scientific account of the association-process in animals is evident. Apart from the desirability of knowing all the facts we can, of whatever sort, there is the especial consideration that these associations and consequent habits have an immediate import for biological science. In the higher animals the bodily life and preservative acts are largely directed by these associations. They, and not instinct, make the animal use the best feeding grounds, sleep in the same lair, avoid new dangers and profit by new changes in nature. Their higher development in mammals is a chief factor in the supremacy of that group. This, however, is a minor consideration. The main purpose of the study of the animal mind is to learn the development of mental life down through the phylum, to trace in particular the origin of human faculty. In relation to this chief purpose of comparative psychology the associative processes assume a rôle predominant over that of sense-powers or instinct, for in a study of the associative processes lies the solution of the problem. Sense-powers and instincts have changed by addition and supersedence, but the cognitive side of consciousness has changed not only in quantity but also in quality. Somehow out of these associative processes have arisen human consciousnesses with their sciences and arts and religions. The association of ideas proper, imagination, memory, abstraction, generalization, judgment, inference, have here their source. And in the metamorphosis the instincts, impulses, emotions and sense-impressions have been transformed out of their old natures. For the origin and development of human faculty we must look to these processes of association in lower animals. Not only then does this department need treatment more, but promises to repay the worker better.

Although no work done in this field is enough like the present investigation to require an account of its results, the *method* hitherto in use invites comparison by its contrast and, as I believe, by its faults. In the first place, most of the books do not give us a psychology, but rather a *eulogy*, of animals. They have all been about animal *intelligence*, never about animal *stupidity*. Though a writer derides the notion that animals have reason, he hastens to add that they have marvellous capacity of forming associations, and is likely to refer to the fact that human beings only rarely reason anything out, that their trains of ideas are ruled mostly by association, as if, in this latter, animals were on a par with them. The history of books on animals' minds thus furnishes an illustration of the well-nigh universal tendency in human nature to find the marvellous wherever it can. We wonder that the stars are so big and so far apart, that the microbes are so small and so thick together, and for much the same reason wonder at the things animals do. They used to be wonderful because of the mysterious, God-given faculty of instinct, which could almost remove mountains. More lately they have been wondered at because of their marvellous mental powers in profiting by experience. Now imagine an astronomer tremendously eager to prove the stars as big as possible, or a bacteriologist whose great scientific desire is to demonstrate the microbes to be very, very little! Yet there has been a similar eagerness on the part of many recent writers on animal psychology to praise the abilities of animals. It cannot help leading to partiality in deductions from facts and more especially in the choice of facts for investigation. How can scientists who write like lawyers, defending animals against the charge of having no power of rationality, be at the same time impartial judges on the bench? Unfortunately the real work in this field has been done in this spirit. The level-headed thinkers who might have won valuable results have contented themselves with arguing against the theories of the eulogists. They have not made investigations of their own.

In the second place the facts have generally been derived from anecdotes. Now quite apart from such pedantry as insists that a man's word about a scientific fact is worthless unless he is a trained scientist, there are really in this field special objections to the acceptance of the testimony about animals' intelligent acts which one gets from anecdotes. Such testimony is by no means on a par with testimony about the size of a fish or the migration of birds, etc. For here one has to deal not merely with ignorant or inaccurate testimony, but also with prejudiced testimony. Human folk are as a matter of fact eager to find intelligence in animals.

They like to. And when the animal observed is a pet belonging to them or their friends, or when the story is one that has been told as a story to entertain, further complications are introduced. Nor is this all. Besides commonly mis-stating what facts they report, they report only such facts as show the animal at his best. Dogs get lost hundreds of times and no one ever notices it or sends an account of it to a scientific magazine. But let one find his way from Brooklyn to Yonkers and the fact immediately becomes a circulating anecdote. Thousands of cats on thousands of occasions sit helplessly yowling, and no one takes thought of it or writes to his friend, the professor; but let one cat claw at the knob of a door supposedly as a signal to be let out, and straightway this cat becomes the representative of the cat-mind in all the books. The unconscious distortion of the facts is almost harmless compared to the unconscious neglect of an animal's mental life until it verges on the unusual and marvellous. It is as if some denizen of a planet where communication was by thought-transference, who was surveying humankind and reporting their psychology, should be oblivious to all our inter-communication save such as the psychical-research society has noted. If he should further misinterpret the cases of mere coincidence of thoughts as facts comparable to telepathic communication, he would not be more wrong than some of the animal psychologists. In short, the anecdotes give really the *abnormal* or *super-normal* psychology of animals.

Further, it must be confessed that these vices have been only ameliorated, not obliterated, when the observation is first-hand, is made by the psychologist himself. For as men of the utmost scientific skill have failed to prove good observers in the field of spiritualistic phenomena,[1] so biologists and psychologists before the pet terrier or hunted fox often become like Samson shorn. They, too, have looked for the intelligent and unusual and neglected the stupid and normal.

Finally, in all cases, whether of direct observation or report by good observers or bad, there have been three other defects. Only a single case is studied, and so the results are not necessarily true of the type; the observation is not repeated, nor are the conditions perfectly regulated; the previous history of the animal in question

---

1. I do not mean that scientists have been too credulous with regard to spiritualism, but am referring to the cases where ten or twenty scientists have been sent to observe some trick-performance by a spiritualistic 'medium', and have all been absolutely confident that they understood the secret of its performance, *each of them giving a totally different explanation.*

is not known. Such observations may tell us, if the observer is perfectly reliable, that a certain thing takes place, but they cannot assure us that it will take place universally among the animals of that species, or universally with the same animal. Nor can the influence of previous experience be estimated. All this refers to means of getting knowledge about what animals *do*. The next question is, 'What do they *feel*?' Previous work has not furnished an answer or the material for an answer to this more important question. Nothing but carefully designed, crucial experiments can. In abandoning the old method one ought to seek above all to replace it by one which will not only tell more accurately *what they do*, and give the much-needed information *how they do it*, but also inform us *what they feel* while they act.

To remedy these defects experiment must be substituted for observation and the collection of anecdotes. Thus you immediately get rid of several of them. You can repeat the conditions at will, so as to see whether or not the animal's behavior is due to mere coincidence. A number of animals can be subjected to the same test, so as to attain typical results. The animal may be put in situations where its conduct is especially instructive. After considerable preliminary observation of animals' behavior under various conditions, I chose for my general method one which, simple as it is, possesses several other marked advantages besides those which accompany experiment of any sort. It was merely to put animals when hungry in enclosures from which they could escape by some simple act, such as pulling at a loop of cord, pressing a lever, or stepping on a platform. (A detailed description of these boxes and pens will be given later.) The animal was put in the enclosure, food was left outside in sight, and his actions observed. Besides recording his general behavior, special notice was taken of how he succeeded in doing the necessary act (in case he did succeed), and a record was kept of the time that he was in the box before performing the successful pull, or clawing, or bite. This was repeated until the animal had formed a perfect association between the sense-impression of the interior of that box and the impulse leading to the successful movement. When the association was thus perfect, the time taken to escape was, of course, practically constant and very short.

If, on the other hand, after a certain time the animal did not succeed, he was taken out, but *not fed*. If, after a sufficient number of trials, he failed to get out, the case was recorded as one of complete failure. Enough different sorts of methods of escape were tried to make it fairly sure that association in general, not association of a particular sort of impulse, was being studied. Enough animals were taken with each box or pen to make it sure that the results were not due to individual peculiarities. None of the animals used had any previous acquaintance with any of the mechanical contrivances by which the doors were opened. So far as possible the animals were kept in a uniform state of hunger, which was practically utter hunger. That is, no cat or dog was experimented on when the experiment involved any important question of fact or theory, unless I was sure that his motive was of the standard strength. With chicks this is not practicable, on account of their delicacy. But with them dislike of loneliness acts as a uniform motive to get back to the other chicks. Cats (or rather kittens), dogs and chicks were the subjects of the experiments. All were apparently in excellent health, save an occasional chick.

By this method of experimentation the animals are put in situations which call into activity their mental functions and permit them to be carefully observed. One may, by following it, observe personally more intelligent acts than are included in any anecdotal collection. And this actual vision of animals in the act of using their minds is far more fruitful than any amount of histories of what animals have done without the history of how they did it. But besides affording this opportunity for purposeful and systematic observation, our method is valuable because it frees the animal from any influence of the observer. The animal's behavior is quite independent of any factors save its own hunger, the mechanism of the box it is in, the food outside, and such general matters as fatigue, indisposition, etc. Therefore the work done by one investigator may be repeated and verified or modified by another. No personal factor is present save in the observation and interpretation. Again, our method gives some very important results which are quite uninfluenced by *any* personal factor in any way. The curves showing the progress of the formation of associations, which are obtained from the records of the times taken by the animal in successive trials, are facts which may be obtained by any observer who can tell time. They are absolute, and whatever can be deduced from them is sure. So also the question of whether an animal does or does not form a certain association requires for an answer no higher qualification in the observer than a pair of eyes. The literature of animal psychology shows so uniformly and often so sadly the influence of the personal equation that any method which can partially eliminate it deserves a trial.

Furthermore, although the associations formed are such as could not have been previously experienced or provided for by heredity, they are still not too remote from the animal's ordinary course of life. They mean simply the connection of a certain act with a certain situation and resultant pleasure, and this general type of association is found throughout the animal's life normally. The muscular movements required are all such as might often be required of the animal. And yet it will be noted that the acts required are nearly enough like the acts of the anecdotes to enable one to compare the results of experiment by this method with the work of the anecdote school. Finally, it may be noticed that the method lends itself readily to experiments on imitation.

We may now start in with the description of the apparatus and of the behavior of the animals.[2]

Description of Apparatus

The shape and general apparatus of the boxes which were used for the cats is shown by the accompanying drawing of box K.

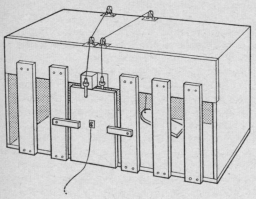

Figure 1

Unless special figures are given, it should be understood that each box is approximately 20 inches long by 15 broad by 12 high. Except where mention is made to the contrary, the door was pulled open by a weight attached to a string which ran over a

2. The experiments now to be described were for the most part made in the Psychological Laboratory of Columbia University during the year '97–'98, but a few of them were made in connection with a general preliminary investigation of animal psychology undertaken at Harvard University in the previous year.

pulley and was fastened to the door, just as soon as the animal loosened the bolt or bar which held it. Especial care was taken not to have the widest openings between the bars at all near the lever, or wire-loop, or what not, which governed the bolt on the door. For the animal instinctively attacks the large openings first, and if the mechanism which governs the opening of the door is situated near one of them the animal's task is rendered easier. You do not then get the association process so free from the helping hand of instinct as you do if you make the box without reference to the position of the mechanism to be set up within it. These various mechanisms are so simple that a verbal description will suffice in most cases. The facts which the reader should note are the nature of the movement which the cat had to make, the nature of the object at which the movement was directed, and the position of the object in the box. In some special cases attention will also be called to the force required. In general, however, that was very slight (20 to 100 grams if applied directly). [. . . .]

6 W. T. Shepherd

Some Observations and Experiments of the Intelligence of the Chimpanzee and Ourang

W. T. Shepherd, 'Some observations and experiments of the intelligence of the chimpanzee and ourang', *Amer. J. Psychol.*, vol. 34 (1923), pp. 590–91.

The experiments and observations reported herein were made on two apes, Sokker, a male chimpanzee 7 years old, and Rufus, a male ourang 4 years old, in the National Zoological Gardens, Washington, D.C.

Purposes: I. To test their mentality for (1) ideas, ideation, (2) reasoning powers, and (3) imitation as involving ideation.

II. To test them by experiments similar to experiments made by the present writer on Rhesus monkeys some years ago; to ascertain if their intelligence is equal to, or greater than, that of other monkeys, so far as these tests would indicate.

III. To verify conclusions reached previously in tests on other apes (the trained vaudeville stars Peter and Consul) observed and previously reported on by the present writer.

IV. To test their intelligence as compared with that of dogs and cats in similar experiments made by the writer at the George Washington University.

Tests of reasoning

In this test, as in those on Rhesus monkeys, dogs, and cats, referred to above, I suspended a piece of apple (for which the apes have a liking) by a string in front of the cage beyond their reach; it had a piece of stick run through it, one end of which was pointed toward the cage in which the animals were kept; that end of the stick was within the reach of the apes if they would pass their hands through the wire of the cage. The problem was to see if they would reach out and seize the end of the stick, and draw in and thereby secure the piece of apple.

Sokker, the chimpanzee, reached through the wire, seized the end of the stick, and drew in the piece of apple: in the first trial, in 5 sec.; in the second trial on that day in 4 sec. Rufus, the ourang, succeeded in securing the piece of apple in the same manner: in his first trial, in 8 sec.; in his second trial on that day in 6 sec.

These experiments were repeated the next day. Both animals did the act, and in shorter time. In this experiment both gave what I consider to be clear indications of a low form of reasoning, – what I have called, in the previously reported experiments on Rhesus monkeys, Adaptive Intelligence.

Tests of ideation

To test the animals I employed a plan formerly used with Rhesus monkeys. I placed a light board, 30 in. long and 8 in. wide, outside the cage and at right angles to it, upon an improvised platform on a level with the floor of the cage. One end of the board was within reach of the animals through the wire of the cage; the other end was beyond their reach; a piece of banana, for which the animals have a fondness, was placed out of reach on the board. The problem was to see if the apes would take hold of the end within reach, pull the board in, and thus secure the banana.

Both the animals did the act successfully. The figures are: Sokker, first trial, 20 sec.; second trial, 15 sec. Rufus in the first trial took 25 sec.; in the second trial 16 sec. We might remark that Rufus appeared somewhat fearful and cautious. The next day the experiments were repeated. Sokker secured the banana in the first trial in 8 sec., and in the second trial in 6 sec. Rufus took 9 and 6 sec. respectively in his first and second trial on that day.

Tests of imitation

In these tests I employed a method used by Hobhouse in England on a chimpanzee and Cebus monkey, and by Watson at Johns Hopkins University on monkeys. I had employed the plan in tests on Rhesus monkeys, reported in Monograph Supplement No. 52 of the Psychological Review. In these tests on the monkeys, I had secured only negative and partially positive results.

A T-rake was used; food, a piece of banana, was placed in front of the cage and in the apes' sight but beyond their reach; the T-rake was placed with the end of the handle within their reach; the problem was to see if they would take hold of the handle and draw in the food, after seeing me do it; if they would imitate my actions. I demonstrated the use of the rake three times, and then gave each separately (they were in different cages) a chance to imitate my act, and thereby to secure the piece of banana.

Sokker in the first trial immediately seized the end of the rake handle and pulled it under the lower part of the wire into the cage; he examined it carefully, and played with it; but he made no effort to use the rake to draw in the food as I had shown him how to do. The banana was, of course, within the sweep of the rake, if he had used it. He was given 2 min. to get his ideas together, if he had any, in the matter. In his second trial, he repeated the actions of the first trial; he made no attempt, so far as I could observe, to use the rake to secure the banana. He at times looked, or appeared to look, at the banana. In similar tests next day, two trials under similar conditions and time, he entirely failed.

Rufus, on the first day, first trial, was allowed 2 min. He repeated essentially the actions of Sokker. He seemed, perhaps, to be more fearful and cautious. He failed likewise in the second trial.

Consideration of results

A comparison of the results of the experiments on reasoning (of the low form) shows that the apes did the acts the Rhesus monkeys did, and in quicker time. The experiments with the apes were fewer in number, but seem to me to be significant. Their mentality, as compared with that of the Rhesus monkeys, seems to be superior, so far as these experiments show. The dogs and cats tested failed entirely or almost entirely in similar experiments. But we should bear in mind that the latter have not the motor equipment, that is, the hands, that the apes and other monkeys possess. In every way, however, they seem to be inferior in intelligence.

In the tests on ideation, in general the apes surpassed the Rhesus monkeys, and by far the dogs and cats tested. That is, they did all, or nearly all the acts the monkeys did, and in shorter time; their understanding of a given situation, like these here reported, was better.

In the test for imitation here reported, two of the Rhesus monkeys did made a success, or at least a partial success, in similar trials. But they were allowed many more trials than the apes. They did not succeed in the number of trials given the apes. For myself, I am not convinced that the apes under similar conditions of more trials would not have done as well as, or better than, the Rhesus monkeys, supposed biologically to be their inferiors. I suggest that they probably would have done so.

Summary

I. The superior motor equipment of the apes accounts in large measure for their apparently superior intelligence.

II. Their semi-erect and biped position accounts in part for their alleged superior intelligence.

III. (1) They give indications of ideas, probably of a crude and unanalysed type. (2) They give evidence of a form of intelligence which may roughly be called a low form of reasoning – as is shown by the suspended-apple experiments here reported.

IV. Observations and experiments, as well as the theory of evolution, appear to give the apes, at least the chimpanzee and ourang, a place above all other sub-humans, in intelligence, as in anatomical structure.

The writer is fully aware that the experiments here reported are few in number. But they suffice, taken together with other observations, to make him reasonably confident of these conclusions.

Part Two DELAYED RESPONSE

The delayed response task requires the subject to identify the location of a reward signified by a stimulus after that stimulus has been removed. The length of the enforced delay has been varied from a few seconds in some experiments to days in others. Correct response, despite the absence of an external cue, suggests that the animal retains a representation of the original stimulus during the delay interval. Such a representational factor was thought to be one of the highest forms of complex ideation.

This notion was dramatically reinforced by unimpeachable data which showed that monkeys in whom the frontal lobes of the brain were removed failed in this task while succeeding with simple discrimination problems. Subsequent research showed that success in delayed response was dependent on attention, motivation, learning and retention rather than on conceptual prowess. Nevertheless, it remains a sensitive indicator of behavioural proficiency and is useful in the study of anoxia, radiation injury, pharmacological damage and a variety of other physiological insults which produce behavioural deficit.

7 O. L. Tinklepaugh

An Experimental Study of Representative Factors in Monkeys

Excerpt from O. L. Tinklepaugh, 'An experimental study of representative factors in monkeys', *J. comp. Psychol.*, vol. 8 (1928), pp. 197–202.

I. Introduction

Hunter and other experimenters have shown that after a stimulus is removed various animals can successfully respond to the position in space in which this stimulus was seen. No experimental evidence has been available, heretofore, which showed conclusively the nature of the cues used by animals in this problem. Was their response predicated on representative factors which stood for the position of the stimulus in space, or was it to be explained by some mere preferential accent at an unconscious level? There arises the further question of whether there were present, in the animal, factors which stood for the reward and not merely for the position of the same in space.

In the present investigation methods were developed whereby the representative factors used by monkeys in the delayed reaction could be studied, and an effort was made to determine the nature of these factors.

II. Historical

1. *Hunter's delayed reaction experiment*

The delayed reaction experiment was first performed in a preliminary way by W. R. Hough and H. B. Reed, graduate students, at the University of Chicago. The first extensive study of this problem was made by Hunter (3) at the same University, in the years 1910 to 1912.

In Hunter's experiments a subject was confined in a compartment so arranged that it was confronted by three doors in as many different directions before it. Each door led to a food compartment. A light was situated behind each door. Food was placed in one of the compartments; the light behind the corresponding door was turned on for a few seconds; a delay followed with the light off, and then the animal was released. If he went through the door from which the light had been visible, he received food.

Before the animals used would respond to the light stimulus in the manner described, Hunter found it necessary to give them a training series of from 150 to 500 trials or over. First they were taught to respond to the door in which the light remained lighted. In several succeeding trials the light was turned off when the animal was *en route* to it. By successive steps made in this manner the animals finally were trained so that they would respond to the door in which the light had been seen prior to the period of delay.

Hunter tested the maximal delay for rats, dogs, raccoons, and children. Rats could delay successfully for ten seconds; dogs, five minutes; raccoons, twenty-five seconds. Children in an analogous situation, i.e., in a suitably arranged room instead of the box-like apparatus, delayed for from fifty seconds to twenty-five minutes, depending upon age and other factors. The probability was that the time for the older children could have been increased to hours or days. Hunter (4) later used a somewhat different method in experimenting with his daughter, Thayer, while she was thirteen to sixteen months old, and before she had developed language habits. She gave 88 per cent correct choices with three to seven second delays, 72 per cent with eight to ten second delays, and correspondingly lower percentages for longer intervals.

Hunter's rats and dogs could only react successfully when part or all of their bodies had been oriented in the direction of the proper choice. With the raccoons and children, this was not necessarily the case. At times tendencies toward bodily orientation were noted in them, but the correctness of their responses was not disturbed by the absence of such orientation. From these facts Hunter (3, p. 80) concludes that the rats and dogs probably used 'overt orienting attitudes' as the cues for correct response, while 'some intra-organic (non-orientation) factor not visible to the experimenter must be assumed in order to explain a significant number of the correct reactions of the raccoons and all of the successful reactions of the children'. 'These cues,' he adds, 'fulfilled an ideational function.' Seemingly in keeping with the principle of Morgan, he concludes that 'sensory thought', of an imageless nature, as contrasted with the higher imaginal thought, 'represents the highest grade of behaviour in raccoons and probably also in children of some two and one-half years of age'.

2. *Other experiments on delayed reaction*

a. Ulrich (9) studied the 'posturing' of rats in connection with delayed response. He found that only when there was orientation, a series of forward movements, or scratching at a certain spot in the retaining chamber, was there a definite direction in the rat's progress. He pointed out that posturing may occur inside of the release box, or it may be reinstated outside the box. His rats responded correctly after an interval of 40 seconds.

b. Cats delayed for as long as four seconds in a three-compartment box, and eighteen seconds in a two-compartment box, in an experiment performed by Yarbrough (12). He concluded that they solved the problem by gross motor attitudes of all or part of the body.

c. Cowan (2) experimented with a Persian cat in its home environment. The rooms of the house were used for the experimental setting. The appearance of the experimenter with a dish of food at one of two doors was the stimulus. This animal reached a delay interval of as long as thirty seconds with 68 per cent correct choices. The animal showed no evidences of bodily orientation.

d. Walton (10) worked with dogs, using four parallel alleys for food compartments. His subjects delayed successfully for one minute, when the retaining cage was turned through an angle of 90° during the delay.

e. A monkey observed by Buytendijk (1) seized a piece of apple thrown in one direction, and at the same time watched the throwing of three others in different directions. He ate the first piece and went and got the second and ate it before a window. After securing and eating the third piece he watched a flying bird, scratched himself, turned around and sought the fourth piece which had fallen under a board. After eating it, he sat peacefully looking out of a window.

f. Nellmann and Trendelenburg (8), when working with a monkey, used a box the door of which was hinged at one side and which opened at the opposite side. If the box was turned through 180 degrees after the food had been placed in it, the monkey observed the turning and always approached the correct side. If a delay of half a minute was introduced after the turning, the monkey failed to remember which side of the box to approach.

g. The chimpanzee, Ioni, which Kohts (7) trained to match objects from a sample, failed if a delay of over 15 seconds was

79

inserted between the showing of the sample and the choice of the similar object.

h. Köhler's chimpanzees (6) immediately located food which had been buried in sand outside their cage, after a delay of sixteen and one-half hours.

i. Yerkes (13) found that the gorilla, Congo, located buried food after 48 hours delay. When he used four boxes, similar except in color, and placed them to either side, in front of and behind the subject, Congo was successful after delays of three hours. As will be seen in the paper by Robert M. and David N. Yerkes (14), chimpanzees also found buried food after delays of forty-eight hours, and with the four box arrangement, delayed successfully for from three to four hours.

3. *Criticisms of delayed reaction experiments*

a. Watson (11) is naturally critical of Hunter's work, for the findings conflict with his behaviorism. In discussing implicit behavior – behavior 'involving only the speech mechanisms (or the larger musculature in a minimal way)' (p. 19) he points out 'that when explicit behavior (involving general musculature) is delayed (i.e., when deliberation ensued), the intervening time between stimulus and response is given over to implicit behaviour (to "thought processes")'. He also asserts (p. 20) that an incoming impulse cannot, as commonly stated, be held in *statu quo* for long periods of time, until it can obtain possession of the motor field. In discussing Hunter's work (pp. 224–7) he suggests that the raccoons may have responded to cues from the experimenter, to after-glow of the light, temperature, odor, or the like. 'The case of the long delays of the children may be explained by the use of language habits.' (Hunter had not yet performed the experiment with his thirteen to sixteen months old daughter who was still without language habits.) But Watson declared there was no known mechanism to account for the behavior of the raccoons.

b. Köhler (5), though not referring specifically to delayed reaction experiments, is critical of all mechanical choice training problems which afford no basis for insight. He points out that chimpanzees, in spite of their excellent behavior in tests requiring intelligence, make a relatively poor showing in problems of this other type. Lower vertebrates which could not pass the tests of insight, learn to perform tasks of the other kind in approximately the same time as apes. This result he believes is due to the fact that the choice training experiments depend, for their solution, upon superficial accustoming and experience, and do not afford any connection comprehensible to the ape. Köhler suggests a new method suited for discrimination and other similar problems with primates. The subject sits behind a grating. Containers with sufficiently different perceptual qualities are placed before him outside. One of them is slowly filled with fruit before his eyes. They are closed. A curtain is lowered in front of the containers, and under cover of it the containers are moved or changed in whatever manner is desired. Then the curtain is raised and the animal is permitted to designate his choice of containers. As can be seen, this is essentially a delayed reaction experiment. A modification of this method was used in the present investigation.

References

(1) BUYTENDIJK, F. J. J.: Considerations de psychologie compar propos d'experience faites avec le singe cercopithecus. Arch. neer. de physiol., 1921, t. 5, 42.

(2) COWAN, Edwina Abbott: An experiment testing the ability of the cat to make delayed response and to maintain a given response toward a varying stimulus. J. Comp. Psych., 1923, iii, 1.

(3) HUNTER, W. S.: The delayed reaction in animals and children. Behav. Monog., 1913, ii, no. 1.

(4) HUNTER, W. S.: The delayed reaction in a child. Psych. Rev., 1917, xxiv, no. 1, 75–87.

(5) KÖHLER, W.: Uber eine neue methode zur psychologischen untersuchen von menschenaffen. Psych. Forsch., 1922, i, 390–397.

(6) KÖHLER, W.: The Mentality of Apes. New York, 1925.

(7) KOHTS, N.: Untersuchungen uber die erkenntnisfahigkeitne des schimpansen. Moscow, 1924. (Summarized by R. M. Yerkes and A. Petrunkevitch, J. Comp. Psych., 1925, v, 98–108.)

(8) NELLMAN, H. and TRENDELENBURG, W.: Ein beitrag zur intelligenzprüfung neidere raffen. Zeitschr. f. vergl. Physiologie, 1926, iv, 142–200.

(9) ULRICH, John L.: Integration of movements in learning in the albino rat. J. Comp. Psych., 1912, i, no. 2, 184–199.

(10) WALTON, A. C.: The influence of diverting stimuli during delayed reaction in dogs. Jour. Animal Behav., 1915 v, no. 4, 259–291.

(11) WATSON, John B.: Behavior. New York, 1914.

(12) YARBROUGH, J. U.: Delayed reaction with sound and light in cats. Jour. Animal Behav., 1917, vii, 87–110.

(13) YERKES, Robert M.: The mind of a gorilla: II. Mental Development. Genetic Psych. Monog., 1917, ii, no. 6.

(14) YERKES, Robert M., and David N.: Concerning memory in the chimpanzee. Jour. Comp. Psych., 1928, viii, no. 3, 237–271.

Part Three   TOOL USING

Few types of intelligent animal behaviour have caused as much controversy among scientific workers as has tool using. The development of this capacity has long been regarded by many as one of the most significant steps in the evolution of man, and this view itself is controversial. Köhler's and Yerkes' studies of chimpanzees (regrettably, too long to be included here) in which methods developed by Hobhouse were extended, showed that this species could purposefully rearrange the environment, interrelating disparate elements of it in order to solve a problem. Subsequent investigators tried to demonstrate that animals are capable of foresight and planning, the appreciation of cause and effect, the isolation of the essential elements in a problem and the role of the tool as an extension of the hand. Others, generally, it should be noted, those working with different methods, questioned the existence of such capacities. They emphasized rather the role of innate manipulative tendencies and of learning in such behaviour, and at the same time pointed to flaws in the experiments of their theoretical adversaries.

Interesting species differences were observed; for example, the Cebus monkey from Central and South America was particularly adept at using tools. It was therefore presumably highly intelligent. However, a cautionary note was sounded regarding the interpretation of such findings when it was observed that many phylogenetically inferior animals, particularly birds and marine animals, behaved comparably under appropriate circumstances and yet they could not be regarded as highly intelligent.

8 K. R. L. Hall

Animals That Use Tools

K. R. L. Hall, 'Animals that use tools', *Animals*, vol. 7 (1965), pp. 16–21.

Tools and weapons have been described as 'extra-corporeal limbs' which can be changed or discarded as circumstances dictate. Essentially, an animal's performance may be defined as 'tool-using' if it takes hold of some object in its hands, claws, jaws, beak, or trunk, and then proceeds to use that object as a kind of extension of its own body to reach something it could not otherwise reach, to break open something it could only break at the risk of damaging its teeth, or to repel something threatening or alarming.

Before dealing with the problem of 'explaining' or 'evaluating' such performances, it will be best to consider a few well-known examples from recent animal studies. Among birds, one of the most interesting examples is that of the Galapagos woodpecker-finch, *Camarhyncus pallidus*, whose remarkable, indeed unique, feeding techniques, first reported in 1919 by Gifford, have been described by Lack and studied recently in great detail by Eibl-Eibesfeldt.

When a woodpecker has excavated in a branch for an insect, it inserts its long tongue into the crack to get the insect out. *Camarhyncus pallidus* lacks the long tongue, but achieves the same result in a different way. Having excavated a hole, it picks up a cactus spine or twig, 1 or 2 inches long, and holding it lengthwise in its beak, pokes it up the crack, dropping the twig to seize the insect as it emerges. If a twig or spine is too short or too pliable, it will reject it and break off or pick up another. Sometimes the bird carries a spine or twig about with it, poking it into cracks or crannies as it searches one tree after another. Eibl-Eibesfeldt found that the bird may use the tool to drive the insect out or to impale it, or just to locate it. Twigs or spines not well suited for the purpose are sometimes worked on by the bird.

Another of the few recorded uses of tools by birds, is the behaviour of the satin bower-bird, *Ptilonorhynchus violaceus*. Many of the males hold a bark wad between the tips of the beak so that a black, tacky material – made from a mixture of charcoal compounded with saliva – which they have taken into their bills can be forced between the mandibles and applied as a plaster to the inside sticks of the bower. Obviously, the 'function' of the tool-using in these two instances is entirely different: in the first, for food-getting, in the second, as an adjunct to a territorial or courtship display.

Among wild mammals other than primates, performances of any kind that fit the broad definition of tool-using are exceedingly rare. There have been reports of polar bears casting or rolling blocks of ice on to walruses to kill them, and elephants have been observed scratching themselves with sticks held in their trunks, and so on. Not a single instance of tool-use for food-getting is at present known except that of the California sea otter, *Enhydra lutris*. This otter is found off the coast of California, south of San Francisco, and off the Aleutian and other groups of islands lying roughly between Alaska, Japan, and Kamchatka.

For many years it was considered to be extinct, at least in the Californian part of its range, as a result of indiscriminate killing to obtain its valuable fur. Then, in the 1930s, it was rediscovered near Monterey, and, through careful protection, the populations of this delightful animal both in the south and north have increased satisfactorily. Soon after its rediscovery, Edna Fisher published the first account of its unique tool-using behaviour. Then, in 1963, when George Schaller and I were in California, we made a study of this behaviour in the Point Lobos Nature Reserve, with the object of getting quantitative data on the tool-using and of obtaining further information about its general behaviour and diet.

These otters feed close inshore, but, in the south they apparently never haul up on to rocks as they do in the Aleutians. They were easy to observe through binoculars and a spotting telescope, so we worked mostly together on the same otter, one of us observing, the other recording the observations. An otter would feed by swimming along the coast and diving to the sea bed from which it then brought to the surface crabs, urchins, mussels, or a large univalve, the abalone, which is a speciality of the many sea food restaurants in California. It would then float on its back, placing the food it had brought up from its dive on its chest.

If, for example, it had a live crab on its chest, it would hold the crab between its paws and up to its mouth while eating it, and might occasionally bang the crab with a paw. When the otter was feeding off mussels, however, it would come to the surface with a stone, about 5 inches in diameter, and place this on its chest as an anvil. The mussel, which was held between the paws, would be banged repeatedly against this stone until the shell was broken sufficiently for the otter to open it up and eat the contents. We watched one otter feeding entirely off mussels for 1 hour 26 minutes, during which time it brought up and cracked open 54 mussels, requiring a total of 2,237 bangs on the anvil.

Occasionally an otter retained the same stone for several feeding episodes, diving and surfacing again and again with the same one. Apparently the otter retained the anvil stone in its armpit while diving and collecting another mussel. Once, after an otter had fed on mussels in this way, it dived with the stone, only to reappear with two crabs. After eating the crabs, it reached under its right arm and produced and placed on its chest the same distinctive stone it had used during the previous feeding episodes. Exactly how the otters prise the large abalones off the rocks is unknown. The base of a shell often shows signs of scoring, as though the otter might have banged it with a stone, and sometimes a large section of shell is broken off before it is brought to the surface.

Two further points about the sea otter's feeding habits require comment. The first is that the otter pup is dependent on its mother for its food supply until it is about 15 months of age.

The pup dives when the mother dives, stays under a shorter time, and usually does not bring up any food. When the mother surfaces with food, the pup takes some of it from her chest or is, occasionally, handed bits by the mother. The second is that the California otters engage in this mussel-cracking behaviour far more frequently than those in the northern range. Observations of this behaviour are very rare in the Aleutians, except amongst the young, although long studies of the animals have been carried out. Russian workers have not reported its occurrence at all.

Let us now consider what kinds of tool-using occur in wild monkeys and apes, supposedly the most 'intelligent' of animals because they belong to the same order as ourselves. It is noteworthy that, in spite of all the recent field studies of baboons, macaques, and other monkeys, as well as gibbons, gorillas, and chimpanzees, only the chimpanzees observed by Jane Goodall in Tanganyika were found to use tools for obtaining food. The way they do this resembles the methods used by the woodpecker-finch. For example, they poke sticks into ants' nests, leave them there for a moment, and then withdraw them covered with ants which they put into their mouths and eat. The same technique is used for obtaining termites from holes.

Some chimpanzees are quite discriminating in their choice of tools for this purpose. When working at an exceptionally deep hole, one male, after trying with several grasses of the usual length, looked round intently, got up, and went to pick a long piece of vine growing several yards away. One male carried a grass stalk in his mouth for half a mile, while he examined, one after the other, six termite hills, none of which was ready for working. Baboons in the same area would sometimes watch the chimpanzees engaged in this activity, but never apparently learned the technique.

In the Cape of South Africa, I have frequently observed baboons feeding off quite large mussels. They never hammer them, but bite them open with their strong jaws. Apart from these extremely interesting observations on the chimpanzees, Darwin quotes an account of South American cebus monkeys breaking open oyster shells with stones, but this has yet to be confirmed.

At the beginning of this article I mentioned a kind of behaviour that might be classed as tool-using, in which the animal tries to repel something threatening or alarming. Chimpanzees, for instance, brandish sticks as a part of an intimidation display amongst themselves, but, when they actually fight, such 'weapons' are abandoned in favour of teeth and hands. Many instances are recorded in field studies of objects, such as branches or fruit being cast down in the direction of an intruder by monkeys and apes, probably the first of these coming from A. R. Wallace's observations of the orang-utan in the 19th century.

An interesting recent example is provided by Kaufmann's study of the coatis on Barro Colorado Island, off Panama. He saw a group of capuchin monkeys chase some coatis from a tree, then proceed to drop nuts and debris from a palm tree on to them. The coatis ignored this shower of missiles except to pounce on and eat the ripe nuts that were among them. Other much less clear instances came from observations of baboons or macaques rolling rocks down on to intruders; it is usually very difficult to know whether such rock falls are due to the agitation of the animals or to more 'purposeful acts of aggression'.

We now need to consider briefly the broader comparative significance of these acts of tool-using. Whether we are dealing with the woodpecker-finch, the sea otter, or the chimpanzee, we are likely to be interested in trying to find out how far such performances are due to learning and to what extent they are the result of some kind of inborn propensity. The standard method used in working out this sort of problem is to compare the behaviour of one set of animals, living in the natural social situation from birth onwards, with another set of animals of the same species, living in the highly unnatural situation of social isolation where there is no opportunity for the normal processes of learning and practising to occur.

If the sea otter pup, for example, were to be reared in complete isolation from its mother and from other sea otters during the formative months, would it, when adult, be able to break open mussels in the way seen in California? No such study has been made, but the answer is almost certainly that it would not readily acquire the habit. Probably, however, it would show an inherent tendency to manipulate or play with all sorts of loose objects and even perhaps to bang them against other objects. It would not know how to apply this tendency to specific food objects because it would normally learn this from its mother.

With the woodpecker-finch it is probable that learning plays a less important part in the performance, only leading to some individual improvement, through trial-and-error, in the skill with which the tool is applied. With the chimpanzee, the evidence from captivity studies strongly indicates that practice in manipulating objects of all sorts, even if only in play, is essential if tool-using performances, such as those studied by Köhler, are to be efficiently and quickly carried out. We are also fairly sure that the opportunity to learn by imitating others of the species is even more important as an aid in the acquiring of such techniques than it would be in the sea otter.

These comments are intended to put the tool-using examples I have described in a proper perspective, allowing for the fact that there is still a great deal more to find out about them. Although the performances of the chimp and the finch look very much the same, that of the chimp may be much more versatile than the finch's which is a kind of specialized adaptation to a feeding need. In fact, but for our definition of tool-using, and the rarity of this sort of performance in birds, there is no particular reason why we should be any more impressed by the finch than by the thrush's hammering of snails on stones or by the nest-building techniques of weaver-birds. And this may also be true of the sea otter's skill. Although it is certainly a fascinating performance to observe, and has the thrill of being a unique piece of mammalian behaviour, it may not be any more significant to the naturalist than the playfulness of other otters or the construction work of beavers.

Animal – particularly monkey and ape – tool-using has sometimes received a greater emphasis than other kinds of 'intelligent' behaviour. This is mainly because those who are interested in trying to reconstruct the course of human evolution from fossil remains have tended to associate humanness with tool-making. In order to be able to make tools, it is presumably necessary to know how to use objects as tools first. The so-called ape-men (*Australopithecus*), which were quite small-brained bipedal creatures, were apparently not only able to use tools but also to make simple implements by chipping stones.

Later species, definable as *Homo*, were larger-brained and showed evidence of a tool-making culture. Their tools were standardized in their manufacture and presumably had a wide range of usefulness in food-getting, hunting, and defence. Probably the way of life and the social organization of these early men were vastly different from that of any present-day monkeys and apes. The inference, then, seems to be that tool-using is not a particularly significant kind of behavioural adaptation, unless it is allied with powers of foresight and memory, with general characteristics of adaptability, and with social factors that can only be guessed at. The ape that was the precursor of the ape-man and of man may have been behaviourally and socially a very different animal from today's chimpanzees.

9 M. R. A. Chance

Kohler's Chimpanzees – How Did They Perform?

M. R. A. Chance, 'Kohler's chimpanzees – how did they perform?' *Man*, vol. 60 (1960), pp. 130–35.

Kohler's book *The Mentality of Apes* has had world-wide fame, and yet the more it is read the more difficult it is to reconcile this with a clear definition of what has been achieved. Apart from the originality of the study, which makes it fascinating, could it be considered as a model for future studies? Clearly, many think that he has demonstrated in chimpanzees intelligent behaviour of the kind familiar in humans. Frankly, this is not proven. We have no concepts yet with which to make the comparison and, although it may sound strange, I do not think that we have the requisite concepts for studying our own behaviour adequately. So the comparison is not possible, even if there is something in the conception that Kohler has made a start on the study of the behaviour of chimpanzees.

Apart from chimpanzees, the gorilla, the orang-utan, the cebus and the macaque monkeys (Warden *et al.*, 1940) show similar, though in some instances a less ready, ability at problem-solving of the type under discussion, but our present purpose is best served by sticking to the study of chimpanzees' performance.

Kohler undertook his work 'to gain knowledge of the nature of intelligent acts' as he put it, but when he elaborates upon his intention he says that he wants to find out whether his chimps behave 'with intelligence and insight under conditions which *require* such behaviour'.

Kohler does not clearly define what he means by 'intelligence or insight' in the context of his studies, but it is nevertheless possible to give definition to these terms from much of what he has written and I shall return to this point later. Consider the part in the passage above where he mentions the *requirements* of the task. No sooner does he specifically state that he is going to try to find out the nature of their intelligence than he brings in the notion of the *requirements* of a task, which introduces an element describing the physical set-up of the problem and which is, therefore, not itself a part of the way in which the chimp behaves, but is really a way of assessing the functional adequacy of behaviour. Because these two elements – the way the chimp actually behaves and the functional achievements – have nowhere been clearly separated, he arrives at a position from which it is impossible for him to take note of an act unless it is part of a direct sequence which can be seen to have functional significance.

Now such a criticism needs justifying, so I shall quote a passage from Kohler's book:

When a man or an animal takes a roundabout way (in the ordinary sense of the word) to his objective, the beginning, considered by itself only and regardless of the future course of the experiment, contains at least one component which must seem *irrelevant*. In very indirect routes there are usually some parts of the way which, when considered alone, seem *in contradiction to the purpose of the task*, because they lead away from the goal. If the sub-division in thought be dropped, the whole detour, and each part of it considered as a part of the whole becomes full of meaning in that experiment.

'Meaning' here refers to the relationship of the parts to the whole and, in particular, that part which is singled out in thought as irrelevant, but careful consideration of the nature of the irrelevancy as construed in this passage shows it to be made up of two parts: (1) A directional component ('in very indirect routes') which must be dealt with as a separate issue and, (2) those parts which seem in contradiction to the purpose of the task.

'In contradiction to the purpose of the task' and 'meaningless in relation to the task' are thus synonymous and clearly imply that the behaviour is seen always in relation to the function it performs. The implications go deeper since 'meaningless in relation to the task' implies that a single part and thus all the separately distinguished parts are related, not one to another as may be ascertained by discovering the pattern of their relationship in time, but their relation one to another is not recognized unless they contribute to the execution of a function defined by the task or the properties of the tool. *Only if* the function becomes apparent are the parts of the behaviour assumed to have any meaningful inter-relationship.

This shows how, when the structure of the behaviour is not considered separate from the function, an element of selection enters which can go unnoticed. The separation of these two is essential for an understanding of the way in which the material will be considered by us. This rigid exclusion of functional considerations of behaviour at the start of the study distinguishes ethological method from most other ways of studying behaviour, and enables patient observation of the movements to be made so that their relation one to another in time may be considered first of all without necessarily any reference to external events once these have been standardized. A picture can then be built up of the structure of the behaviour as it is at any moment or in any phase of the life of an animal. This procedure means that precedence is given to a knowledge of the internal factors

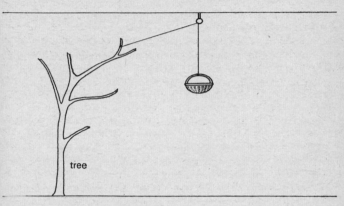

Figure 1 Kohler's basket of fruit.

which to a large extent determine what acts are available, and in what proportion, when an animal is roused. This we shall have to try to do for the problem-solving behaviour of Kohler's chimps and it is an eloquent vindication of his powers of observation, despite his heavy selection of material by the approach which we have just noticed, that his records enable us to distinguish some structural elements. Let us take an example (fig. 1).

'A long thin string is tied to the handle of a little open basket containing fruit' – the basket hangs six feet from the ground on the string, which passes through an iron ring on the roof of a large cage. The end of the string is tied in a wide loop and put over a stump on the branch of a tree.

A chimpanzee by name of Sultan, who has been fed from the basket many times before, is led into the cage and left alone. After some time he suddenly makes for the tree and climbs quickly up to the looped end of the string, stops a moment, then, watching the basket, pulls the string till the basket bumps against the ring, lets it go again, pulls a second time more vigorously so that the basket turns over and a banana falls out. He comes down, takes the fruit and gets up again, and now pulls so violently that the string breaks and the whole basket falls. He clambers down, takes the basket and goes off to eat the fruit.'

The chimp Sultan saw the basket, string and tree and then went to the point where the string was connected to the tree, but his subsequent behaviour was difficult to interpret since 'the best solution of the problem, which could be expected, would be that the animal should take the loop . . . off the branch . . . and simply let it drop'. Sultan's persistence in pulling the string – rather than taking the loop off the branch – remained not very clear to Kohler even at the end of his investigations.

Figure 2 Climbing a pole before it falls. (Figures 2–4 after Kohler.)

As I am as much concerned to find out how to investigate the behaviour of chimps and thereby to highlight, if possible, the distinctive contribution of ethology, we will look at the range of functional competence shown by the group of nine chimpanzees available to Kohler. As you probably know, most of the tasks which they were set involved obtaining a lure not immediately accessible by hand or by going to the spot. The lure could only be obtained indirectly by means such as stacking of boxes, use of a stick or pole, fitting together of sticks (figs. 2–4), pulling-in of string, the removal of an obstruction or making a detour. For our purposes, however, the distinction between these different problems is immaterial as very much the same range of performance was evident between the individual chimps performing any one of these types of task.

Let us look back at the example I have quoted. Although the action was smooth and direct, a criterion essential for what Kohler regards as an intelligent solution, the behaviour contained a singular rigid and stereotyped element, the persistent pulling of the string until the food dropped or the string broke. These stereotypes are much more evident in other examples of the problem-solving behaviour, as when Grande tries to balance one box on its point on top of another repeatedly over a period as long as two years, or when Chica tries to combine her stick with a box by placing it on the upturned edge of the box, again repeatedly, or when Rana repeatedly tries to jump up sticks which are too short even to take her off the ground. More intelligent near solutions are achieved by placing one box on another just as Grande did. Then, however, the chimp learns that they will not stay there if lifted on their point, but only if laid flat on the other box. Even chimps which show this advance show no great interest in the goodness of fit or the ways of building a stable structure.

From these examples, which Kohler curiously calls 'good errors' because they appear to have, so to speak, got the idea, he describes every gradation of performance up to the following example which appears to show great competence.

Figure 3 Box-stacking.

Tschego made her first experiments with a stick, pulling fruit with it towards the bars of her den. Now the lower part of the bars are covered with fine-meshed wire netting, and the animal cannot get hold of the fruit which she has drawn towards her, although it lies so close, either through the tight meshes, or over the netting, which is too high for her arm to reach over it to the ground. About one metre further along, the net is lower; after Tschego has once reached down in vain, she seizes the stick again, pushes the fruit with one clear, continuous movement sideways to where the net is lower (that is, away from where she is sitting), quickly goes to the place, and seizes the fruit without further ado.

The solution, let us note, was achieved in two parts. First, the drawing-in of the food towards the cage and then as a separate act, after trying to reach it with its hand, taking the stick and sweeping it to the side where the wire netting was low. In effect, therefore, the problem appears to have been tackled in two parts: the first act having failed, it was immediately followed by a second of a different kind. Assuming that the acts immediately follow the awareness of the different features constituting obstacles in the way, they appear to arise directly out of that awareness.

This second example, therefore, supplies all the requisites of the solution which appears to be, and could be, the result of an awareness of the essential geometric relations. It occurs without previous experience, is deliberate in the sense that it arises without delay, is continuous, but is not quite the simplest of the actions required in a situation where the solution requires more than a direct movement. This would have been to sweep the fruit in an arc to one side and towards where the wire netting was low.

Evidence, therefore, exists which is compatible with the assumption that the chimpanzee becomes aware of the necessary features and that these features and the relationship of the different parts do guide the series of acts with which he obtains his objective. As we shall see, however, these are not frequent, but in most of the examples the sequence of behaviour does not meet these criteria; nevertheless, they often lead to a solution.

We have, therefore, a wide variety of performances between different individuals, with prominent amongst the elements of actual behaviour stereotyped acts which in all instances, but especially in the less intelligent solutions, appear to conflict with the assumption that the chimp was acting on the basis of full comprehension. Is this so?

Kohler's findings have been the subject of three subsequent studies, one by Harold Bingham, which, mainly I think because he was satisfied with insight as an explanatory concept, did no more than demonstrate in greater detail how chimps solved problems by box-stacking, the movement of objects or detour behaviour. On close examination one must admit, I think, that neither Kohler nor Bingham actually formulated a precise working hypothesis. In the nature of things, therefore, it is not surprising that they did not reach any definite conclusions, but Bingham was perhaps more modest in his claims when he stated that he 'is disposed to accept as ideational the behaviour of his chimpanzees'!

Birch, working with young naive chimpanzees, made an inconclusive, but suggestive, attempt to find out if experience played a part in the solving of problems which involve the use of a stick.

The third person to enter this field was Paul Schiller and here we move into very different territory. Schiller asked himself 'Are the unlearned motor patterns of a chimpanzee conducive to instrumental behaviour?' He approached this from the developmental angle, and, as a means of investigating this aspect, he worked out a stepwise series of tests by which he could compare the problem-solving abilities of chimpanzees of different ages. From this he discovered that there was a large maturational component in the ease with which animals solved a given type of problem, *e.g.* five chimps of one to two years old could not learn to solve problems higher than stage E, whereas six youngsters of three to four years old learnt up to G. Those of five to eight years old could start at D and proceed more rapidly onwards from there to the most difficult – K.

Prior experience was, however, necessary before the use of the various instruments, particularly the sticks, was developed and with this experience the older animals advanced more rapidly to higher levels of complexity than the youngest ones.

Schiller, however, paid very close attention to the exact way in which the chimpanzees used their tools and he became intrigued at the way all the animals handled the sticks before they began to use them. He was aware of the approach to behaviour which Konrad Lorenz was the first to make known in this country and so he was quite prepared to believe that such careful observation might reveal important indicators of the processes underlying the way the chimps used their sticks.

The oldest animals all started to use the stick in the same way and without reference to the lure. They drew in the stick, then licked, smelt and chewed the end. He at once recognized the similarity of this behaviour to that recorded for the chimpanzee Sultan, one of Kohler's chimps. This six-year-old chimp solved the drawing-in problem by putting together two bamboo sticks that fitted together at either end. Sultan's performance was first produced in play, but was utilized immediately afterwards. In the description given by Kohler he pulled out the stopper which prevented the joining of the sticks and before he attempted to insert one into the other, he bit off the head of one of them to 'make it match the hole', as Kohler had put it. Schiller noticed the inconsistency in this description, for the sticks were designed so that they fitted into each other; the biting-off of the end was, therefore, irrelevant to the purpose of the task and suggested that even in this example the biting was another stereotyped element. Schiller comments on this incongruity as follows:

None of these activities need be regarded as having any reference to the problem situation. The manipulation of sticks by older animals

Figure 4 Fitting two sticks together.

that have had no prior opportunity of handling jointed sticks when there is no food to be reached shows all of these varieties of activity. Licking, chewing, stroking and splitting the stick, banging, poking, hammering with it, and thrusting the end into any available openings are responses that occur frequently and constitute the basis of complex motor patterns of utilizing sticks as tools.

Therefore his next step was to give two fitting sticks to 48 new chimps without any problem to solve. Of these 32 fitted the sticks together within the hour. Of 20 adults in the group 19 fitted them together within five minutes and repeated the performance several times (the single exception was a pregnant female). Of 16 between five and ten years old 11 fitted the sticks together within five minutes and of 12 less than five years old only one joined them within the hour (and this had had previous experience).

The infants played almost exclusively with one stick at a time. Those of the bigger animals who did not join them showed, nevertheless, elements of this pattern by inserting a finger into the hole, putting the point of the peg into some crack in the floor or fence. Those who connected the sticks usually chewed the end of the peg before inserting it into the hole and after this they took the peg out and licked it. The hole was often filled with food, water, or dirt, and these substances were then sucked out of it. Some active chimpanzees repeatedly poked through the fence, shaking the sticks in the face of the experimenter or other animals. As the experimenter approached, the chimpanzee withdrew suddenly as if chased, or prepared to attack with the other hand or both hands, if the stick were offered in the mouth.

The dramatic construction of a tower by piling boxes or cases 'in order to' climb on top and jump for food suspended high above is most likely based on naturally preferred playforms also. I tested 12 chimpanzees of 6–10 years of age in two 15-minute periods with two of the smallest standardized boxes used by Yerkes and associates. All of them dragged the boxes along the floor, sat and stood on them, rolled them over, carried them carefully balanced to some preferred corner, and used them as pillows. Six of the animals actually stacked them and climbed on the tower jumping upward from the top repeatedly with arms lifted above the head and stretched toward the ceiling. For the human observer it was hard to believe that there was no food above them to be reached. Needless to say none of these animals had ever been tested in box-stacking problem situations.

Complex responses are, therefore, not based on perceptual organizations, but on innate constituents which are motor patterns. This is true not only of the chimpanzee, but also the macaque (Mason *et al.*, 1959). Once avoidance, grasping, banging, waving, poking, chewing, etc., are established any familiar surroundings which fit dimensionally to these activities will elicit them in a way which can appear insightful. All that is required in the simplest instance is that these activities should be brought into juxtaposition to a lure and a solution will soon be hit upon. A suitable arrangement and condensation will then take place and be all that is necessary to produce a set of acts which could be taken to indicate that the chimpanzee has insight into the overall relationship of the situation. So far we have only considered examples which do not fit this interpretation as well as they fit the type suggested by Schiller, but I myself am not convinced, despite the obvious part played by innate motor patterns in determining the form of a solution to a problem, that we are yet able to exclude insightful solutions.

What is clear, however, is that an analysis of the innate forms is required before any further progress can be made into this problem. We need to examine the arousal patterns just as much in examining 'intelligence' as in social behaviour where the elements are more complex sequences or postures, but where experience has shown that the underlying structure may be revealed by more detailed observation. Then, and only then, does analysis begin. Then we should ask how large and of what kind are the units? One twitch, a whole sweep of the arm, an oriented posture; which are the basic elements? What changes and recombinations take place in development and in different states of motivation?

Just as is now familiar from the work of many ethologists studying the social behaviour of lower vertebrates, arousal in particular conditions is found to lead to an interaction between a complex of innate components, so here we have a varied bag of tricks, so to say, laid down by hereditary factors and requiring only the opportunity for play in order to perfect the operational competence with sticks and – we may note – the same motor patterns are displayed towards sticks and boxes alike.

What this means for the insight we may gain into the evolutionary history of a species of primate once we know its innate patterns is considerable, for the method is in essence applicable to man, despite the preponderance of cultural influences.

If we accept Schiller's hypothesis, then the 'intelligent' chimpanzees are as much under the influence of the predetermined motor elements as are the 'stupid' chimps which are more obviously so because of the repetitive way in which they employ the same element time after time. The difference is simply that the so-called 'intelligent' ones had a greater repertoire available to them. In the early phases of attempts to solve a problem they search in a sequence which has no apparent relationship, not only to external stimuli, but also to the order of acts which eventually go to make up a smooth effective sequence. As Schiller comments about the play, 'since no external stimulus is definitely associated with the response it is fair to replace the term "response" with that of "emittance" of patterns determined more by the internal state of the organism than by the external stimulus'. Thus the ability to search through a repertoire and try out many types of 'emittance' in succession provides the wherewithal of success. We are used to the idea of animals searching through external objects, but perhaps till now it has not been clear that much successful behaviour depends on searching through a repertoire which we may have acquired by the luck of our birth, from experience, or the two combined.

Do we need to assume, as Schiller does, that the solutions are *only* the result of serialization and condensation and that, as he says, 'whichever components are reinforced by the responses of the outside world, those will be produced in the proper sequence, omitting repetitions, and develop into a unified pattern that the human observer calls a problem solution'? This may, in itself, be as facile an interpretation as the alternative hypothesis that a 'correct solution is the result of an awareness of the requirements of the simplest solution to the exclusion of other possible, but less appropriate, alternatives'.

In both instances we are dealing with a complete solution and one which, because of its completeness, does not allow for much variability on repeated occasions, either because it is the terminal form of a reinforced series or because, on the other hand, of a functional adequacy which has distracted attention so far from the fact that it was largely preformed.

Quite clearly these motor patterns, as long as they are unmodified, determine the form and, by this very fact, will prevent the expression of insight if and when it is present. Thus, the possibility of demonstrating solutions based on insight must depend upon the extent to which the original motor patterns can be modified.

In many instances of what Kohler calls 'good errors' it is possible to see that the attention of the chimpanzee is severely restricted, often to the manipulative aspects of tool-using and not to any aspect of the set-up other than the lure. This restriction of attention may itself be a product of the predominant place which motor patterns occupy in the behaviour of the less capable chimp. Therefore, a ready ability to switch from one type of emittance to another may go hand in hand with a corresponding diversity of attention which brings within the chimp's comprehension many more relevant aspects of the environment.

Pulsating through this work of Kohler's is a vibrant sense of the marvellous performance of these creatures and he imparts it to everyone who reads his book. The genuineness of the solutions is not in question; but for Kohler, one of his main obsessions was that people would not believe that they solved problems and he set out to convince them that these were solutions and not mere fortuitous occurrences. When his feelings burst forth he says:

For one who has actually watched the experiments discussions like the above have something comic about them. To secure these facts against misinterpretation seems almost pedantic.

In such passages his propagandizing zeal on behalf of the chimps' abilities prevents him from seeing that much critical enquiry arises from interest and not disbelief. Certainly no-one now would maintain that chimps do not solve problems. His achievement has been to bring forward into the light of day this remarkable feature of ape behaviour.

In conclusion, may I make a plea for the great apes who are now in danger of extinction? Surely their preservation is a matter of major concern for all interested in the behaviour of man and his near relatives.

References

Bingham, H. C., *Comp. Psychol. Monog.*, Vol. VI (1929), p. 1.

Birch, H. G., *J. Comp. Psychol.*, Vol. XXXVIII (1945), p. 367.

Kohler, W., *Mentality of Apes* (in English translation), London (Methuen), 1927.

Mason, W. A., H. F. Harlow and R. R. Rueping, 'The Development of Manipulatory Responsiveness in the Infant Rhesus Monkey', *J. Comp. Physiol. Psychol.*, Vol. LII, No. 5 (1959).

Schiller, P. H., *Psychol. Rev.*, Vol. LIX (1952), p. 177.

——, in C. H. Schiller (editor), *Instinctive Behaviour*, New York (Int. Univ. Press), No. 99 (1957), pp. 264–87.

Warden, C. J., A. M. Kock and N. A. Fjeld, 'Instrumentation in Cebus and Rhesus Monkeys', *J. Genet. Psychol.*, Vol. LVI (1940), pp. 297–310.

10 P. H. Schiller

Innate Constituents of Complex Responses in Primates

Excerpt from P. H. Schiller, 'Innate constituents of complex responses in primates', *Psychol. Rev.*, vol. 59 (1952), pp. 177–91.

Adaptive behavior is recognized as constituted of unlearned patterns, *modified* by repetition or reinforcement. What the original responses are like, however, before they are modified by learning, is not frequently analyzed in the literature. Yet how can modifications of behavior be studied if we do not have a basis of comparison in the *unmodified* patterns analyzed as extensively as the learning series? Some comparative psychologists do not seem to study the animal before training; consequently they are inclined to hold that all adaptive responses are learned and do not conceive of any complex response as native.

As a matter of fact, many a conditioned response has been found to be paralleled by unconditioned responses that appear when the animal becomes adapted to an originally ineffective stimulus. The organism has a changeable reserve of responses, influenced by general and specific levels of activity. This level varies with the internal state, the motivation and adaptation of the organism, as well as with the frequency and consequences of a particular behavior pattern. Since we cannot control all internal stimuli, we had better start with comparative studies of early behavior and make a complete inventory of the animal's repertoire.

Just which response is complex and which simple is not easily decided in the light of embryological behavior studies. Elements of complex responses are admitted to be ready prior to specific learning, but the question is whether the organism is not producing the compounds we observe without any training, just as its effectors mature. Experiments on maturational factors *versus* experience have led to contrasting results with various species and various tasks. In a long forgotten study Spalding (21) has shown that flying in birds was unimpeded after he prevented early practice. Essentially the same was found by Carmichael (5) in the swimming of tadpoles, by Gesell (6) in the climbing behavior of human twins. On the other hand, Shepard and Breed (19) recorded that chicks have to learn how to peck seed in a few days of practice, whether freshly hatched or fed artificially for a considerable period allowing for maturation. Similarly Stone (22) and later Beach (2) have found severe impairment of copulating behavior in rats isolated from early contact with mates.

The contradiction in these results can be resolved by a dichotomy. The *constituents* of the motor pattern themselves mature. Due to internal, prefunctional factors, they appear at a certain stage of development (many of them traced in embryos) ready formed. Their *application* to external stimulus configurations is something that must be learned. Such a dichotomy was reported by Moseley (13) who found that pecking, striking and swallowing were unlearned responses whereas seizing of the grain was formed by practice. [. . . .]

There can be no doubt that adaptive behavior is shown in typical 'instinctive' patterns. But similarly rapid and definite adaptive modifications occur in some cases of complex learning too, in problem-solving behavior, described as 'insightful'.

The animal seems to have an understanding of the actual situation and behaves as if steered by orientational cues. In studies on the detour behavior of various animals I have arrived at a composite notion of behavior adjustment rather similar to the cooperation of internal and external factors derived from the aforementioned investigations on instinctive constituents. Direct attack and giving up (fish, 15, 16), exploratory responses and nest-building incipients (rats, 1, 17), seeking and covering (octopus, 18) constitute the complex plan of the detour pathway chosen in every new situation. A familiarization process extinguishes the repetition of local reactions and lowers the threshold for orientational stimuli. After repeated exposure to a frustrating situation, the originally independent reactions are integrated in time. Strictly speaking, the animals do not learn to make a detour. They make it in reference to the presently governing stimulus conditions produced by their own behavior. It is the consistency of external events, their lawful sequence and intrinsic relations that secure a consistency of organismic responses to them. The performance actually observed is a change of speed in the serial elicitation of previously determined response patterns.

Since the clearly innately determined activities and the rather complex learning processes thus appear to follow identical laws in orienting the animal in its adjustment, it seems worthwhile to summarize some as yet unpublished data of mine under this viewpoint. [. . . .]

[The section *Do Certain Visual Configurations Elicit Unlearned*

Motor Responses? containing experiments 1 and 2 has been omitted.]

Are unlearned motor patterns conducive to instrumental behavior?

The results reported in the previous section cast considerable doubt upon the value of visual organization as the sole guide to complex learning. It is an interlocked sensorimotor integration, rather, that seems to be responsible for adjustment. The sudden changes in perceptual organization, inferred from the insight type of problem solving, are not based on specific processes coordinated readily before any functional practice. The efficient relation between perceptual patterns and displayed motor patterns must be acquired in the course of use. As a matter of fact, we shall see that rather comprehensive motor complexes appear without any specific training, but their application to external situations is due to habituation or experience.

The pioneer studies on using a stick to obtain food beyond reach in the orangutan and the gorilla by Yerkes (24), in the chimpanzee by Köhler (11), gave the impression that a relational perception of food and tool is sufficient for the overt response that leads to a more intimate contact between these separately presented entities. Occasional observations of Jackson (10) and systematic experiments by Birch (3, 4), however, have shown that some experience with the handling of a stick is necessary for 'insight' or 'ideation' to be expressed. Both found rapid generalization, once an initial learning was obtained. The generalization was tested by Birch in single trials with 10 different stick problems, for each of which a full hour of trial time was allowed. Only 3 of the 10 problems were solved by all 6 animals used, and those who solved all the problems took an average of several minutes and only 12 of the total of 60 trials were positive within one minute. No immediate success was thus generally obtained.

3. I have analyzed the stick problem in 25 chimpanzees of 1 to 15 years of age. Contrary to Birch's findings I have found no significant improvement in the use of the stick by providing young animals with an opportunity to play with sticks for days or even weeks. On the other hand, a maturational gradient was found. Older animals solve varieties of the stick problem much more rapidly than younger ones. Even they require some *specific* training with the stick in order to use that tool efficiently. A gradual introduction of more difficult problems after the easier ones furthers the achievement.

I have built up a procedure, beginning in the youngest animals

105

with a *string* baited first at the closest end within reach (*a*), then on the farthest end out of reach (*b*); after this the *rake* was introduced, with the food at first between the rake and the animal (*c*), later to the side of the rake. The *straight stick* was first used in an *oblique* position, the food in front of it, so that its drawing in will bring the food closer (*d*); then it is *vertical* to the plane of grill behind which the animal is working and the food is within the sphere of sweeping an area of 90° toward himself (*e*); later the food is presented farther aside and even *behind* the stick so that the latter has to be adjusted to the location of the food before pulling in (*f*). After this adjustment has been made the stick is given *in the cage* and the food without, beyond reach of the naked arm (*g*). If this problem is mastered, the stick is put in a place where it cannot be seen simultaneously with the food and cannot be hit upon by accident (*h*). These two-platform experiments are continued after having introduced a *second*, shorter, *stick* that serves to procure the longer stick that is needed to get the food (*i*). The most complex problem studied utilizes *three platforms*, one for each of the two sticks and one for the food, all including an area of 270° around the chimpanzee (*j*). The ablest animals were given two sticks, one with a hollow, the other with a peg-like end so they can be *joined by insertion* to form an elongated single stick (*k*).

The five youngest chimpanzees, of the age of 1 to 2 years, learn this series only up to the point where they need not adjust the stick to a location of the food behind or beside it, that is through (*e*) of the above list. Even these simplest problems require a repetition of trials up to a few hundred, to be readily solved. It is very much like a result of conditioning, for the animals just learn to do something to the stick before obtaining food. The infants will try just to touch it, or pull it straight, or push it aside and display, after this performance, every sign of expectation of food. Since the effective sweep alone is rewarded (plus some 'good' but by chance inefficient trials, in order to avoid discouragement), the best way of doing it will be gradually built up.

Six youngsters of 3 to 4 years of age learn essentially in the same manner but considerably faster. Roughly a hundred trials suffice to bring them to master even more adaptive problems, up to the stick in the cage that has to be put out to the food in a proper position to get it in, through task (*g*).

Eight chimpanzees of the age between 5 and 8 (probably corresponding to Köhler's animals) take roughly a score of trials, with the straight stick alone, to reach the level of the younger group and then proceed in another score of trials with a spread of generalization to solve the more complex tasks. These animals have no difficulty with multiple platforms. It is not so much the optical separation of the sticks and food that makes such tasks difficult, but the fact that a longer series of single responses has to be integrated into one complex pattern. All animals of the group solved two-stick problems $(i; j)$ even on 2 and 3 platforms, the older ones certainly in fewer trials than the younger ones.

The group of 9 to 15 years old animals, pubescents and young adults, contained two of those used by Birch. All of them had to learn gradually, by specific experience too, stepping from the simpler to the more difficult problems, as did Köhler's chimpanzees. The experience which two of these animals had many years before did not show up in their performance. They were not advanced as compared to those closest in age to them. Even the adults needed almost the same amount of specific experience as the pubescent animals, but the former generalized faster. I started the series with this group by presenting to the animal food behind the accessible stick. All of them reached first for the food across the stick and then, after some hesitation, took the stick and pulled it in with no reference to the food, licked, smelled, and chewed it. Much later only did they put the stick out again and push it toward the food. Then they suddenly swept or angled for the food, at third or fourth trial, and rarely made any more mistakes. Silly behavior sometimes occurred, especially as the multiple platform problems were introduced. Like the younger ones, these big animals tried to reduce their efforts and just push or pull a bit on the stick and then look alternately to the food and to the experimenter.

This series of tests shows that there is an important maturational element in the adaptive use of the stick as a rake by chimpanzees. Experience in the handling of sticks is necessary for the solution of the rake problems, but with equivalent amounts of experience in the use of the stick as a rake, the older animals advance to a more complicated level of performance than the younger. (The conditions of caging at Orange Park are such that even the adult animals tested have had practically no opportunity for practice in rake using prior to these experiments.)

The jointed stick problem gives especially clear evidence of the interrelations of maturation, experience and insight. Köhler (11) gave a classical description of a male chimpanzee, Sultan, aged about 6 years, who solved the drawing-in problem by putting together two bamboo sticks that matched on either end. Sultan's performance was first produced in play but was utilized 'immediately' and was repeated the same and the next day several times, even with three sticks. Moreover, he pulled out a stopper that prevented joining the sticks before he attempted an insertion and bit off the too-broad end of a board to make it match the hole.

None of these activities need be regarded as having any reference to the problem situation. The manipulation of sticks by older animals that have had no prior opportunity of handling jointed sticks when there is no food to be reached shows all of these varieties of activity. Licking, chewing, stroking, and splitting the stick, banging, poking, hammering with it, and thrusting the end into any available openings are responses that occur frequently and constitute the basis of complex motor patterns of utilizing sticks as tools.

4. To test stick-joining without the motivation of the food and rake problem, two short sticks, of which the end of one could be fitted into the other, were given to each of 48 chimpanzees. Thirty-one of these fitted the sticks together in play within one hour (tests made in four 15 minute periods). Of 20 adults in the group, all but one (a pregnant female) joined the sticks repeatedly and the majority did this within the first 5 minutes. Of 16 animals between 5 and 10 years, 11 fitted the sticks together within 5 minutes. Of 12 chimpanzees less than 5 years old, only one joined the sticks within an hour. She was a home-reared animal that had been taught similar tasks.

The infants played almost exclusively with one stick at a time. Those of the bigger animals who did not join them showed, nevertheless, elements of this pattern by inserting a finger into the hole, putting the point of the peg into some crack in the floor or fence. Those who connected the sticks usually chewed the end of the peg before inserting it into the hole and after this they took the peg out and licked it. The hole was often filled with food, water, or dirt, and these substances were then sucked out of it. Some active chimpanzees repeatedly poked through the fence, shaking the sticks in the face of the experimenter or other animals. As the experimenter approached, the chimpanzee withdrew suddenly as if chased, or prepared to attack with the other hand or both hands, if the stick were offered in the mouth. Sometimes they actually gave the stick and then presented back, shoulder, or rump to be scratched. All of these activities occurred in series of many repetitions before variation. Vocalization, especially that characteristic of grooming situations, frequently accompanied this social play and the exploration of cracks and holes by poking.

There are some correlations of the play activity with age and need factors. Older chimpanzees manipulated more persistently than the younger ones (see Table 1) and had a larger variety of manipulation forms. While younger animals handle the stick as a passive thing with no relation to other objects – just chew and scratch it, carry it or rest on it (with shoulder, neck, or head) – older ones use sticks to mediate activity, poke at or batter another object, eventually combining both sticks. The same patterns of handling objects constitute components of 'instinctive' activities like investigation and grooming, building of twig-nests, and sexual games. There seems to be a difference in the frequency of types of manipulation according to the prevalent needs. Hungry animals lick and chew the sticks, and socially isolated ones perform mostly exploratory and grooming-like activities as described above. Raising the level of any particular activity by developing needs or habits may facilitate its utilization in the composition of problem-solving stereotypes.

Fitting the sticks together and using them as a rake are independent activities, not immediately associated. Six adult animals, which had united the sticks within 5 minutes in play and had joined and pulled them apart many times, failed to join them within three 15-minute test periods, when there was food to be reached. The frustration in the problem situation seems to inhibit the natural play activities. The behavior of one of these, Sinbad, a 12-year-old male, is typical of the reactions of the inexperienced chimpanzee when given the disjointed sticks with food on a platform beyond reach with the single sticks. Only on the fourth 15-minute trial did he join the sticks. He first tried to reach the food with a short piece but soon gave up attempts to get the food and resorted to play. He took both sticks into the cage, inserted the peg in the hole and had lots of fun holding the double stick upright, putting it to his shoulder and in his lap, rolling the constructed 'tool' on the floor and even poking with it across the bars of the grill toward, but not for the food (several minutes of play). At the end of this session he accepted another, long enough, single stick and swept his food in cleverly. Play and work are distinct spheres of activity, not yet integrated at that stage. Next day he again began to play after a few minutes spent in the problem situation, but played only for one minute with the double stick, then he poked it through the grill and dropped it. He soon picked it up, placed its end behind the food, and swept in quietly (46 minutes total of 4 test periods). At next trial he made this whole sequence rapidly, so we could proceed to the multiple platform tests, which he solved with good adaptation, connecting the sticks in the cage between two reachings and sweeping in smoothly in about 20 seconds every time.

In none of the animals tested was there any evidence of the immediate perception of a relation between the united sticks and the distance of the food to be reached. Most typical was the

Table 1

Amount of Spontaneous Manipulation and of Learning Needed to Solve a Problem with a Stick

	Order of magnitude of			
	Seconds spent in spontaneous activity as indicated in a 15-minute period		*Trials taken to reach the indicated level of solution*	
Animals	*Number of subjects*			
Spider monkey	30 stick passive	5	3 Straight pull only	500
Rhesus monkey	45 stick passive	5	2 Straight pull only	400
Infant chimps	120 stick passive	6	5 Straight pull only	200
2 to 4 years ch.	240 stick mediates	6	6 Stick adjusted	100
5 to 8 years ch.	540 stick combined	16	8 Multiple tasks	50
Adult chimps	600 stick combined	20	6 Multiple tasks	25

joining of the sticks in the period of play, then pulling them apart and trying to reach the food with a short piece or with the bare arm. The discovery of its utility as a rake mostly followed its abandonment as an object of play.

The dramatic construction of a tower by piling boxes or cases 'in order to' climb on top and jump for food suspended high above is most likely based on naturally preferred playforms also. I tested 12 chimpanzees of 6 to 10 years of age in two 15 minute periods with two of the smallest standardized boxes used by Yerkes and associates (25). All of them dragged the boxes along the floor, sat and stood on them, rolled them over, carried them carefully balanced to some preferred corner, and used them as pillows. Six of the animals actually stacked them and climbed on the tower, jumping upward from the top repeatedly, with arms lifted above the head and stretched toward the ceiling. For the human observer it was hard to believe that there was no food above them to be reached. Needless to say none of these animals had ever been tested in box-stacking problem situations. Nevertheless, the pattern of behavior, developing spontaneously in play without external motivation, duplicated exactly the pattern of using boxes to attain a suspended bait. Furthermore, as in the use of the jointed stick, the introduction of a bait interfered with and delayed the piling of boxes, just as it interfered with the playful joining of the sticks.

There is a definite relation between the amount and variety of non-motivated manipulation and the final achievements of the animals. This is illustrated by a comparison of monkeys and chimpanzees in the rake problem. I have tested 5 rhesus and 5 spider monkeys. They were given sticks and the time and varieties of play with the sticks were recorded. They were then trained to use the stick as a rake to secure food. All learned to sweep in the food when it lay between the stick and the cage. No one of them learned to get the food when it lay beyond the stick; they did not lift the stick over the food. Table 1 compares the amount and type of play activity with the stick and the subsequent training trials required for prompt and smooth use of the stick as a rake by monkeys and chimpanzees of different ages. The monkeys and infant chimpanzees played with the stick for only a few seconds before discarding it and the manipulation was limited to simple handling (passive) without use of the stick in relation to other objects. The 2 to 4 year old chimpanzees used the stick to poke at other objects (mediates) but failed to join two sticks. The older chimpanzees joined the two sticks in play. There is a perfect correlation between the average times of manipulation without external motivation and the learning scores to achieve the highest level of problem solution attained by the group. As the functional abilities of the effectors develop, onto- and phylogenetically, the manipulation shows a higher degree of variety and longer series of activities.

It can be seen that the longer and more varied the spontaneous activity, the shorter the time for adjustment and the more complex the adjustment. Motor patterns at the disposal of the animal, whether learnt or unlearnt, enter complexes of response sequences that are, as they appear, more or less adaptive and become, by provoking repetition with incentives, solidified, smoothly running units of behavior. These adaptive complexes or generalized routines are conducive to problem solution. A compound operant is conditioned by the intrinsic consequences of the behavior proper. It is suggested that behavioral adjustment to environmental entities is a composite result of innate response patterns.

The innate constituents of complex responses are not perceptual

111

organizations but motor patterns. The adaptive use of these patterns depends upon the span of activity that is composed and conditioned as a unit to some elicitor in a generalized fashion. Once avoidance, grasping, banging, poking, etc., are established, any familiar object in familiar surroundings that fits dimensionally to these activities will elicit them in a way that appears insightful. The positional relations of objects can be varied without breaking up the pattern, since it is the inhibition of repetitions and the orienting to subsequently produced cues that is learned.

Discussion

There is no doubt that the motor components of any behavior compound are innately determined; probably larger series are established prior to learning in insects, fishes, and birds than in mammals. How large are the units, that is the question. What is a single response? One twitch, one flexion, one grasp, salivation of one drop, an orientational posture? The comprehensiveness of these innate entities is variable with age groups and animal forms. An analysis of the specific repertoire is needed before we can proceed to a learning theory which is more than a justification of one or the other very restricted method of behavior research.

These motor patterns are the basic units of overt behavior. There is *no* definite stimulus correlated to a more complex motor pattern. The releasers of a pattern may vary within a more or less broad range specific to the receptors of the species. Adaptation changes this range more widely in higher than in lower animals. The modification of behavior produced thereby seems to have two functionally consecutive phases: habituation and condensation. In the first a perceptual, in the second a motor factor is predominant. A duality of learning mechanisms, selective problem-solving as preceded by associative conditioning, was conceived by Maier and Schneirla (12) and, more elaborately, by Mowrer (14). Girden (7), however, asserts that the adaptive pattern is a function of the non-associative adjustment to repeated stimulation and thus there might be a continuity between the allegedly separate mechanisms. Habituation is necessary for condensation to take place. In conventional experiments we usually vary both factors at a time.

A unified learning theory can be attempted on the basis of regarding the original repertoire as consisting of operants. Their governing stimuli are internal. Hess and Brügger (9) discovered diencephalic loci, the direct stimulation of which produces complex sniffing, fighting, and other sequences in cats. These patterns if emitted, however, are immediately applied to crudely fitting perceptual releasers. Such sham-adjustment can be a consequence of structural correspondence between dimensional properties of the effectors and the perceptual field. The centrogenic spitting of cats, e.g., was directed toward persons present in Hess' laboratory. An ape seizes a stick without primary or secondary reinforcement, just because it fits the size of his grasp.[1] In consequence of the response, minor possible coincidences of extero- and proprioception are presented and enable the animal to make more accurate adjustment. Excitement by shock or food creates an emotional climate in which motor complexes are associated to either preceding or following cues (Tolman, 23, recently showed the latter possibility). Maybe this is just another way of saying that motor patterns are activated more readily by stimuli to which the organism becomes sensitive. Anthropomorphically stated: By repetition a new aspect of the situation becomes functional. A piano player learns in a similar way to attend (without knowing it) to proprioceptive cues that enable him, in coincidence with synchronous external perceptions, to speed up a sequence produced originally by independent impulses.

Application of ever more comprehensive motor complexes to involve cue constellations is the basis of adaptability in higher organisms. In order to integrate such complex operants, their elements must be matured or otherwise acquired; the motor patterns must be at the disposal of the animal, the orientation accurate enough and the span of synthesis, persistence, or attention sufficiently comprehensive to permit larger entities of sequences to be built up.

The classical description of smooth and continuous problem-solving in the insight experiment is certainly valid. Its genesis, however, is obscure. My chimpanzees showed the same type of behavior, but they needed a series of specific experiences until it was established. The difference in their learning from some of Köhler's chimpanzees is most likely to be explained in terms of life history. The surroundings of the colony animals in Florida are much more monotonous than were those of the freshly captured Teneriffe animals, and the former surely do not have all the opportunities necessary for unimpaired functional develop-

1. This statement is made deliberately in that absurd way to stress that there is no need for assuming either innate schemata or established connections to account for complex adjustment. There is a preference for larger sticks with growing age (and size of hand), preserved despite experience at variance with it.

ment. In a natural habitat or free colony outside of experimental conditions the consequences of behavior follow the laws of reality. Thus the animal has no other choice but to adjust. The mechanism of adjustments, however, can only be seen in maladjustments, when the experimenter forces strictly controlled arbitrary consequences upon the animal.

It is the failure rather than the adjustment which is conspicuous. The mistakes my animals made were seldom of the 'good error' type that indicates some intention on the part of the animal but, on the contrary, they mostly showed stereotyped routines of the sort produced by Guthrie and Horton (8) in cats or by Skinner (20) in pigeons. The stick is a token, the mere touch of which induces inaccessible food to become accessible. This 'hypothesis' or 'superstition' is soon established as a conditioned operant. It becomes reinforced chiefly in consequence of proper action with the stick and thus the proper components of the initial partial responses become emphasized, their sequence is condensed. The chimpanzee will not poke repeatedly at the stick or push it back and forth twenty times, as in the beginning of his trials, but goes over to the next variety of available response and displays all these immediate responses in rapid succession, integrating temporally a piecemeal pattern into a more unified compound. The sequence becomes elicitable as a composite complex by the original releaser of the first member[2][. . . .]

References

1. BAKAY, E., & SCHILLER, P. H. Detour experiments with rats. *Psychol. Stud.*, Univ. Budapest, 1947, **9**, 123–127.
2. BEACH, F. A. Comparison of copulatory behavior of male rats raised in isolation, cohabitation, and segregation. *J. genet. Psychol.*, 1942, **60**, 121–136.
3. BIRCH, H. The role of motivational factors in insightful problem-solving. *J. comp. physiol. Psychol.*, 1945, **38**, 295–317.
4. ——. The relation of previous experience to insightful problem-solving. *J. comp. physiol. Psychol.*, 1945, **38**, 367–383.
5. CARMICHAEL, L. The development of behavior in vertebrates experimentally removed from the influence of external stimulation. PSYCHOL. REV., 1926, **33**, 51–58.
6. GESELL, A. Maturation and infant behavior pattern. PSYCHOL. REV., 1926, **36**, 307–319.

2. Analyzing Thorndike's learning curves of monkeys (*Animal intelligence*, New York: Macmillan, 1911, pp. 185–187), it becomes clear that multiple manipulations, like his triple tasks, composed of three operations, were the most difficult ones to learn. The same effect is explicitly shown by N. Kohts, Les aptitudes motrices adaptives du singe inférieur. *J. de Psychol.*, 1930, 27, 412–447.

7. GIRDEN, E. Conditioning and problem-solving behavior. *Amer. J. Psychol.*, 1938, **51**, 677–687.

8. GUTHRIE, E. R., & HORTON, G. P. *Cats in a puzzle box.* New York: Rinehart, 1946.

9. HESS, W. R., & BRÜGGER, M. Das subkortikale Zentrum der affektiven Abwehrreaktionen. *Helvet. physiol. Acta*, 1943, **1**, 33–52.

0. JACKSON, T. A. Use of the stick as a tool by young chimpanzees. *J. comp. physiol. Psychol.*, 1942, **34**, 223–235.

1. KÖHLER, W. *The mentality of apes.* New York: Harcourt Brace, 1925.

2. MAIER, N. R. F., & SCHNEIRLA, T. C. Mechanisms in conditioning. PSYCHOL. REV., 1942, **49**, 117–134.

3. MOSELEY, D. The accuracy of the pecking responses in chicks. *J. comp. physiol. Psychol.*, 1925, **5**, 75–97.

4. MOWRER, O. H. On the dual nature of learning – a re-interpretation of 'conditioning' and 'problem-solving'. *Harvard educ. Rev.*, 1947, Spring, 102–148.

5. SCHILLER, P. v. Umwegversuche an Elritzen. *Z. Tierpsychol.*, 1942, **5**, 101–131.

6. SCHILLER, P. H. Analysis of detour behavior: I. Learning of roundabout pathways in fish. *J. comp. physiol. Psychol.*, 1949, **42**, 463–475.

7. ——. Analysis of detour behavior: II. Problem solution in the rat. (Manuscript, preliminary report in *American Psychol.*, Aug., 1947.)

8. ——. Delayed detour response in the octopus. *J. comp. physiol. Psychol.*, 1949, **42**, 220–225.

9. SHEPARD, J. F., & BREED, F. S. Maturation and use in the development of an instinct. *J. Animal Behav.*, 1913, **3**, 274–285.

0. SKINNER, B. F., 'Superstitions' in pigeons. *J. exp. Psychol.*, 1948, **38**, 168–172.

1. SPALDING, D. Instinct and acquisition. *Nature*, 1875, **12**, 507–508.

2. STONE, C. P. The initial copulatory response of female rats reared in isolation from the age of twenty days to the age of puberty. *J. comp. physiol. Psychol.*, 1926, **6**, 73–83.

3. TOLMAN, E. C. Cognitive maps in rats and men. PSYCHOL. REV., 1948, **55**, 189–208.

4. YERKES, R. M. The mind of a gorilla. *Genet. Psychol. Monogr.*, 1927, **2**, 1–193, 375–551.

5. ——, SPRAGG, S. D. SHIRLEY. La mesure du compartement adapté chez les chimpanzées. *J. de Psychol.*, 1937, **34**, 449–474.

11 H. G. Birch

The Relation of Previous Experience to Insightful Problem Solving

H. G. Birch, 'The relation of previous experience to insightful problem solving', *J. comp. Psychol.*, vol. 38 (1945), pp. 367–83.

The present paper is a report on the genesis of stick-using behavior of chimpanzees in problem-solving situations of the 'open' type used by Köhler in his investigations. It is felt, however, that although the data are specific, they apply more broadly to the general, controversial question of the role which previous experience plays in insight, and they are therefore discussed in connection with the general question of the behavior mechanisms involved in insightful problem-solution.

Background of the Problem

The available discussions of the behavior mechanisms involved in the solution of problems by infrahuman primates all tend to be dominated by the insight *versus* trial-and-error controversy. The two major frames of reference into which the bulk of the existent descriptions and interpretations fall are epitomized by the classical reports of Köhler and of Thorndike (11, 16, 17).

Thorndike, on the basis of his experiments on the modes of behavioral adaptation of cats and monkeys in problem-box situations contended that problem-solving was simply the product, or more accurately the sum or end result of a whole series of non-directed, more or less random and aimless acts, in the course of which the animal chanced to perform the one movement or series of movements which yielded an adequate adjustment. These rewarded acts were then retained by the animal and the unrewarded acts eliminated. Thus, the basic processes involved in the solution of a problem according to this point of view are: first, the essential feature of *variability* in behavior which causes animals to make a diverse series of movements in a problem situation; second, the beneficent factor of *chance* which provides the probability of the correct movement being made and finally, the tendency of the animals to retain the rewarded acts in a series, a tendency which has come to be known as the Law of Effect. According to such a view, problem-solving is primates was not considered as a higher level response, but as the eventual sum of a discrete series of responses in no way qualitatively different from less elaborate instances of learning insofar as behavior mechanisms were concerned.

This mechanical approach to infrahuman problem-solving did not fail to elicit criticism from others of the students of the evolution of intelligent behavior. Perhaps the most important of the earlier critics was Hobhouse (4), who contended that Thorndike's descriptions of animal problem-solving left unfilled a major hiatus in the history of mental evolution, namely the phyletic origins of the perception of relations, a kind of perception of fundamental importance in human adjustment. Hobhouse felt that the existence of this gap in our knowledge was at least in part a product of the problem-box method, and so devised and used a number of problem situations, which he felt would make possible the demonstration of the origins of relational perceptions in infrahuman forms. Among the problems he devised to this end were the patterned string test, the single and multiple stick test, the rod and tube test, and the box or stool climbing test. On the basis of a rather unsystematic study of the behavior of a small number of primates including one zoological-garden chimpanzee, Hobhouse concluded that the infrahuman primates, in addition to making adjustments on a trial-and-error basis, were capable of responding to the functional relations which existed among objects in the environment. The responses to such existent concrete relations he termed as manifestations of 'practical judgment', a category which filled the gap between trial-and-error adjustment of lower animals and the higher level human responses in his scheme of mental evolution.

However, despite the objections of Hobhouse, almost all of the studies of an experimental character concerned with the psychological status of monkeys and apes conducted during the years intervening between the early studies and those conducted independently by Köhler and by Yerkes during the period of the first world war continued the Thorndikian trend. Woodworth, working in Sherrington's laboratory, examined the behavior of a chimpanzee in regard to a puzzle-box into which food was placed. The results of this study are reported in Ladd and Woodworth (12). To solve the problems the animal had to open the door by turning one or two door buttons. It was found that the animal 'showed a prompt narrowing down of the field of effort to the right feature of the situation' (namely the door button); but that 'this important factor in the process of learning seemed to be accompanied by a complete absence of insight into the mechanical principle involved'. Shepherd (14, 15) interpreted the behavior of his rhesus monkeys and chimpanzees, and Kinnaman (8) the behavior of his rhesus monkeys in terms of the trial-and-error theory.

The Thorndikian conception, which identified problem-solving and effect learning, was sharply criticized by Köhler whose experiments with the chimpanzee indicated that the problem-solving behavior of the animal, far from being random, had as one of its most significant components directionality of activities. On the basis of his observations Köhler concluded that the chimpanzee was an animal capable of insightful problem solution. By insight he meant a type of behavior in which the animal takes the meaningful functional relations existing in the whole situation into account, and performs in a continuous, sequential manner until a goal is reached. In order to obtain this kind of behavior on the part of an animal it is essential that the situation be one in which such meaningful relations are present and all relevant items are open to inspection by the animal. In Köhler's opinion Thorndike's problem boxes did not meet this criterion and his results represented an artifact of method rather than a description of the characteristic mode of adjustment of the animal. Yerkes, contemporaneously with, but independently of Köhler, interpreted the behavior of the higher primates in a manner similar to Köhler (18, 19, 20, 21, 11).

Ever since its enunciation the concept of insight has been subjected to a double fire of criticism. In the interests of theoretical and expositional clarity it is essential that two aspects of the opposition to the doctrine be sharply distinguished one from the other. This can be done by dealing with the two distinct uses to which the term, *insight*, has been put, the one categorical, the other explanatory.[1]

In its categorical sense, insight simply represents a new quality of behavior. That is to say, it is a method of adjustment which has characteristics different from other modes of adjustment demonstrated by animals in response to problem situations.

1. That the act of categorizing has implicit in itself an explanatory element is practically a methodological truism, in the sense that any grouping of phenomena into classes represents the first step of all explanation, namely, designation. However, the validity of the contrasted use of the terms *categorical* and *explanatory* in the present connection seems to be warranted by the manner in which the insight concept has been both used and criticized.

Further, it represents a behavioral modality for which the concepts of chance variability, and the law of effect are inadequate as explanatory behavior mechanisms. This categorical use of the term insight leaves as unanswered the nature of the underlying behavior mechanisms, and poses their exploration as the next problem of research. For this meaning and application of the term insight only one valid question is possible, and that is: Does insightful behavior represent a type of performance qualitatively different from the earlier described trial-and-error behavior, or are the so-called insightful solutions simply manifestations of skills previously acquired by the animals in a trial-and-error fashion?

The attempt to use the concept of insight as an explanatory device in the interpretation of animal behavior has been essentially anthropomorphic. The problem-solving behavior of the animal has been interpreted as the product of an *awareness* of functional relations existing in the problem situation by the animal, which is identical in kind to the phenomenon of consciousness in human beings. Thus, the behavior is seemingly explained by means of an intuitively derived statement of the identity of animal problem-solving experience and common human experiences in similar situations. This kind of 'explanation' through the medium of communal experience is completely unverifiable and is dependent for its acceptance not upon demonstrable fact, but upon faith in the validity of intuitive judgments. It is not the intention here to discuss the utility or otherwise of the intuitional method as a scientific device, but merely to indicate that it is with the categorical rather than with the intuitional aspect of insight that the present paper is concerned.

The results of two decades of primate research have served amply to answer the categorical question, and there remains very little basis for doubting the validity of the term insight as descriptive of a distinct category of behavior. The work of Bingham (1), Yerkes (19), and Klüver (9) provides ample data in support of such a classification of behavior. However, there still remains lacking any conclusive evidence concerning the genetic development of insightful problem solutions, and the part played by the previous experiences of the animal in problem-solving has served as an item of speculative contention rather than as a problem for research. No conclusive answer is possible on the basis of the data which are given in the earlier studies, because the subjects used were captured animals whose backgrounds of experience were unknown, and the possibility of whose previous contacts with situations similar to the problem situations could only be inferred.[2]

Actually the question of the relation of previous experience resolves itself into two distinct problems. First, does the problem-solving behavior of chimpanzees characterized as insightful by Köhler represent a new performance never before stereotyped in the course of previous experience? Second, if there is a type of behavior which can be called insightful, does it have any basis in previous experience, or does it occur independently of the animals' experimental background? That is: Does insight arise directly from the effect of a given objective situational structuring on an animal possessing cortex of a given innate complexity, or does the experiential background of the organism play a significant part in determining the way in which it will perceive and manipulate external reality? It is the purpose of the present paper to attempt an answer to these two questions.

Subjects

To examine the problem of the part played by previous experience in insightful problem solution, it was essential that the subjects used be naive animals whose previous background of activities and experience was well-known. The subjects used in this study were six young chimpanzees all of whom were between 4 and 5 years of age. The group consisted of four males, Alf, Bard, Ken and Art, and two females, Jenny and Jojo.

All of the animals had been used as subjects in previous studies of an observational character and had worked at a series of six patterned string problems, but none had ever had any experience in working in stick-using situations. They were, therefore, naive subjects insofar as the problem situations used in the present study are concerned.

The background of experience of all of the subjects was uni-

2. This lack of genetic information has been remarked upon by other workers in the field. Fischel (3), and Klüver (10), have both posed the question, though in somewhat different ways, while Zuckerman (22) has despaired of its solution and has stated that: 'The sort of animal one would have to observe in order to learn exactly how a chimpanzee reacts to the single situation of "a banana out of reach and a stick near-by" does not exist. It would have to be an animal that had been brought up from birth alone and without food in an empty grey room. The chimpanzees one can observe already know how to solve the problem.' (Page 163.) Fortunately, as the results of this study will indicate the environmental restrictions need not be quite so severe, nor the outlook so pessimistic as Zuckerman has implied, for an understanding of the genetic development of primate problem-solving to be obtained.

form to an extraordinarily high degree. This was the result of the fact that they had all been used in the infant development studies at the Laboratories. Every one of the animals had been separated from its mother within two weeks after birth, and had been raised under controlled and uniform conditions in the nursery at the Yerkes Laboratories of Primate Biology. Complete diaries were available for each animal, and covered all of its observed behavior, physical changes, and temperamental manifestations from the time of birth to the present.

All six of the subjects had for the last 20 months been living together in an open air enclosure containing a tree and a slide, both of which were frequently climbed upon by the animals. In the course of this outdoor existence, all of the animals have gained an extensive experience in climbing, and all have on occasion been observed to handle branches and twigs torn or fallen from the trees.

Only one of the animals, Jojo, has made a regular practice of stick using, and on numerous occasions has been observed to reach through the mesh of her indoor cage and flick the electric light switch off and on with a stick. She has developed, also, the further habit of unscrewing an electric light bulb by reaching through her cage-mesh with a stick. The origin of this unique behavior on the part of Jojo is not known. The important point, however, is that none of the other animals had been observed to use a stick as a reaching instrument up to the time at which the present study was begun.

Procedure

Before being subjected to any test situations the animals were given a series of adaptation sessions in the cage in which the tests were to be administered. A detailed description of the experimental set-up is presented in another paper (2). The adaptation sessions were continued until the animals showed no signs of being excited in the cage, and had learned to extend their arms through the grill and remove food from the table without any hesitation. After the adaptation sessions had been completed, the experiment proceeded through the following steps:

(1) The animals were tested individually on what has been considered the simplest of the stick using tests, the hoe problem (see figure 1). Four of the subjects failed to solve this problem in the course of a thirty-minute test period. The two animals who solved the problem did so by very different methods.

(2) After the initial test session the animals were returned to

121

Figure 1

their open air enclosure, into which a dozen 1″ × 1″ sticks of
lengths varying from 16 inches to 30 inches were put, in order to
determine the manner in which the opportunity to use a stick in
the course of general play activities would affect the performance
of the animals in the stick using situation. The sticks which were
placed in the enclosure were not hoe-sticks, but ordinary straight
sticks. The behavior of the animals was observed during four
observation periods a day for three days. Each observation period
lasted for 30 minutes, and detailed notes of the behavior of the
animals were taken. Two of the periods occurred in the morning
and two in the afternoon, so that the four periods of daily observation represent progressive time-segments of the development
of the animals' behavior in regard to the sticks.

(3) After the three-day period of stick-play opportunity, the
six animals were retested on the hoe problem.

(4) Following the hoe retest, work on the problem of the relation of motivational state to problem-solving efficiency was resumed. The results of this investigation are reported elsewhere
(2); however some of the behavior observed in the course of the
motivational study are relevant to the problem under consideration in the present paper, and shall be referred to, with appropriate attention to procedure, in the final section of the results
to be presented below.

Results and Discussion

(*A*) *Responses of the animals to the initial presentation of the hoe
problem*

In the first presentation of the problem only two of the animals,
Jojo and Bard, achieved a solution. The remaining four subjects
failed to solve the problem in the course of the thirty-minute work

period. The solutions and the failures at solution are summarized in the following paragraphs:

Of the two subjects who solved the problem only one, Jojo, an animal who, as has already been mentioned, was frequently occupied in playing with twigs and fallen branches, solved the problem in a smooth, direct, and rapid fashion. She went to the grill, looked at the food, glanced at the stick, and at once reached for the stick, *picked the stick up*, and in one smooth sweep (counterclockwise) brought the food into reach. She then laid the stick on the table, picked up the food with the same hand that had held the stick (right), and ate. Time for solution was 12 seconds.

The behavior of the other successful subject, Bard, was quite different. He went to the grill, looked at the food, and at once began to reach out directly for the food with his hand. After three futile attempts at direct reaching within a period of one minute, he desisted in his direct reaches for the food, hooted, turned away from the food and began to solicit the experimenter. This solicitation continued for approximately a minute, after which he wandered about the cage and solicited intermittently. After 4 minutes had elapsed from the time of his entrance into the test cage, he returned to the grill and resumed his direct reaching for the food. In the course of this direct reaching, his thrashing arm happened accidently to brush against the stick, causing it to move about 3 inches to the right. The center of the stick was blocked by a small obstruction on the table surface and so the stick moved in a pivotal manner sweeping the food along through a short arc. Bard immediately paused in his reaching and looked carefully at the stick and the food. He then reached out deliberately and shoved gently at the side of the stick, while he watched the food. The food moved. Bard then grasped the stick between two of his fingers, and pulled it in with the same technique as that which he had used in string-pulling, and after several tugs he brought the food into reach, took it up in his hands, and ate.[3]

3. It is of interest to note at this point, the near identity of our description of the accidental solution of the problem arrived at by Bard, and the description of the initial accidental solution of a stick-problem made by the young female gorilla (*G. Beringei*), Congo, estimated age 4–5 years, in Dr. Yerkes' investigation (19). In both cases an accidental shove against the stick caused the food to move and initiated a series of responses which led to the attainment of the lure. Further incidents of interest in connection with the initial adjustment to problem-situations, of young chimpanzees are available in the reports of infant development by the Kelloggs (7) and by Jacobsen *et al.* (6).

It is important to note at this point that the manner in which the stick was utilized was fundamentally different for the two successful subjects. Jojo picked the stick up from the table and severed its direct spatial connection with the food before she reached out with it and swept the food into reach. Bard, however, at no time separated the stick from the food, and behaved as though the food were attached to the stick in the same manner as the lure was attached to the string in the patterned string-problems. Thus for Jojo a functional connection seemed to exist between the stick and the act of reaching, while for Bard there appeared to be a functional and physical connection between the stick and the food.

The behavior of the unsuccessful subjects was of two kinds, with one variety exemplified by Alf, and the second type exhibited by three animals, Jenny, Ken and Art. When Alf was presented with the problem he responded by reaching out directly for the food. He persisted in making direct attempts at reaching the food alternated with periods of soliciting the experimenter or wandering about the cage for the entire 30 minutes of the test period. At no time did he make any attempt to use the stick and, as a matter of fact, at no time during the entire test period did he touch the stick at all.

The remaining three unsuccessful animals behaved in a manner which was different from that of Alf, but typical among themselves. Their first responses in the situation were a series of unavailing direct reaches for the food. After a few direct reaching attempts of this kind the animals desisted in their direct reaching and turned their attention to the stick. They hit at the stick angrily, and thrust it aside with sufficient violence to throw it from the table. When the thrust-aside stick was reset by the experimenter, these animals pushed it aside once again and persisted in making direct, non-instrumental attempts at reaching the food, alternated with solicitation of the experimenter. This pattern of behavior was persisted in for the entire thirty-minute test period. They behaved as though the stick were perceived as an obstacle or barrier between the food and themselves.

To summarize: There appear to exist four distinct types of perception of functional relations among our six young chimpanzee subjects in the first stick-problem situation, indicated by their behavior. (1) For Jojo the stick represents an extension of the arm. (2) For Bard there appears to exist a functional and physical connection between the stick and the piece of food. (3) For three of the subjects, Jenny, Art, and Ken, the stick appears to be viewed as a barrier between themselves and the food, or perhaps more parsimoniously, bears no positive functional value in the situation. (4) Finally, in the case of Alf, the stick does not seem to be responded to at all.

(B) The behavior of the animals during the period of stick availability and familiarization

After being tested on the hoe problem, the animals were all returned to the open air enclosure and provided with the opportunity to handle sticks in their play in order to determine the effect of such general, non-problem-directed experience upon the manner in which they would use a stick in a problem-solving situation. When the sticks were first placed in the enclosure, the animals examined them, picked them up, handled them, and carried them around either in their mouths or in their hands for short periods of time. None of the animals showed the least sign of being afraid of the sticks, which makes it extremely improbable that the earlier failures to use the stick in the hoe problem was the result of timidity.

During the early part of the first day in which the sticks were in the enclosure the animals tended to carry the sticks about. Sometimes an animal would wander around carrying a stick in each hand in addition to one held in its mouth. In the course of the first two observation periods of the first day every animal had reached at least once for objects with the hand in which the stick was being carried. *The object was not reached for with the stick, but with the hand, with the stick appearing to play no functional role in the reaching-contacting pattern. The object (a twig, a piece of food, or another of the chimpanzees) was contacted with the hand and not with the stick.* However, in the course of this reaching, the animals, after having established manual contact with the object, sometimes poked at and touched it with the stick. Further, during the course of the first two periods of observation, some of the animals poked at the ground and at the enclosure fence with the stick.

In the third observation period of the first day the animals were seen to reach out and touch distant objects, usually another of the chimpanzees, with the stick. By the end of the first day during which the sticks were available to them, every one of the subjects had on several occasions used the stick as a functional extension of the arm. That is, they had all been observed *to reach out with the stick* and touch some animal or object distant from themselves. The nature of this reaching with the stick as a functional extension of arm-reach is quite different from the earlier behavior of the animals during which objects were reached for with the hand and only touched with the stick by accident, or after they had been manually apprehended. In the later behavior it was quite clear that the object at a distance from the animal was being reached for with the stick, and not with the hand.

During the second enclosure-day the animals were observed to be using the stick more frequently as an arm extension, and several times fights were started when one chimpanzee poked another sharply with a stick. On the third day, the animals seemed to be responding to the sticks as a prominent and attractive part of the environment. The activities already described for the second day were continued and extended, with several of the animals developing the somewhat annoying habit of poking at the experimenter through the enclosure mesh, and Art, especially, was prominent in using his stick in the frequent launching of play-attacks on his enclosure mates.

The changes in the behavior of the animals toward the sticks during the three-day-period of opportunity for stick-play in the enclosure can be summarized as follows:

(1) The sticks tended to become a significant part of the environment in connection with which many general activities were associated.

(2) The animals had gradually integrated the sticks into their previously existent reaching patterns, with the stick coming to be used as a functional extension of the arm.

(3) The sticks were not seen to be used to sweep objects into reach, but to establish contact from a distance.

(*C*) *Responses of the animals to the hoe problem after they had had general experience with sticks in play*

The behavior of the animals in the food-hoe problem-situation after they had had the opportunity to handle sticks in their play activities was markedly different from what it had been in the initial test involving the use of the hoe as an instrument for bringing food into reach. To begin with the most obvious change, it was found that whereas in the initial test only two of the six subjects were capable of using the stick in any manner as an instrument for overcoming the distance between themselves and the food, now, after the time spent in play with sticks, every one of the six animals was able to solve the problem without the least sign of difficulty. Jojo, the animal who had solved the problem on its first presentation, was again the most efficient worker, and swept the food into reach in 5 seconds. However, the other animals were not very much slower, with the slowest worker, Alf, taking 20 seconds in which to solve the problem.

In addition to the gross change in the number of successes made in the problem by the animals, some of the more subtle modifications in the modes of response are worthy of mention. It will be recalled that Bard, the only subject in addition to Jojo to solve the problem on its initial presentation, arrived at his first solution on the basis of seeming to perceive a direct physical connection to exist between the food and the stick. In his first solution of the problem, prior to the provision of opportunities for stick-play in the enclosure, he treated the stick as though it were a string, and pulled in the food by means of the same technique as that which he had used in the patterned string tests. His behavior in the test which was given subsequent to the stick-play experience was quite different. Upon being placed in the problem cage, he ran to the grill, *reached out and picked up the stick*, thereby breaking its direct connection with the food. The stick was held with the four fingers of his right hand. He then swept the food into reach, picked it up and ate. This sweeping with the stick was a movement distinctly different from the pulling movement which had characterized his first successful attempt at the problem. While in the first solution Bard perceived the stick as something attached to the food, in the second solution, arrived at after stick-play experience, the stick was perceived as a functional extension of the arm,[4] and not as an object having a direct connection with the food.

The behavior of the animals who had failed to obtain the food in their initial attempts at the problem was, upon retest after the stick-play opportunity, similar to that already described for Jojo and Bard. Upon being admitted to the problem cage, they ran at once to the grill, picked up the stick and swept the food into reach, took it in hand and ate. The responses were all smooth and direct in character. None of the animals repeated its previous performance of thrusting the stick out of the way, and only one animal, Alf, prefaced his use of the stick with an attempt directly to reach the food by means of a non-instrumentally augmented direct extension of his arm. Alf made one such direct-reaching

4. The idea that the use of a stick as a problem-solving instrument is genetically linked to the prior development of the stick-arm extension pattern, has been hypothecated by Professor T. C. Schneirla in his lectures on comparative psychology. The data obtained in this study seem to represent a confirmation of this hypothesis.

attempt, it was unsuccessful, and he at once desisted, picked up the stick and swept the food into reach with it.[5]

(*D*) *The behavior of the animals in the subsequent series of more complicated problems which required the use of sticks for their solution*

The data to be reported in this section of the paper represent selected items from the behavior protocols of the animals in a series of problem-situations designed to demonstrate the effect of different motivational states on the ability of the chimpanzee to solve problems of the type used by Köhler. Although the analysis of these protocols as a whole is presented in another paper (2) in connection with the question of the relation of motivation to problem-solving, the items reported here, bearing as they do upon the question of the relation of previous experience to insight, have not been presented before.

When the behavior of the animals in a series of ten stick-using situations is considered as a whole, it is found that once the basic pattern of the use of a stick as an extension of the arm-reach is established the animals are capable of using sticks in a wide variety of situations. At this point, however, we shall report in some detail the activities of the animals in only two of the eleven stick-problems used in the motivation study because of the especial relevance of the behavior for the question of the part played by previous experience in the appearance of insightful problem solutions. The behavior to be discussed here occurred in the first and in the ninth problems of the series. Problem 1 was a simple stick-using situation, in which the food was placed on the table beyond the reach of the animal and a straight stick was placed on the table with its near end 3 inches from the grill, and its far end directly alongside, and in contact with, the food. Problem 9 was a food-in-pipe problem, in which the food was

5. Some significant ancillary data on another young chimpanzee subject, Velt, is provided in Jackson's report (5) on stick-using. This young male was given ten trials on a single-stick problem, each trial lasting about five minutes. The animal 'failed utterly, making no attempt to use the stick to get the food'. However, after being permitted to play with a stick for two hours a day for fourteen days, he solved the problem on its re-presentation in a 'deliberate manner', and 'manifested the skill of an animal that had used a stick dozens of times'.

It is important to remember, that at no time during the stick-play period were any of our animals or Jackson's animal observed to use the stick as an instrument by means of which a distant object was swept into reach. What was developed in the case of our animals was an arm-stick-extension pattern and not a stereotyped reaching sweeping movement.

placed inside a pipe in the presence of the animal; the diameter of the pipe was too small to permit the admission of the hand, but a long stick was available on the floor directly beneath the pipe. The task involved the use of the stick as tool by means of which the food could be pushed out of the pipe. In the case of problem 1 the food was one-half an orange; in problem 9 the food was a whole medium-sized banana. It is to be remembered that each of the animals was working under a different condition of motivation in these problems.

When they were confronted with problem 1 of the motivation series, three of the animals, Alf, Bard, and Jenny, all made the same initial responses to the problem. They went to the grill, looked out at the stick and food, and then reached out and pulled in the straight stick that extended from the grill to the food, in exactly the same manner as that in which they had pulled in the strings or the hoe. Their behavior seemed to indicate that the stick was being reacted to in terms of a direct equivalence, with the straight stick being treated as the stimulus equivalent of the strings and the hoe. However, when they saw that the food did not move into reach as the stick was drawn in, the animals paused, thrust the stick out onto the table once again, picked it up and used it smoothly to sweep the food into reach. The behavior of Jojo, whose stick-using propensity and proficiency has already been referred to, was quite different. She went to the grill, reached out, and at once picked up the stick and swept the food into reach. The two remaining animals, Ken and Art, who were working under the most intense conditions of drive, *i.e.* after periods of 36 hours and 48 hours of food deprivation respectively, made the initial response of pushing the stick aside and then reaching directly. However, after a short time both of these animals picked up the stick and swept the food into reach.

The behavior of the animals in problem 9, the food-in-pipe situation, provides an interesting illustration of the manner in which previous learning may interfere with the utilization of a familiar object in a new manner in a problem-solving situation. The animals were tested on the pipe-problem after they had all had experience in working at the first eight problems in the stick-using series. In all of these previous problems the food had been situated on the table before the grill. Now when the animals were tested on the pipe-problem, five of the six animals tested, although they had all seen the banana being placed in the pipe by the experimenter, at some time during the test carried the stick to the grill and reached out with it over the empty table. It was quite clear visually that the table was devoid of food, yet five of the six subjects went to it and reached out over it with the stick.

Only three of the animals eventually solved this problem in a test period of one hour. Of these three, two of the subjects, Bard and Jojo, both carried the stick to the grill and reached out over the table with it as their initial response to the pipe-problem. After one such reaching attempt, Jojo made no further reaches over the table, but Bard stopped working at the pipe and made two further table-reaches before he finally mastered the food-in-pipe problem. Of the three animals who failed the food-in-pipe test, each made a single table-reach. In every case this attempt occurred early in the test period and was not repeated by the animal.

It seemed that the animals had begun to develop a stereotyped approach to the total problem situation, and were beginning automatically to respond by carrying a stick to the table and reaching, without taking the objective features of the problem into account. However, the animals were capable of discarding this stereotyped response rapidly, and of readjusting their behavior to the requirements of the problem.

Some Theoretical Considerations

For Köhler the principal controversial question to be considered in an examination of the problem-solving behavior of chimpanzees seemed to be the inadequacy of the doctrines of chance and of trial and error as explanations of the manner in which chimpanzees solve problems. On the basis of his reports when taken as a whole, and on the basis of the behavior of the animals reported in the protocols of the present study, it is quite clear that chimpanzees are capable of behaving in a way that is characterized by responses which are indicative of what may be termed insight into the nature of the functional relations existing in the situations with which they are confronted. The animals do not appear to solve the problems on the basis of the direct application of previously learned patterns to the new problem, nor do they succeed in mastering the problems on the basis of the selection of certain rewarded acts from among a series of random activities in the course of which the correct response happens to occur by chance.

However, in rejecting the doctrines of trial and error and of chance as adequate theoretical approaches to the question of chimpanzee problem-solving, Köhler seems to have failed to give sufficient weight to the role which the previous activities and experiences of the animal play in its problem-solving efforts. Although he has taken 'for granted that every chimpanzee above a certain low age' (p. 204) has had some experience in the handling of sticks or branches in the course of its general activity, he has attempted to explain the problem-solving of the animal in terms of its supposed innate capacity to perceive certain relevant relations existing in the problem-situation in terms which are purely situational–visual in character. In his discussion he states: 'In the field of the experiments carried out here the insight of the chimpanzee shows itself to be principally determined by his optical apprehension of the situation; at times he even starts solving problems from a too visual point of view, and in many cases in which the chimpanzee *stops* acting with insight, it may have been simply that the lay of the land was too much for his visual grasp (relative "weakness of shape perception"). It is therefore difficult to give a satisfactory explanation of all his performances, so long as no detailed theory of shape (*Gestalt*) has been laid as a foundation. The need for such a theory will be felt the more, when one remembers that *solutions* showing insight in this field of intelligence necessarily take part in the nature of the structure of the situations, in so far as they arise in dynamic processes *co-ordinated with* the situation.'[6]

The tendency to deal primarily with the objective structuring of the problem-situation and only assumptively if at all with the animal's experiential background to a certain extent was the inevitable product of circumstances beyond Köhler's control. The subjects which he used in his experiments were captured animals the nature of whose previous experiences could only be inferentially known. However, his failure to make explicit the *relevance* of such experiential conditions to insightful behavior seems to be a function of an entirely different circumstance. It appears as an artifact of the Gestalt method, which is essentially non-historical, and thus tends to approach the problem of the mechanisms underlying problem-solving in immediate situational terms, on the basis of an assumed identity of situational and cortical dynamics.

This situational emphasis, although it has stimulated research that has given us a good deal of information about the character of problem-solving difficulties which arise as a result of the spatial configuration of the problem-situation, has not provided sufficient evidence for understanding the active interrelation between

6. Italics in original.

organism and situation which is essential if the dynamics of problem-solving are to be understood. The extensive work carried out by psychologists adhering to the Gestalt school of thought has created an extensive and highly significant body of knowledge concerning the manner in which the structure of the objective situation influences the character of an organism's problem-solving efforts. This literature on the *Einstellung* effect is, however, a highly directionalized spotlight which has served to illuminate only one side of the problem, namely the way in which external field organization tends to evoke a given predominate direction in the responses of a behaving organism. The other side of the question, the manner in which experiential factors influence the character of the animals' perceptions of the externally objective reality, has remained relatively unexplored.

The experimental evidence seems to indicate that far from the directly available perceptual field determining behavior, in many cases the character of the field itself may well be determined by the condition of the perceiving organism. Therefore, any attempt at an explanation of problem-solving in terms of the external field properties alone becomes a device of doubtful value. Any attempt then at a non-experiential explanation of problem-solving perforce must leave as unresolved the basic problem which the behavioral data pose. That is, in an ambiguous situation such as a problem-solving situation there seems to exist no *a priori* 'good' configuration, the perception of which leads directly to elicitation of the requisite adequate response. On the contrary the ability of the animal to shift from one of the possible perceptual organizations of the situation to another appears to be fundamentally necessary if an adequate ordering of the field is to occur. Under such conditions the immediately perceived organization may have to be discarded, and a new, more relevant organization of the situation developed in its stead. This new configuration is thus not simply inherent in the external field properties, but is the emergent product of the interaction of organism and field.

In the present study, the behavior of the animals in the first stick-using situation provides some important data on the question of the role of previous experience in problem-solving. As has already been reported the only animal who showed a clear-cut perception of the functional relations which existed in the problem-situation between the available T stick and food placed beyond direct reaching distance was Jojo, an animal whose earlier behavior had included many instances of stick-using. Of the other animals, only one, Bard, solved the problem on its initial presentation. He did this on the basis of accidentally hitting the stick with his arm in the course of making a direct reach for the food. The food moved a little. Bard saw this, pushed at the stick once again, deliberately this time. The food moved once again, and he then took the stick between his fingers, and behaving much as though the stick were a string, an instrument with which he had had previous experience in the patterned string problems, he pulled the fruit into reach. The remaining four animals either ignored the stick, or treated it as though it were an obstacle between the food and themselves.

After the animals had been given an opportunity in handling sticks in their home environment for three days, they all solved the T stick problem within a period of 20 seconds. It seemed that in the course of playing with the sticks, the animals gradually learned to use the stick as an extension of their arm-reach. This learning took place in several stages. At first the animals did not appear to be reaching for things with the stick. They seemed merely to be reaching for objects when the stick was in the hand, and the stick then served accidentally as an extension of the animals' reach. It was not until after this had been done that the animals picked up the stick and used it deliberately as an extension of the arm-reach.

On the basis of this evidence it appears that the animals only perceive a *given functional relation* to exist between the stick, the food, and themselves in the stick-using situation after they have had an opportunity to learn something about sticks and their possible use on the basis of previous experience. Only then, in the problem-situation, is the stick viewed as a part of the situation which bears a positive functional relationship to the food. The stick is no longer ignored or thrust aside by the animals, as though it were an obstacle between themselves and the goal, but is utilized in the solution of the problem.

There were thus several different kinds of perception of the relations existing in the problem-situation demonstrated in the behavior of our animals, who were initially incapable of solving the stick problem. The first existed prior to their having experience with sticks, and the second appeared after they had been given the opportunity to acquire such experience. The perception of relevant functional relations does not appear to be the directly determined product of the action of a given situational pattern upon an organism of given cortical complexity, but to be organized on the basis of the dynamic interrelation between the matrix of available past experiences and the characteristics of the given objective situation.[7]

Such a conclusion does not mean that features of the situational pattern do not affect the difficulty or the ease with which an organism can solve a given problem. However, it does mean that discussion of situational factors alone is insufficient to explain problem-solving behavior.

Once the animal has learned to use the stick as an extension of its arm-reach, it is capable of utilizing this knowledge in a wide variety of ways. *This ability to reorganize previous experiences in accordance with the requirements of a new problem-situation is the essential feature of problem-solving.* The ability to select from the available repertoire of recall and reorganize into new patterns of response previously learned, *but not contiguously learned* items of experience, makes possible an enormous expansion of the adjustive possibilities of an organism. As Maier and Schneirla (13) put it, 'In the ability to reorganize experience, the animal is released from stereotyped forms of behavior which are laid down by learning. With the development and dominance of this ability, learning takes on a new role. Past experience ceases to furnish the patterns of response, and instead furnishes the data from which new patterns may be formed. This ability frees the animal from a particular bit of learning and makes possible almost unlimited patterns of response' (p. 479).

Summary and Conclusions

Six young chimpanzees, aged between four and five years, were used to investigate the relation of previous experience to the insightful solution of problems of the type used by Köhler, in his studies of primate intelligence. The animals had all been born in captivity and had been raised under controlled nursery conditions, so that records of their early development and experiences were available. The specific problem selected for investigation was stick-using.

The animals were first tested as to their ability to solve a simple

7. Klüver (10) has stated that the utilization of an object as a problem-solving implement is dependent not only upon the recognition of a number of significant situational relations, but also upon knowledge acquired in previous experiences of the properties of the objects themselves. The results of the present study support this hypothesis, and indicate further (1) that the functional relations which are perceived are dependent upon prior experience with the objects present in the situation, and (2) that the animal not only has obtained specific knowledge of a property of an object, but has also generalized this knowledge.

problem involving the use of a hoe to secure a piece of food. Of the six animals, only two arrived at a solution in the course of a thirty-minute test period, while the remaining four animals failed to solve the problem. The two animals who were successful in their problem-solving efforts, arrived at very different solutions, which indicated that while one of the animals perceived the situation as one in which the stick had a direct, physical connection with the food, the other animal, whose history of stick-using was extensive, perceived the stick as an instrument which was capable of being used as a functional extension of the arm.

The animals were then given a number of sticks in their home enclosure, and the subjects' behavior in connection with the sticks was observed. In the course of three days of playing with the sticks, the animals evolved a pattern of response, which was characterized by the gradual acquisition of the use of the stick as a functional extension of the arm. The animals were retested on the hoe problem after they had had the opportunity to use sticks in the course of their play activities. In the retest every one of the subjects succeeded in solving the problem within a period of 20 seconds. Further, the evidence indicated clearly that the functional relations which were perceived in the situation were fundamentally modified by the general experience in stick-using.

The evidence was interpreted as demonstrating:

(1) That the perception of functional relations in a situation is dependent in large part upon the previous experiences of the animal.

(2) That insightful problem solution represents the integration into new patterns of activity of previously existent part-processes developed in the course of the animals' earlier activities.

(3) That any interpretation of insight in situational terms alone, or even predominately in situational terms, is invalid.

(4) That the functional relationships which are perceived in a given problem by the animal, and which serve as the basis for an insightful response, are the product of the dynamic interaction of (*a*) the available repertoire of experiences (superimposed upon the basic species characteristics), with (*b*) the objective features of the situation.

(5) That in insightful problem-solving, in contrast with trial-and-error solution, previous experience provides the materials out of which an adequate pattern of response may be fabricated, rather than the stereotyped problem-solving response itself.

References

1. BINGHAM, H. C.: Chimpanzee translocation by means of boxes. Comp. Psychol. Monogr., 1929, **5**, No. 3, 91 pp.
2. BIRCH, H. G.: The role of motivational factors in insightful problem-solving. In press, 1945.
3. FISCHEL, W.: Methoden zur psychologischen Untersuchung der Wirbeltiere. Handb. Biol. Arb. Meth., 1932, VI, 233–338.
4. HOBHOUSE, L. T.: Mind in Evolution. London: Macmillan, 1901.
5. JACKSON, T. A.: Use of the stick as a tool by young chimpanzees. J. Comp. Psychol., 1942, **34**, 223–235.
6. JACOBSEN, C. F., JACOBSEN, M. M., AND YOSHIOKA, J. G.: Development of an infant chimpanzee during her first year. Comp. Psychol. Monogr., 1932, **9**, No. 1, 94 pp.
7. KELLOGG, W. N., AND KELLOGG, L. A.: The Ape and the Child: a Study of Environmental Influence upon Early Behavior. New York: Whittlesey House, 1933.
8. KINNAMAN, A. J.: Mental life of two *Macacus rhesus* monkeys in captivity. Amer. J. Psychol., 1902, **13**, 98–148, 173–218.
9. KLÜVER, H.: Behavior Mechanisms in Monkeys. Chicago: Univ. Chicago Press, 1933.
10. KLÜVER, H.: Re-examination of implement-using behavior in a *Cebus* monkey after an interval of three years. Acta Psychol., 1937, II, 347–397.
11. KÖHLER, W.: The Mentality of Apes. (Trans. E. Winter.) New York: Harcourt, Brace, 1925.
12. LADD, G. T., AND WOODWORTH, R. S.: Elements of Physiological Psychology. New York: C. Scribners Sons, 1911.
13. MAIER, N. R. F., AND SCHNEIRLA, T. C.: Principles of Animal Psychology. New York: McGraw-Hill, 1935.
14. SHEPHERD, W. T.: Some mental processes of the *Rhesus* monkey. Psychol. Rev. Monogr., 1910, **12**, No. 5, 61 pp.
15. SHEPHERD, W. T.: Some observations on the intelligence of the chimpanzee. J. Anim. Behav., 1915, **5**, 391–396.
16. THORNDIKE, E. L.: Animal intelligence; an experimental study of the associative processes in animals. Psychol. Rev. Monogr., 1898, **2**, No. 8, 109 pp.
17. THORNDIKE, E. L.: The mental life of monkeys. Psychol. Rev. Monogr., 1901, **3**, No. 5, 57 pp.
18. YERKES, R. M.: The mental life of monkeys and apes: a study of ideational behavior. Behav. Monogr., 1916, **3**, No. 1, 145 pp.
19. YERKES, R. M.: The mind of a gorilla. Genet. Psychol. Monogr., 1927, **2**, Nos. 1 and 2, 1–193.
20. YERKES, R. M.: The mind of a gorilla. Part II. Mental development. Genet. Psychol. Monogr., 1927, **2**, No. 6, 377–551.
21. YERKES, R. M., AND YERKES, A. W.: The Great Apes: a Study of Anthropoid Life. New Haven: Yale University Press, 1929.
22. ZUCKERMAN, S.: The Social Life of Monkeys and Apes. London: Kegan Paul, Trench, Trubner & Co., 1932.

12 K. R. L. Hall

Tool-Using Performances as Indicators of Behavioral Adaptability

Excerpt from K. R. L. Hall, 'Tool-using performances as indicators of behavioral adaptability', *Current Anthropology*, vol. 4 (1963), pp. 479–94.

Introduction

The use by an animal of an object or of another living organism as a means of achieving an advantage has been commonly regarded by comparative psychologists as an indication of intelligent adaptability. The mediating object is required by definition to be something extraneous to the bodily equipment of the animal, and its use allows the animal to extend the range of its movements or to increase their efficiency. Phrases like 'functional extension' have been applied to such performances, whose crucial characteristic is manipulation of something in the environment, in appetitive or aversive behavior or, much more rarely, as part of an instinctive display or nesting operation.

Many problems arise as to the origin, in ontogeny and phylogeny, of such performances. It is rarely clear whether a performance is characteristic of a species, or whether individual variations due to local ecological conditions modify it. Nor is it clear whether a performance, once it has occurred in an individual given or in a group of animals, can be transmitted to form a 'tradition', in the sense of a habit learned and retained, or whether the more likely evolutionary process is selection, on the basis of the advantage of the performance; in the latter case, the learning is a matter of trial-and-error application of the tendency, comparable to the way in which any number of inherited tendencies may be ecologically employed. Thorpe (1951, 1956) has examined much of the evidence along these lines, with particular reference to birds. In the present paper it is intended to carry the analysis into the realm of nonhuman primate behavior; some of the well-authenticated studies of other animals will be cited to give the necessary comparative perspective.

On evaluating performances as falling inside or outside the category of tool-using, it will be evident that they vary greatly in their flexibility and apparent behavioral complexity. All performances are conventionally excluded if they involve simply applying a 'primary' object, for example, food, to a 'secondary' object, such as a rock. Thus, the snail-breaking by thrushes or the dropping of shells by gulls or crows onto a hard surface can be excluded. Included can be performances as manifestly unlike as the carrying of actinians in the claws of crabs and the enlisting of aid among chimpanzees in the cooperative solving of problems beyond the ability of a single chimpanzee, or the inducement of one chimpanzee by another, through food-begging or threat, to bring it food.

Tool-using Other Than for Defense or Food-seeking

The classic example of tool-using in insects, that of the solitary wasp, *Ammophila urnaria*, was reported by Peckham and Peckham (1898); to be sure, Williston (1892) had already made similar observations on another species. In each instance, the act consisted of holding a small pebble in the mandibles and using it as a hammer to pound dirt into the nest burrow. The Peckhams commented: 'We are claiming a great deal for *Ammophila* when we say that she improvised a tool and made intelligent use of it, for such actions are rare even among higher mammals . . . .' (p. 223). Whether this is to be counted as an 'individual' achievement rather than characteristic of a species is not certain, and the problem is not, at this level, of importance except in the way it parallels the situation in 'higher' animals. So unexpected and interesting were these observations to the early comparative psychologists that they tended to jump to the conclusion that 'intelligent purpose' and 'perception of the relation of means to an end' (Morgan, 1900) were involved, while McDougall (1923) was somewhat more lyrical, saying:

Are we then to regard each of these two wasps as a lively *bahnbrechende* genius, leading their species onward to the use of tools; individual sports comparable to the man, or ape, who first took a stone in his hand to crack a nut and so foreshadowed the genius of Nasmyth? I see no other plausible interpretation of the facts. [p. 91]

The best known and most reliably reported instance of tool-using among birds occurs in the Satin bower-bird, *Ptilonorhynchus violaceus*. This species was said by Chisholm (1954) to use a 'tool', such as small wads of bark, to aid in the painting of the inside walls of its bower. He commented:

. . . it had been supposed that these served the office of a brush, but it is now thought more probable that each one acts as a cork, or stopper, to prevent the paint oozing from the tip of the mandibles while the bird is plastering the walls of the bower with the sides of the bill. [p. 381]

Marshall's study (1960) provides the behavioral context of these performances in the Satin bower-bird species, as well as a very full description of them:

... many, but not all, adult males begin to plaster their bower with a thick, black, tacky material made from a mixture of charcoal compounded with saliva. With a bark wad held between the tips of the beak, the plaster is forced between the mandibles and so transferred to the inside sticks of the bower. [p. 207]

A similar kind of behavior is reported of some male members of the genus *Chlamydera*: painting their bowers with dry grass mixed with saliva. These performances occur during displays which serve partly to attract females to the display grounds, partly to repel other males, so that pair-formation can occur: 'Remarkable as they are, the bowers and display paraphernalia of bower-birds are no more than an extension of the territorial and display impulses to be found in other birds' (p. 208), and the whole performance of bower-construction and painting is interpreted by him as the outcome of a 'displaced nesting-drive', the male taking no part in nest-building or incubation. Marshall commented that bower-birds are no more intelligent than other highly developed passerine species, and there is, indeed, no valid reason for supposing they might be simply on the grounds that an elementary act, definable as tool-use, is incorporated into the display. The *rarity* of any such performance among birds or other animals in such a context suggests that it is a special case of behavioral adaptation which has no particular significance in the evolution of 'intelligent' tool-using.

Seemingly the only instance in this miscellaneous category known in mammals is that of the Burmese elephant, which, according to Williams (1950), picks up a long stick with its trunk to scratch its body. Although in captivity monkeys and apes are known to cover themselves with sacking or other materials, apparently as protection from cold or wet, no such instances are known from field studies.

Tool-using as a Part of Agonistic Behavior

Not a single authenticated instance of tool-using as an element in agonistic behavior is known in animals other than that of the monkeys and apes which use a tool in repelling predators or intruders. According to Duerden (1905), the carrying of actinians by the crab *Melia tessellata* may have protective function. The crab travels with the actinians expanded and directed forward, sometimes waving them from side to side; when irritated, it moves its chelipeds toward the source of irritation, thereby placing the actinians in what may be considered the most favorable aggressive or defensive attitudes. It is possible, however, that this function is secondary and incidental, for the crab reacts in the same way whether it is carrying the actinians (as food-getting 'instruments') or not.

In considering such evidence as there is of the 'agonistic' use of objects by monkeys and apes, trying to analyze the observations in terms of function and context of the act, we should first examine reports on wild animals, in which no training by or imitation of human beings is presumably involved. Some of the sources of information (Table 1) are personal observations of trained field-workers, others, those of naturalists and hunters (Wallace; Merfield and Miller; Hingston), and the rest, of unknown source. The two major field studies of baboons (DeVore 1962, etc.; Hall 1962a and b, etc.) include no observations of agonistic object-use. In both of these studies, the investigator's objective was to study the baboons without disturbing them by his presence, and hence, the very situations most likely to elicit agonistic behavior in a group usually were lacking. The unexpected presence of parties of travellers or soldiers in baboon country may produce great agitation in the animals, eliciting a more intensive reaction.

In analyzing the function and context of these 'primitive instrumental acts' (Carpenter 1934), we shall need to refer chiefly to the few studies in which sufficient detail of observation is available. In general, it is implicit in most early reports that the animals roll stones or drop or throw branches and other objects *with intent* to hit or drive away intruders. Aim or purpose in the act is assumed, and hence the whole act is usually thought of as intelligent or learned rather than instinctive or emotional. Lacking detailed and careful observation, one alternative was that these happenings are the 'accidental' result of some agonistic behavior pattern characteristic of the species. Thus, excited macaques may dislodge stones in scrambling up a slope away from an intruder, or members of an arboreal species may chance to break off branches while making threatening gestures. Zuckerman (1932) inclined to the view that the many instances of this sort of behavior could be explained as the more or less accidental outcome of emotional displays, and thus did not need to assume the animal's perception of a relationship between such acts and the possible consequence of driving away an intruder.

This explanation seems correctly to emphasize the emotional origin of such acts but probably incorrectly assumes that animals noted for their learning ability would not readily carry out the emotional gesture with a very elementary directedness rather than in a supposedly random fashion.

Analysis of two sets of observations may help to clear the way for a critical evaluation of the status of the behavior involved. Carpenter (1935) describes the reactions to man of red spider monkeys in Panama as including the following: (1) barking; (2) frequently, approach; (3) in trees within 40 to 50 feet of the observer, shaking of the branches associated, almost invariably, with vigorous scratching; and (4) 'breaking off and dropping of branches . . . close . . . to the observer'. 'This behavior cannot be described as throwing, although the animal may cause the object to fall away from the perpendicular by a sharp twist of its body or a swinging circular movement of its powerful tail.' Sometimes the dropping is delayed for a few seconds, as an observer approaches; feces and urine are also dropped. All are 'instrumental acts' carried out with reference to objectives.

This account indicates that: (1) the approach of the monkeys is an aggressive action; (2) the vigorous scratching represents a displacement activity, which is known experimentally to occur in agitated monkeys that, because of caging, are unable to act out their escape or aggressive tendencies more directly (Hall 1962c); (3) shaking of the branches probably represents a redirection of the aggressive tendency; (4) breaking off and dropping the branches would seem to be a natural carryover of the aggressive movements, no new type of movement being involved; (5) the delay in dropping and the imparting of direction to the branches is 'purposive' or 'instrumental' in the elementary sense that the consequence of this variation is anticipated as being more rewarding than the consequence of no aiming; in other words, a simple process of operant conditioning is at work, whereby the 'aimed' variation is reinforced over the 'unaimed'.

The objections to such a formulation stem mainly from the lack of information as to the frequency and variability of 'directed' performances in these animals. Nevertheless, the learning postulated is of so elementary a kind that all it requires is a very slight modification in the agonistic behavior repertoire apparently characteristic of the species in such circumstances. It is not easy

Table 1

Some Sources of Evidence on the Agonistic Use of Objects by
Monkeys and Apes in the Wild

Species/genus	Author	Behavior and situation recorded
Gorilla	Merfield and Miller (1956)	When hunted, tearing off branches and flinging in direction of hunters below, 'after peering about to locate them accurately'
	Schaller (1963)	Various forms of throwing of branches in agonistic display; not reported to be directed at source of disturbance
Orang-utan	Wallace (1902)	Throwing down of branches and heavy fruits in direction of intruder
	Schaller (1961)	Breaking off and hurling branches in direction of the observer
Gibbon	Carpenter (1940)	Breaking off and dropping dead branches in direction of observer
Howler	Carpenter (1934)	Breaking off and dropping dead limbs towards observer; also defecation and urination from directly above observer
Red spider	Carpenter (1935)	Breaking off and dropping branches close to observer
Cebus	Kaufmann (1962)	Dropping nuts and debris onto coatis
Baboons	Brehm (1916), Hornaday (1922), and other sources of unknown reliability	Geladas meeting Hamadryas and rolling stones down upon them; rolling of rocks toward human intruders
Macaques	Kinnaman (1902), quoting another source Hingston (1920) Joléaud (1933) and other sources of unknown reliability	Deliberate tilting-up and rolling of stones down slope; throwing down of pine cones by Japanese monkeys at passers-by
Patas	Boulenger (1937)	Directing 'fusillade' of sticks, stones, etc., on river travellers in W. Africa

to imagine simpler learning performances, given the usual threat-gesture system of monkeys, for no new act is involved.

For all other species of new and old world monkeys, only a single, very brief statement about the behavior of a *Cebus capucinus* group on Barro Colorado Island has added to our knowledge. During his two-year study of coatis, Kaufmann (1962) on one occasion saw the monkeys chase some coatis from a tree, then go on to drop nuts and debris from a *Scheelea* palm onto them. The coatis ignored the shower except to pounce on and eat the ripe nuts that were included. This observation is of particular interest in view of the reputation of *Cebus* in laboratory experiments and because it is the first by a naturalist of behavior of this type involving non-human intruders.

Among the apes, Wallace's observations (1902) on the orang-utan and Schaller's confirmation and elaboration of them (1961) suggest a similar pattern. One of Schaller's observations was as follows:

A female with a large infant spent 15 minutes throwing a total of about 30 branches varying in size from twigs to limbs 10 feet long and 3 inches in diameter. Considerable effort was expended at times in tearing off the larger branches. Limbs were thrown in three ways: (*a*) she merely held the branch at her side and dropped it limply; (*b*) she looked down at me and swung the branch like a large pendulum, and at the peak of the arc closest to me she released it; (*c*) she lifted branches either as high as her chest or above her head with one hand and hurled them down forcefully. Whatever interpretation is given this behavior, there is no doubt that it induced me to jump nimbly at times and that it kept me effectively away from beneath the tree. [p. 82]

Wallace's account concerned the throwing down of branches and of the fruits of the Durian tree by an adult female with young ones near her; and he supposed that the ape's parental instinct may have been specially aroused. However, the essential features of the situations in which this and the resulting behavior occur are similar to those in the Red spider monkey account, namely disturbance by a human intruder eliciting agitation and re-direction of aggression onto the most readily available objects, and an effective directing of the objects toward the observer.

The explanation already proposed seems to need no revision to include the orang-utan data or any other data of similar performances in free-ranging monkeys or apes. This does not imply that such displays always or even usually have a 'direction'. Schaller's (1963) full account of the mountain gorillas' repertoire of gestures in such circumstances does not suggest that branches or leaves are, in the physical sense, aimed at the observer. The amount and kind of learning involved in 'aiming' are such that many other mammals below the primates might achieve this behavior very readily *if* they had happened to evolve the sort of manipulatory and agonistic repertoire which seems to be a general simian characteristic. To underline this point, we may briefly consider the agonistic and the feeding repertoire of baboons in the wild (Hall 1962a and b). First, baboons frequently turn over stones when searching for food. Second, they may pull violently back and forward on tree branches or rocks while staring at and otherwise threatening an observer. Third, they may hit away, with a swift underarm movement, a noxious or unfamiliar small object or living organism as a sequel to, or component of, a startle behavior sequence. These three aspects of their behavior readily dispose these animals to the simple instrumental act involved in tipping a rock toward an intruder. There would be no mystery if it were shown that baboons or chimpanzees, for example, throw sand, stones or sticks, toward a predator on the same horizontal plane. All that is necessary is that the hitting-away movement be combined with the most elementary of feeding acts, that of grasping some object in the hand and 'aiming' it in the same way that a threat-gesture or movement is usually directed *toward* an adversary. Because the use of objects as missiles has tended to be confused with the use, and even fashioning, of objects as offensive weapons, the complexity of the behavior involved seems to have been greatly exaggerated.

Linking behavior of this kind with that observed to occur spontaneously in captivity adds very little to the over-all picture. Many reports are available of agonistic scooping/throwing in captivity (Kortlandt and Kooij, 1963), but all that need be added as commentary is that horizontal aiming is an extension of the threat-display, involving nothing more than the co-ordination of two acts basic to the repertoire. Brandishing of a stick and using it to beat another animal, as described by Cooper and Harlow (1961) in an individual *Cebus fatuellus* and in several chimpanzees, is an interesting elaboration of threat-display against other animals, but the significance of such performances must again be regarded first in their functional context, and only later against the supposed evolutionary background. The kind of brandishing action reported is very similar to that which baboons (Hall 1962a) and other monkeys and apes may engage in throwing a sack or a stick over a food-object.

We are not primarily concerned here with sifting through the varied kinds of evidence and deciding as to their reliability and accuracy. It is not yet possible to make valid comparisons of the various species or for example, of terrestrial monkeys and anthropoid apes, of old world or of new world types, and the like, with respect to their 'ability' to engage in this kind of instrumental behavior. Chimpanzee, capuchin, and baboon may turn out to demonstrate this propensity more readily and more flexibly than other nonhuman primates, but it is all too easy to fit the inadequate observational evidence into whatever evolutionary model one chooses – as Kortlandt and Kooij (1963) have done. It is simply the interaction of the processes of learning with the components and sequences of the naturally practiced behavior repertoire that requires a clear and straightforward analysis. The key to the instrumental learning successes of many types shown in the wild and in captivity by these animals is the exploratory–manipulatory tendency, of a quite general kind, which makes it easy for transfer or generalization to take place from one kind of situation to another, and over a wide range of objects or stimuli. Although we can thus simplify the behavioral analysis in such a way as to show that performances of the kind reported are readily to be expected in these animals, it still remains necessary to consider very carefully the kinds of environmental conditions which elicit or inhibit or just fail to elicit these performances.

Tool-using in Extension of the Feeding Repertoire

The use of an object as a means of obtaining food which the animal cannot reach or which if within its reach, the animal cannot obtain directly, is contrary to the preceding class of performance, reported in birds in several instances, occasionally and rather uncertainly in marine invertebrates, and once only, with two other insufficiently substantiated instances, in subprimate mammals. For monkeys and apes, there is an extensive experimental literature, many observations on animals in captivity, and extremely few field data that provide evidence for analysis. The data will merely be sampled, as in the previous section, to illustrate points that seem significant for the whole comparative picture. Inevitably, this means paying most attention to the areas where most reliable knowledge is available.

The case of the crab, *Melia tessellata*, and actinian 'commensalism', described by Duerden and others, is a curious example of the use of a living organism as a tool to aid the feeding of another. Although Duerden says the crabs do not restrict themselves to one species of anemone and may also, as already noted, hold them forward as a kind of defensive aid, the performance need not be classed as more 'intelligent' than other sorts of behavioral adaptation to ecological need in which no tool or accessory is involved.

In birds, there are two sorts of performance which have been much discussed, namely, the string-pulling achievements of *Parus* and other passerines, and the use of a cactus-spine or twig as an extension of the bill to probe out insects or larvae in the so-called Galapagos woodpecker-finch, *Cactospiza pallida*. The former type of behavior clearly has some parallel in the probable factors involved here and in similar performances of primates. There may be an 'inherited tendency' to pull upon and manipulate with beak and foot grasses, hair, bents, and other long flexible materials, in the course of nestbuilding or perhaps in obtaining certain sorts of food. This factor and practice can be supposed to account for the ease with which some of these birds seem immediately to tackle the task of pulling in a string on the end of which a bait is attached. We may note that the direct pulling-in of a string or stick to the end of which the food-object is attached seems to be a task requiring very little modification of existing repertoire other than trial-and-error application.

The tool-using performances of the woodpecker-finch are usually considered a remarkable example of behavioral adaptation to fit it into the special ecological circumstances of the Galapagos Islands bird population. According to Lack (1947, 1953), this primarily insectivorous finch resembles a woodpecker in that it climbs up and down vertical trunks and branches in search of its food. But whereas the woodpecker, having excavated in a branch with its beak, inserts its long tongue into the crack to get the insect out, the finch has evolved the alternative method of picking up a cactus spine or twig, holding it lengthwise in its beak and poking it up the crack, dropping the twig to seize the insect in its beak as it emerges. It has been seen to reject a twig if it proved too short or too pliable, and sometimes the bird carries a spine or twig about with it, poking it into cracks or crannies as it searches one tree after another. Bowman (1961) added further observations on this behavior. He saw it most frequently in the dry season in the arid zone, where almost every bird of the species was seen carrying a cactus spine in its bill. He also reported two cases of what appeared to be attempts of the bird to adjust the size and shape of its probe to fit the cranny or crack in which it was searching: (1)

One such bird was holding a spine about six inches long. Only about two inches of the spine protruded from the tip of the bill, the remainder passed along one side of the face and neck. Apparently the bird realized that the stick was excessively long, for it made an unsuccessful attempt to twist off approximately three inches of the spine by holding it with the feet. [p. 33]

(2) He quotes an observation made by Mr Kastdalen in 1956:

I was looking at a finch the other day, and it convinced me that the stick habit is intelligent and not instinctive. One of them was working in a hole ... which seemed to be full of bugs, so it had to drop its stick several times to catch the bugs. Each time it went for a new stick, but after a few times it came with a forked stick, and tried to get it into the hole a couple of times, but in vain. Then it saw what was wrong and turned the stick around and broke it off at the fork, and started working. [p. 33]

Ignoring the terminological points about the bird's 'realizing' what it was doing and the distinction between 'intelligent' and 'instinctive', it is evident that something definable as 'tool-making', that is, an attempting to work upon the tool-object, is here involved. However, it is likely that nothing more worthy of note is involved in such an attempt than what is routine in nest-constructing activities.

While it is indeed remarkable that this finch should have evolved a behavioral adaptation supposedly more appropriate at the primate level of evolution, the chief significance of such a performance, in the comparative behavior framework, is perhaps to emphasize the fact that *tool-using as such*, and even tool-making, taken outside of the total behavioral context in which it occurs, is not a criterion of adaptability that should be assigned any special weight. If in rare cases a species of crab or bird evolves a behavioral, rather than a physical, adaptation to deal with some ecological condition, this may be interesting evidence of the versatility of evolutionary processes but involves no more complex type of *learning* than, one may suppose, the sort of trial-and-error adjustments which these 'remarkable' species have in common with other crabs and other birds.

Among subprimate mammals, we have already cited Williams' (1950) report of elephants using sticks to scratch their bodies, and he also describes how 'Many young elephants develop the naughty habit of plugging up the wooden bell they wear hung around their necks with good stodgy mud or clay so that the clappers cannot ring, in order to steal silently into a grove of cultivated bananas at night' (p. 78). While the performances of elephants in captivity indicate that their potential in tool-using is probably greater than that of any other nonprimate animal, there is no systematic evidence of the variety of their performances in the wild. It can merely be noted in passing, however, that the way in which they pull down or push over trees to get at foliage otherwise beyond their reach is an 'instrumental act' at least on a par for behavioral complexity with patterned string or string-pulling performances. It is also, for the elephant, a much more economical way of feeding than would be, say, its attempt to knock off fruit or leaves by brandishing a stick in its trunk.

Apart from elephants, another class of mammal that may be found to use tools as a feeding aid in the wild are bears. The readiness with which they stand on hindlegs and use their paws in manipulations would predispose them to develop such skills where need arises, and Harington (1962) interestingly reviews the evidence that polar bears dislodge or pick up and cast down blocks of ice onto the heads of sleeping walruses. The only sub-primate mammal for which there are reliable reports is the sea otter, *Enhydra lutris*. Studies made of its feeding habits show that in the Aleutians as well as in California, mollusks form a substantial part of the diet. In California, abalones are also commonly brought up and eaten, but it is not known whether rocks are used to aid in the process of removing these large shellfish from their sites. Fisher (1939) was the first to give a detailed account of this animal's use of a stone as a tool:

It is a not uncommon thing to hear a sharp clicking sound and then to locate its point of origin ... This sound is always made by an otter that is trying to crack open something with a very hard stonelike shell. The object that the otter has in its paws is too small to see – possibly it is some mollusk. The object is held with both paws and with full arm action from well over the head it is brought down hard on a piece of rock that rests on the otter's chest. These pieces of stone are brought to the surface at the same time as the food. It may take several severe blows before the object is cracked enough for the otter to get the food out. These rocks are not small but appear to be almost as large as the large abalones. When the otters roll over they hold both the rock and the food on their chests. This clicking sound is so distinct that it can be heard for some distance above the noise of the waters. [p. 28]

Murie (1940) confirmed this observation on the California animals, and Hall and Schaller (1964) have obtained quantitative data on this performance; they reported that it is usually mussels that are banged against the rock anvil, although occasionally other animals, such as spiny lobsters, may be pounded in this way. Krear (personal communication), who spent from late July until mid-December 1957 on Amchitka in the western Aleutians, watching sea otters most of the time, observed only one young animal traveling with its mother that used a rock as a tool: 'The immature was observed on three occasions to bring rocks to the surface, and on these he would pound and crack his food items, most of which were little blue mussels.' It is probable that the mussels in the Aleutians did not require tool-use of the sort so frequently seen off the California coast, but that the propensity for such performances is readily available, as is strongly indicated by Kenyon's account (1959) of how an adult otter, captured in the Aleutians, used rocks as anvils on which to pound clams.

The sea otter data suggest very little at present as to the origin, variability, and other characteristics of this behavior. So far as is known, no developmental observations are available, other than the one instance quoted. It is also likely that the pup acquires the habit by observing the behavior of its mother, for it swims for many weeks very close to her, takes food from her chest, and is occasionally offered food by her (Hall and Schaller, 1964). It is thus highly probable that the pup must learn its discriminations of food objects and of behavior appropriate to deal with them by observing the corresponding behavior in the mother. The fundamental dependency relationship is such that 'following', both perceptually and in the locomotor and manipulatory senses, is necessary for the pup's survival. This is generally true of mammals and is mentioned here only because it may help to explain the origin of the habit.

Considering now the nonhuman primates, detailed evidence from field studies indicates that only one, the chimpanzee, uses tools; this it does in reference to a probably minor feeding behavior, probing termites out of holes with twigs (Morris-Goodall, 1962). Beatty (1951) reported that chimpanzees in Liberia break open palm nuts by hammering them with rocks, and Merfield and Miller (1956) described how chimpanzees poke long twigs into the entrance holes of the ground nests of bees and withdraw the twigs coated with honey. The distance at which this observation was made was 50 yards, using binoculars. Pitman (1931) mentioned seeing a free-living gorilla using a stick to obtain fruit otherwise out of its reach, but Schaller (1963) had no record of such behavior in 12 months of field study.

This lack of evidence of tool-using comes as a surprise to the many investigators familiar with the ease with which other species of great ape and several species of monkey learn spontaneously in captivity, as well as with progressive training procedures, to use sticks, sacks, boxes, or even live rats (Klüver, 1937) to haul in food objects otherwise out of reach. *Cebus capucinus* and perhaps other *Cebus* species appear to be particularly adept in this respect (Klüver, 1933; Bierens de Haan, 1931), while individuals of the *Papio ursinus* species (Bolwig, 1961; Hall, 1962a) show a similar kind of aptitude. The surprise of the laboratory investigators is due to the apparent discrepancy between the *potential* that these animals have for such performances when given situations designed to elicit them in captivity and their failure to make use of the potential as an aid in increasing their dietary repertoire in the wild. Two of the main factors accounting for this discrepancy are: (1) Systematic field evidence is still far too scanty for us to know how great the discrepancy is; for example, very little is known of the details of the feeding habits of free-ranging *Cebus*. (2) The discrepancy is not a behaviorally significant one but is rather due to a misconception as to the degree of transfer or generalization involved when the wild-born animal is given the usual run of instrumentation tasks in captivity. This point requires a brief elaboration.

If we take as an example the natural feeding behavior of the baboon and the more or less continuous processes of exploration and manipulation of objects that go with it, some of which have already been mentioned, we find that the animal is practicing, either in play or in actual feeding, a variety of skills which are readily generalized in the experimental situation. The young ones carry sticks or branches in their mouths or in one hand and do not use them in feeding. All of them at some time or other break dead branches from bushes in searching for food, as when, for example, they are searching for larvae or ants' nests (Hall 1962a). They push over slabs of rock, and they tend to investigate almost any strange manipulable object that lies in their path. They pull upon telegraph wires, open the doors and windows of unoccupied huts and cars, and so on. In short, they show a generalized tendency to fiddle with and try out objects that may or may not be instrumental in obtaining food. These animals appear to have a surplus of exploratory–manipulatory energy for which there may seem to be no immediate ecological need. However, it is perfectly feasible to suppose that it is just this kind of generalized activity which has enabled baboons to be sufficiently adaptable to survive over large areas of Africa in a very wide variety of habitats, for example, allowing them to be omnivorous in some regions (although they are classed as predominantly vegetarian in all areas where the diet has been adequately scheduled, according to Washburn and DeVore [1961] and Hall [1962a]). Thus, given the behavior repertoire the baboon is known to possess, the learning involved in obtaining food that is out of reach would appear to be of a rudimentary kind.

Similar evidence as to the maturation of the necessary manipulatory coordinations (Schiller, 1957) and as to the effective role of natural and instrumental practice (Nissen, 1931; Birch, 1945) has been put forward for the chimpanzee, and there is no need to review it. One comment of Schiller's is particularly appropriate, however, because it indicates how, in chimpanzees and other species, the 'emotional' repertoire of gesture may be readily utilized in differing contexts:

> That a chimpanzee breaks off a branch if excited has nothing to do with his desire to get the food [in an experimental situation]. Once he has the stick in his hand, he will use it sooner or later. Such a sequence can easily be reinforced in a couple of trials, then it appears to be a coherent, continuous pattern. [p. 275]

General Evaluation

Tool-using performances have tended to be treated as though they represented some kind of behavioral homology at the different levels of organism in which they have been recorded. This view seems to be incorrect, however, because it seems evident that the application of a common term to so varied an assortment of performances has led to the glossing over of fundamental differences in adaptive significance. While the criterion of tool-using is no longer used by anthropologists to signalize a supposedly critical stage in the transition of ape to human, it is still not unreasonably inferred that tool-using was an important behavioral adaptation somewhere in primate evolution, and that the *making* of tools derived from a prevalence in tool-using far in excess of that now discernible in any living nonhuman primate (Washburn, 1950). For anthropologists, behavioral evidence of living nonhuman primates in the wild is thus of interest to the extent that it indicates 'transitional' ingredients of essentially hominid characteristics such as the carnivorous tendency and tool-using (Oakley, 1951).

In the general framework of animal evolution, we have seen that instances definable as tool-using occur in highly specialized ecological settings, as in the woodpecker-finch, crab-actinian commensalism, and probably the *Ammophila*. These are basically behavioral adaptations that are probably produced by trial-and-error learning, like that commonly found in almost all living organisms. These adaptations do not appear to give their possessors any selective advantage over other species which have evolved alternative forms of adaptation. Rather, they simply enable their possessors to survive at a certain population level in their ecological niches. In other words, such performances are only worthy of special note because of their entirely superficial, indeed one might almost say fortuitous, resemblance to human tool-using. The case of the string-pulling performances of some passerines is of the same order. While one allows that birds of the *Parus* genus, as an example, show a certain aptitude in this kind of problem, as in others, such as pecking open milk bottle tops, no one, but for the human analogy, would probably be disposed on this ground to give this species a specially high rating for adaptability. As others have clearly indicated (Thorpe, 1956; Tinbergen, 1960), birds may evolve certain rather restricted propensities enabling them to learn through what one might call a special aptitude. The natural practice of food-seeking and nest-construction may fit into the scheme. A performance classifiable as tool-using may in fact be less significant as an adaptability indicator than one which cannot strictly be so considered, such as the performances of thrushes, gulls, or crows in breaking open hard food-objects.

The observations of the sea otter were reviewed at length to refute the view that its performance indicated that a new process had appeared at the *Mammalian* level of evolution. The apparent uniqueness of this performance and its occurrence in the context of a particular marine ecological situation for which the animal shows other peculiar behavioral and physical adaptations, such as lying on the back when feeding, indicate that there is no reason to judge this animal's performances as of any greater evolutionary significance than those for which other marine mammals, such as seals and dolphins, are noted.

In the evaluation of what is known about the non-human primates' performances and potentialities, we have to consider two main types of tool-using; that in the service of agonistic behavior and that in obtaining food. It is in the former category that by far the most evidence is available, suggesting that 'instrumental acts' with some degree of direction or purpose are quite a widespread and general characteristic in monkeys and apes, as a straightforward function of fear-threat motivation and manipulatory endowment. And indeed it seems, as the quotation from Schiller indicated, that we have here a behavioral adaptation of a fairly general and simple kind which evolved primarily in the context of agonistic tendencies toward opponents that inhibit direct attack. Associating this with the fact that no such instances have been reliably reported in any other class of animal, one can infer that this is the fundamental behavioral situation from which all other instances of primate tool-using have been derived. There is, in most monkeys at any rate, an arousal of fairly strong agonistic tendencies in any food-to-be-gained situation in which they are frustrated. They tend easily, in such circumstances, to show displacement activities or redirections of aggression (Masserman and Pechtel, 1953), and their tool-using attempts often consist of throwing actions which are hardly distinguishable from threat-gestures. It will be only through systematic developmental studies of young primates that we shall be able to trace the course of these performances and to study the relationship between frustration responses and the emergence of tool-use in general.

Summary

Tool-using performances in animals have often been considered important indicators of relative intelligence, but no comparative analysis of their probable origin and place within the total ecological and behavioral setting has been available. The usual definition has tended to emphasize features that performances at different phyletic levels have in common, while glossing over the underlying and even overt differences.

The many examples in the literature are sampled with reference to the use of tools: (1) in agonistic behavior; (2) in extending the feeding habits of a species; and (3) in courtship display (Satin bower-birds), nest-hole construction (*Ammophila* spp.), and, possibly, body care (elephants).

Examples of the second category include what appear to be special behavioral adaptations that are functionally equivalent to physical extensions or modifications, as in the case of the crab-actinian relationship in *Melia tessellata*, the Galapagos woodpecker-finch, *Cactospiza pallida*, and possibly also in the sea otter, *Enhydra lutris*. To varying degrees, the tool-using adaptation has importance in the life of the species. In the crab and the finch, it seems to involve a basic feeding adjustment, while in the sea otter it is reportedly used only with respect to one major item of food, mollusks, and it may be much more prevalent in the

153

southern limits of distribution than in the north. Among non-human primates in the wild, tool-using of this sort is rare, not being known in baboons and macaques, and only reliably reported, among the anthropoid apes, in the chimpanzee which appears to use a food-getting tool to obtain a supplementary rather than a staple item of diet.

Examples of the first category occur only in nonhuman primates. In systematic field studies in the wild, 'primitive instrumental acts' of breaking off and casting down branches, twigs, or leaves in the direction of the observer have been reported of howlers and red spider monkeys, gibbons, and orang-utans. Gorillas include throwing gestures in their complex and apparently stereotyped displays when disturbed, but no 'directing' toward the source of disturbance has been noted. Terrestrial monkeys of the *Macaca* and *Papio* genera have been reported to push or roll stones towards intruders. There are, however, no detailed field observations of this behavior, and, if it occurs, it is probably elicited in groups of monkeys that are highly disturbed and unused to human intrusion and would not be seen under the noninterference conditions in which the field observer usually tries to work.

Controversy over the reliability of the evidence on tool-using, particularly in nonhuman primates, and over the explanation of such instances as are irrefutable, seems to stem from the following: (1) a tendency to overestimate the significance of such performances as indicators of behavioral adaptability, largely because of the urge to discover equivalences to stages in human evolution; (2) a failure to analyse in detail the context and function of such performances. It is suggested that the 'primitive instrumental acts' involve only an elementary form of operant conditioning imposed upon the agonistic repertoire of the species, and that 'direction' of aim with objects is no more surprising than the fact that threat gestures without objects are normally aimed at an intruder.

The discrepancy, commented upon by laboratory investigators, between the apparent ease with which many monkeys and apes use tools to gain food in captivity situations and their apparent failure to use this propensity to advantage in the wild, has no real significance. Possibly the 'primitive instrumental acts' provide the primary emotional bases from which any kind of tool-using arises, the transfer to other situations, such as food-getting, being conditioned by the way in which the animals manipulate objects not directly related to food.

The present evaluation of the comparative data has, as its purpose, the clarification of the confusion caused by inadequacy of behavioral evidence and by the biasing of such evidence to fit some evolutionary scheme. The hypothesis that the 'emotional' use of tool objects by monkeys and apes may provide the lead to an understanding of the origins, in phylogeny and ontogeny, of such performances in human beings is suggested by the fact that no comparable agonistic performances are known in any other class of animal. On the other hand, tool-using as a feeding adaptation occurs in several different types of animal but has so far proved very rare in monkeys and apes.

Comments

By R. J. Andrew, New Haven, Conn., U.S.A.

My comments will be brief, since I agree with all the principal points made by Professor Hall. It seems clear that our main attention should be concentrated on the use of tools by primates in the field. There is very little information to be obtained concerning the evolution of tool use by studies in which primates are trained by investigators to use tools.

However, even in the absence of such field data, it is possible to investigate in captive animals the normal range of motor patterns used by a species in grasping or manipulating the objects with the hands. As Schiller (1957) emphasised, the number of such patterns is far fewer even in the chimpanzee than might be expected. A recent study by Bishop (1962) in my laboratory has shown that only one grasping gesture is used by the Lemuroidea and only one (a different one) by the Lorisoidea, the second being adapted to catching insects. Unlike the Ceboidea or Cercopithecoidea (Napier, 1960; Bishop, 1962) their power and precision grips are the same. Current work in our programme of comparative studies of primate behaviour suggests that a single manipulative pattern may function in several different contexts and so be exposed to widely differing selection pressures. One interesting example is the pattern of grasping an object with both hands, and then rotating the hands outwards so that they separate distally. This, when used in grooming, serves to part the hair and make the skin accessible to the lips and teeth. When used in grasping an object, it has two functions. In the case of a solid unyielding object it results in the object being turned, since one of the hands ceases to oppose the other and relaxes for long enough to allow some rotation. A series of such movements permits the animal to investigate the object from all sides. In the case of a soft object the opposing rotation of the two hands may break the object. It is as yet impossible to decide in what context this pattern probably first appeared. It is present in both Cercopithecoidea and Ceboidea from *Saimiri* up.

In the more advanced members of both groups, further grasping and manipulatory patterns appear. In the present article, the hitting away of objects by baboons was mentioned. In *Papio hamadryas* a two handed backward and forward scrubbing of objects on the ground passes with increasing rejection of the object into more lateral movements in which the object is held in one hand and may finally be flung away. Besides finding a variety of uses in foraging the first type of movement is used in punishing young animals (Kummer, 1957). In *Cebus* spp. one-handed banging of an object against the substrate may occur as well.

A more comprehensive knowledge of the distribution and relative ease of elicitation of such manipulative patterns may make it possible to say something definite concerning the ecological determinants of their evolution. This in turn would be relevant to the problem of the origin of tools, in that the first use of tools by human ancestors must have been greatly affected by the range of manipulative patterns which they possessed. However, the data collected by Hall on the use of tools by animals other than primates suggests that the use of tools in the human line, and their almost complete absence in other primates was not due primarily to very advanced manipulative abilities, or even intelligence in our ancestors. It appears that the use of tools can appear without either if the selective pressures for this are strong enough. (A similar argument can be made concerning the origin of vocal mimicking, Andrew, 1962.) It may therefore be most profitable to look for a major ecological difference between the human line and other primates. Co-operative hunting of moderate to large sized prey is perhaps the difference most commonly suggested. The dropping or throwing of objects in defense by primates has been very fully discussed in the present article, and it is no novel suggestion that such behavior might have been critical in the first development of tools.

By C. R. Carpenter, Oak Park, Penna, U.S.A.

The interesting paper by Hall describes *special* performances of animals in natural environments which may indicate *special* behavioral adaptability. The evidence arrayed and the inferences stated oppose attributing tool-using to animals, including non-human primates living in the wild. The conclusions also oppose explanations which include 'intelligence' and 'purpose'. Learning of 'simple' kinds including trial-and-error and 'operant conditioning' are judged adequate to explain 'primitive instrumental acts'. If these statements are correct, then a more descriptive title than the one selected might have been used.

The general definition given of a category of behavior, modified as follows, could be useful: *the use by an animal of an object, or of another living organism, as a means of achieving an advantage indicates adaptability.* Such a definition and inference could include defined acts, defined objects, conditions and other organisms, and the consequences or results of a complex sequence of behavioral events.

I should have liked to have had Hall's definition of tools and tool-using and to know whether or not he accepts the concept that tool making could be defined as the shaping or moulding of material or object to serve repetitively a set of functions. Also, I would have appreciated knowing what is implied by 'primitive instrumental acts'. The aggressive–defensive acts of howlers, spider and cebus monkeys, gibbons and orangs breaking limbs or branches and timing their fall relative to a moving object, person or another animal are rather complex even though 'primitive'.

The non-human primates for which there are reliable observations of breaking, holding, somewhat directing and releasing objects in aggressive–defensive situations are all *arboreal* types. For them, height, availability of obtainable and droppable objects, gravity, and perhaps, other factors provide conditions for the occurrence of the described behavioral patterns. Tree shaking occurs in rhesus monkeys but *not* the breaking off and dropping of objects with reference to sources of disturbances.

How does Hall classify and interpret the *bridging behavior* observed in howler and spider monkeys? When an adult, usually a female but sometimes a male, spans a space, remains suspended and permits a young animal to cross over it, is this too a 'primitive instrumental act'?

Hall seems to have accomplished his objective of raising serious doubt that the evidence supports the hypothesis that behavior which corresponds closely to tool-using, occurs in animals including the non-human primates. However, it does seem that many animals and non-human primates exhibit *naturalistic* behavior patterns which are *instrumental in achieving goal states*. The explanations and functions of these classes of behavior surely are not as simple as Hall seems at times to imply.

By Radomír Čihák, Prague, Czechoslovakia

This interesting paper approaches the problems of so-called tool-using in animals from the standpoint of behavior studies. From the viewpoint of an anatomist studying the development of the human hand in ontogenesis and phylogenesis, I might comment on several points of common biological interest, and then add a comparison with our results of developmental studies of the primate hand.

1. I have to agree with the author's conclusions that problems exist in comparing similar actions in different animals of the same phylum or in animals of different phyletic position.

2. All these problems depend upon the exactness of definition of the terms, *tool*, *tool-using*, and *tool-making*. If the definition of the tool-using performance is to be extended to include all actions of animals – in whatever sense – where we find the use of an object foreign to the body of the animal in question; this multiplies the examples of tool-using animals.

3. The author states:

> Tool-using performances have tended to be treated as though they represented some kind of behavioral homology at the different levels of organism in which they have been recorded. This would not seem to be the case at all, because it seems evident that the application of a common term of classification for so varied an assortment has led to the glossing over of fundamental differences in adaptive significance.

The term 'behavioral homology' presents difficulties. In morphology the term 'homology' indicates body structure in different animals that are of the same relation, principal pattern in the body, and of the *same origin*. For other structures of similar form, but of different origin, the term *analogous* is the only correct one. Hence the observations quoted sometimes concern similar actions of animals at different phyletic levels, i.e., of animals whose structures of the central nervous system, e.g., in insect and mammal, are not homologous at all. The actions described may be similar to the action of tool-using man; this does not mean that it *is* tool-using. Hence, if we extend this terminology to the classification of behavior – the results are *behavioral analogies* at different phyletic levels.

4. The author states that not tool-*using* but tool-*making* signalizes the critical stage in the transition from ape to human; but it ought to be pointed out that tool-making, as '*shaping an object in an imaginary future eventually*' (Oakley, 1961), is the real boundary between ape and man. The real *tool* is the obviously shaped

and obviously used object. Based upon this view we would probably be right in saying that there is no *tool-using* in animals at all; but that there are many examples of using stones, branches, or other objects during reproduction, nesting, feeding, excitation, etc. From the physiological viewpoint, these processes are chains of unconditioned or, sometimes, conditioned reflexes connected with food, reproduction, etc., developed during the phylogenesis of the species concerned as adaptations to the environment. These processes are the same in their physiological base in all species, including nonhuman primates.

5. For some observations greater accuracy, probably followed by a new and reconsidered explanation is necessary; for other observations (elephants plugging their bells so that the clappers cannot ring, or polar bears casting blocks of ice onto the heads of walruses), fundamental revision of the facts registered in the literature is desirable. Many zoological observations tend to express the behavior of animals in anthropomorphistic fashion.

6. There are several problems concerning apes: Köhler's experiments indicate the ability to use bamboo poles in order to obtain fruit which is out of the animals' reach. This use of a pole may occur in a complicated manner, but it is always initiated by seeing the food desired. In Hall's paper, contrary to experimental conditions, apes are reported as using objects during excitation with the implication that this is the probable mode of origin of tool-using in man's phylogenetic past. This may be right, but with the reservation, concerning the above-expressed differences in the definition of the tool, tool-using, and tool-making.

The physiological condition of the brain of tool-using and tool-making man is different from any living nonhuman primate. It is necessary to point out that both recent apes and recent men are ends of *divergent* developmental branches of primates. This divergence is determined by the whole complex of erect posture, the development of the central nervous system, together with tool-using and tool-making hands, and the beginning of social life of early human ancestors.

The differences between recent apes and recent men *even occur in the anatomical pattern of the human hand*. According to our latest studies, differences in situation of muscular layers develop during human ontogenesis. The fusion of two superimposed muscular layers forming the dorsal interossei (i.e., muscles executing fine movements of the fingers) occurs. Complete loss of the so-called layer of contrahentes muscles in its ulnar sector is characteristic only of man (Čihák, 1963). On the other hand, recent anthropomorphic apes possess two muscular layers (functioning as flexors) in place of man's dorsal interossei, and at least the rudiments of the whole contrahentes muscles layer (Forster, 1916).

7. In concluding my comment I should like to express my opinion that it is impossible to explain the development of tool-using in man solely from the comparative behavior evidence; i.e., from the standpoint of a single research field. I see the necessity of joining several standpoints; namely, developmental morphology, the comparative studies of physiology of the central nervous system based upon exact experiments, and consideration of mutual influences of social factors and tool-using in early evolution. From an integration of these multiple complex standpoints, it might be useful to try, retrospectively, to explain various observations of primate behavior and thereby gain more positive results.

By R. Dale Givens, Richmond, Kentucky, U.S.A.

Since I am in essential agreement with K. R. L. Hall, there are only a few comments I wish to make:

1. It may be hoped that additional research will clarify even more the nature of tool using in nonhuman animals since the picture presented here is still far from clear, complete or well documented. This, however, is due more to the lack of data than to any fault of the author. Still, it seems somewhat premature to attempt to explain incipient tool using behavior as 'only an elementary form of operant conditioning imposed upon the agonistic repertoire of the species'. Nor would such an explanation, if verified, make tool using phenomena any less important as a behavioral form of adaptation, as Hall seems to imply.

2. Hall considers the 'use' of one chimpanzee by another to obtain a goal, such as, perhaps, food, as a case of tool using. Classifying social interaction of this type as tool using seems to me to assign too much to the latter concept and to confuse two totally different phenomena. If we follow Hall in this, we would have to call most social relationships, including those found among man, tool using.

3. In view of a recent news report of rudimentary tool making behavior among chimpanzees in the wild, it would appear that Hall's position requires modification. If the Jane Morris-Goodall findings reported in *Newsweek* (May 1963) are accurate, the behavior displayed, that of moistening the end of a stick with saliva to attract termites, can hardly be explained in terms of an extension of agonistic behavior; it is directly oriented toward food

procurement. What Morris-Goodall's report and the present paper both indicate, however, is that the gap between early man and the higher primates is not much greater in regard to mental capabilities than it was already known to be for biological characteristics. Leslie White notwithstanding, the distinction between the mentality of human and nonhuman primates is a matter of degree and not a difference in kind.

By Harry F. Harlow, Madison, Wisconsin, U.S.A.
I totally and highly approve of the article.

By Gordon W. Hewes, Boulder, Colorado, U.S.A.
Chance (1960) calls attention to the role of the repertory of innate motor patterns in much of the seemingly insightful problem-solving observed in apes and monkeys, though insight cannot be wholly excluded. Primate tool-using probably began in manipulatory behavior not directed toward any external goal. Rewarded manipulation, if repeatedly successful in a given environment – enhancing food supply or increasing security from enemies – could be expected to spread by social imitation to the rest of the local population. Hall does not refer to the Japanese macaque studies where behaviors analogous to invention and diffusion of tool-using have been observed (Imanishi, 1960). Higher primates can learn vicariously by observation of the actions of other individuals (Hall, 1963) as anyone who has worked with them can testify. Endowed with this capacity to a very high degree, primates are 'pre-adapted' to persistent, functional tool-using where environmental conditions make it biologically rewarding.

Monkeys approach some of the conditions of tool-preparation and tool-handling in their inspection, peeling, stripping, and other preliminary steps in the eating of wild plant foods. Such behavior is far more deliberate, and far more flexible than the nut-gnawing of squirrels, and is best seen when the monkey is confronted with an unfamiliar plant which may have edible parts. Wild monkeys distinguish carefully between food and containers, as in Kawamura's report of macaques extracting wheat grains from paper envelopes (1959, p. 48 and Fig. 17). A stumptail macaque at the University of Colorado drinks from cups, opens paper boxes, and removes wrappings from any stray packages suspected of having edible contents.

Cord-pulling is also part of the common motor repertory of monkeys. It is evidently easier to pull a cord or stick toward the body to secure a desired object than to get at it by pushing something outward, away from the body. Such preferences in basic motor patterns have undoubtedly affected the evolution of primate tool-using. The primate hand is used regularly with precision not only for food preparation, and feeding, but also grooming. Hall does not mention grooming, nor has this been stressed by other writers on the subject of the emergence of tool-using in primates (Napier, 1962, 1963). Macaques in grooming usually steady the body-part being worked on with one hand, while dextrously probing with the fingers of the other to the base of each hair or clump of hairs, opposing the ball of the thumb to the terminal phalange of the index finger. Transfer of the motor habits and psychological drive toward grooming, to the surface treatment of tool-objects – from decortication of twigs to the systematic removal of surface irregularities on chipped stone implements, and eventually even to tasks such as weeding, does not seem too far-fetched.

Carrying of food, infants, and objects usable as tools has also probably been important. My own ideas as to the relation between Hominid bipedalism and tool-using (Hewes, 1961) differ from those who see a direct relationship between incipient tool-using and bipedal locomotion.

Washing of food, and other 'manipulations' of water, have certain analogies to tool-using. The invention of sweet-potato washing by a Japanese macaque, and its subsequent acceptance as a cultural trait in the entire troop is well known (Kawamura, 1959, Fig. 16). Our captive macaques regularly soak or dunk their hard biscuits before eating them. This would seem to be a step beyond merely peeling or husking, in the direction of more elaborate forms of food-preparation. On the topic of the 'tool' use of water, I have observed gorillas at the Cheyenne Mountain Zoo, U.S.A., using their fingers to direct a stream of water from their water-fountains toward spectators, and with great accuracy. The spectators are safely behind plate glass. Chimpanzees in the same zoo fill their mouths with water and send spurts toward onlookers, in this case unprotected by glass. Under suitable environmental conditions, apes will use brushes and paints (Morris, 1962) to achieve far more than random splashes of color. Although these behaviors do not occur in nature, they illustrate the kind of tool-using potential which is present in infrahuman primates. Hall notes that captive apes sometimes drape themselves with sacking, etc., but that comparable behavior has not been observed in the wild; however, Schaller shows in a sketch a wild infant gorilla who had decked himself in a 'green hat' of lobelia frond (1963, p. 250 and Fig. 63F).

Hall's major contribution to the study of tool-using among nonhuman primates is that it can arise spontaneously in agonistic behavior, as when apes throw sticks or branches toward intruding humans. But it is hard to believe that this action would do more than temporarily annoy a hungry carnivore. Its effectiveness might lie in another kind of situation: Hall observes that monkeys exhibit very strong aggressive responses when competitors prevent them from getting at food immediately present. If their competitors were members of their own troop, the usual dominance signals would be employed rather than stick-hurling. If however the competing eaters were – say, vultures working on a carcass, stick-throwing and stone-throwing by outraged and hungry primates might be the most effective way of driving the birds away. To be sure, modern apes and monkeys do not steal carrion away from vultures, but there are enough references to occasional meat-eating, hunting or killing of small, slow game, and even to winter hare-hunting (by members of one troop of Japanese macaques) to suggest that under some ecological conditions, even existing ape or monkey species might be capable of a more carnivorous regime than they are accustomed to. Scavenging of carcasses left by predators, as I suggested (Hewes, 1961) would have provided for more agonistic missile-hurling as well as for increased transportation of food-burdens to places of greater safety.

Napier (1963, p. 16, Fig. 4, photograph by Jane Goodall) shows a chimpanzee preparing a thin stick or reed as a probe to extract termites from their nest. This is Napier's second stage of tool-using, in which the tool is modified. His first step is the *ad hoc* use of a convenient stick or stone, and his third stage is the making of tools to a pattern. Hall does not sufficiently distinguish between the state of mind of aggressive stick-throwing and the deliberate selection and modification of a natural object as exemplified by this chimpanzee termite-extractor. It is the former, deliberate selection of a tool – as in the stones on the living floors in Olduvai Gorge, or the bones, etc. in the breccias of Makapansgat, rather than in the breaking off of a branch to annoy an intruder that sustained tool-using probably got its start. In connection with bones, captive macaques are capable of a considerable amount of bone-modification by slow gnawing. With no more goal than to obtain the maximum amount of marrow and chewable cartilage, our captive macaque can work a bone down to unusual and unnatural shape. This suggests that once a carnivorous habit had been stabilized, primate bone-handlers would be forever reshaping them through gnawing. The continuing human nervous habit of chewing the ends of implements is perhaps not altogether irrelevant. An object serving both as a tool and as something to chew on has a greater chance of being reused.

Recent field studies of apes and monkeys have made it clear that their present living conditions do not impel them to much if any high-quality tool-using. However, it is not altogether impossible that before the rise to dominance of the genus *Homo*, some groups of apes ancestral to modern apes may have occupied environments in which more tool-using could have occurred, in ways contributing to their survival. This would parallel the situation of certain recent human groups which have been forced into marginal, stone-less alluvial regions, where the entire lithic tradition has been abandoned (to be sure, other kinds of tools have persisted).

I disagree with Hall's suggestion that the ease with which captive apes and monkeys acquire the use of tools together with their failure to exhibit this propensity in the wild 'has no real significance'. To me this is the most significant point of the whole discussion. Conditions of captivity provide tool-using opportunities for these primates while their natural habitats do not. We regularly use tools not because of our impressively larger brains and adept hands, but because we have been trained in cultural environments, in this respect analogous to the conditions of captivity for apes and monkeys. Feral human beings drawn from modern *Homo sapiens* populations, and living in the restricted, tool-less environments of gorillas and chimpanzees, or of baboons, would probably do hardly any better than these animals in developing tools and weapons. Our superior brains might accelerate the process of tool-development by a factor of two or three, so that an Acheulean technology could be achieved in two or three hundred thousand years instead of a million years or more.

What we must explain then is the initial environmental 'push', sufficient to stimulate tool-using among suitably endowed primates, and to sustain it through social learning from generation to generation. Stick hurling in anger appears less promising than the palmnut cracking with rocks reported from Liberia. I see the conditions for take-off, in a changed food-habit, plus the adoption of relatively permanent bases of operation – rock-shelters or living-floors. Dart has stressed the importance of osteodontokeratic litter in stimulating tool-using (1960); such accumulations of bones, horns, and teeth could arise from scavenging as well as from hunting, at least to begin with. Present forest environments used by anthropoid apes do not provide for semi-permanent sanctuaries where trash suitable for tools could accumulate, though the Kwangsi Gigantopithecines evidently lived in caves. Aimless tool-handling could be stimulated by residence in a trash-filled cave or shelter, but practical use of tools requires something more – most likely food in a form which must be crushed, pounded, cut, or broken before it can be consumed; the carcasses of medium to large sized animals represent such a food. The reconstruction of the ecological status of the primordial Hominids is most urgent (Napier, 1963).

To conclude, Hall's paper has stimulated me to suggest some large-scale and undoubtedly expensive experiments, utilizing apes and monkeys in naturalistic environments, but not necessarily in environments identical to their present habitats. In such environments, the animals would be provisioned with foods requiring special preparation – palm-nuts to be cracked with stones, carcasses to be dissected, or even small, slow game animals to be hunted and killed with regularity. We might even try out Washburn's suggestion of supplying baboons with digging sticks, in a range in which such tools would significantly increase their food supply. If the initiation of such behaviors in non-human primates required some deliberate training of selected individuals, this would violate no basic canon of scientific experimentation. If we are interested in the ramifications – technological as well as sociological – of regular tool-using in non-human Primates, we need not wait for fifty thousand years for some ape to discover a simple tool-technique by himself.

I have not commented on Hall's examples of non-primate tool-using, illuminating as they are, since I think our understanding of the emergence of human tool-using and tool-making is most likely to come from studies of primate behavior.

By Harry J. Jerison, Yellow Springs, Ohio, U.S.A.

When animal behavior is treated in purely evolutionary terms and limited to naturalistic field observations, there is an inherent obstacle in the way of scaling the behavior to provide a measure of adaptability. This is due to the assumption implicit in evolutionary analysis that the present state of nature represents a peak of excellence for the measure, or, stated another way, that a given pattern of behavior that is observed in the field is the best that has been achieved for the adaptive niche within which the behavior occurs. It seems to me that Hall's analysis of tool-using as a measure of adaptability illustrates the problem very well. If I read him correctly, he finds that tool-using, when it occurs in the field, is a rare behavioral adaptation to selection pressures associated with particular niches in the environment, and that the very category, 'tool-using', is no more than an anthropomorphically derived identity for behaviors that may differ radically in their bases.

In presenting his interesting and in many ways original review of tool-using, Hall has eliminated this superficial category of behavior from serious consideration as a measure of adaptability. Yet it seems fair to ask him to state his views on the nature of appropriate measures, and, if possible, to suggest some examples of behavior categories that would provide such measures. Is it true, as I have just suggested, that the species-specific nature of much of the behavior that can be observed in the field limits the potential of such behavior for comparative purposes? I think a persuasive argument can be made for this position. Hall's review suggests that, at least in some primates, novel tool-using behavior patterns appear in the unusual environments of laboratories and zoos, and is not the frequency of novel and adequate responses to new situations one of the definitions of adaptability? One might therefore study adaptability profitably in laboratory settings where novel responses, including tool-using, might provide an appropriate comparative measure.

This is a treacherous position, too. I recall my own dismay when working with a very well trained Java monkey (*Macaca irus*) that had to reach through a window and press a lever to avoid or escape a shock after an easily detected signal was presented. Pressing a lever is a classic 'instrumental' act in the psychological laboratory, and it is clearly a bit of tool-using – or is it? In this case I found that when the clearly visible lever was moved back about 2 cm, this was enough to disrupt the animal completely. The monkey went through all of its usual response movements, but it missed the lever every time, because it failed to correct for the new lever distance. One must conclude that at least some 'tool-using' in the laboratory as well as in the field is the result of the interaction of stereotyped (even if learned) movements with movable objects.

These comments are less on tool-using, which is apparently a weak descriptive category for animal behavior, than on the problem of defining and measuring adaptability. I would appreciate additional discussion of this problem.

By Arthur J. Riopelle, Covington, La, U.S.A.

Tool-using by animals has fascinated behavioral scientists for many years. Particularly perplexing has been an apparent comparability of behavior in even widely divergent orders of animals. This is nicely illustrated in this paper by Hall who juxtaposes examples from wasps, crabs, birds, elephants, monkeys and apes. Historically, explanations of this apparent common trait have emphasized either instinct or intelligence. In one case the task is to explain how high up the phyletic chain one sees evidence for instinctive behavior and in the other case how much intelligence and insight is possessed by primitive animals. The popularity of these alternate views has fluctuated from decade to decade, depending on the dramatic strength of the latest data in favor of one viewpoint or the other and with the temper of observations in related sciences.

Similarities and parallels can often be found in different behaviors and in the approaches to the study of them, and the conceptualization of the proper approach in one may be helpful in the other. Imitation and observational learning are cases in point. (Interestingly enough, observational learning, too, has engaged Hall's attention.)

The kinds of behavior that may be classified as imitative are as diverse as the kinds called tool-using. Many factors likely are involved, including the identification of the native elemental responses, the diversity of responses available, the situation surrounding the response, and the motivation and learning components.

Thorndike in 1898 stated the task for studying imitation: 'Now if a bird really gets a sound in his mind from hearing it and sets out forthwith to imitate as mocking birds are said at times to do, it is a mystery and deserves the closest study. If a bird, out of a lot of random noises that it makes, chooses those for repetition which are like sounds he has heard, it is a mystery *why*, though not in the previous case a mystery how, he does it.' (Thorndike, 1898.)

Hall's paper identifies similar components of the problem of tool-using. All species, because of innate response capabilities, are predisposed to execute certain kinds of responses rather than others. (Here Hall is more restrictive than Thorndike.) Out of the responses that are made, some lead to reinforcement, satisfaction, and gratification, whereas others do not. Those reinforced will tend to be repeated. Thus Hall has taken Thorndike's less mysterious route to search for an explanation of the behavior he and others have observed.

167

Hall's report, like Thorndike's before him, is perhaps less of an explanation of tool-using behavior than an identification of the significant components of it. It, naturally, goes beyond Thorndike in its use of concepts, such as displacement activity, which were not available in 1898. It is to be hoped, therefore, that Hall's report will stimulate experimental work on tool-using behavior just as Thorndike's did for imitation.

There is another emphasis in the paper which deserves mention, and that is the breadth of the sources of literature cited. Tool-using is evidently that kind of animal activity which brings together scientists of differing orientation and thus serves as a vehicle for the transport of ideas among them. One cannot help but observe that such communication broadens our sciences and sharpens our concepts. Hall's study will further this process.

By J. P. Scott, Bar Harbor, Maine, U.S.A.

This is an excellent review of the subject and points out the fact that it is difficult to draw a line anywhere in the animal kingdom which will strictly separate human from non-human behavior. The following remarks are intended as addenda rather than criticism.

A distinction should be made between instances where tool-using is a part of the regular behavioral repertoire of a species, and cases where such behavior can be learned and passed along from individual to individual by some form of cultural inheritance, the latter being the more human attribute. However, simple observation does not reveal which of these two alternate explanations of behavior applies to any particular case. The use of stones in cracking mussel shells by the sea otter might belong in either category until it is possible to experiment with animals which have not had an opportunity to learn from their own kind.

A great many animals are capable of instrumental learning; i.e., of performing certain acts, obtaining a result which is rewarding to them and consequently learning to repeat the activity. No high degree of intelligence or capacity for symbolic logic is necessary. The likelihood of learning to use tools under these circumstances is largely dependent upon the species' ability to manipulate objects.

Instrumental learning may have a variety of motivations besides the two basic ones suggested by Hall in connection with agonistic and ingestive behavior. Captive chimpanzees at Yerkes Laboratories used to squirt water and throw feces at passing spectators with considerable accuracy. While the motivation may have been agonistic, it may also have resulted from the simple pleasure of watching the spectators jump and yell.

In general, Hall has shown that tool-using is not a unique human capacity. Rather, human societies excel, but are not unique, in their capacity to communicate tool-using by cultural means. In our search for the beginnings of cultural heredity in other forms, we should not neglect the opposite side of the coin, that human behavior may include a basic repertory of patterns whose development is largely under biological control.

By S. L. Washburn, Berkeley, California, U.S.A.

This paper clarifies a confused subject and offers what may well prove to be a major contribution to the understanding of human evolution. The clear separation of objects used in emotional display behavior from those used in feeding is new and important. I would like to comment briefly on how this supplements available notions on the origins of human tool-using.

In both chimpanzee and gorilla (as described by Morris-Goodall [1963] and Schaller, 1963) the emotional-display throwing occurs when the animals are bipedal and on the ground. In particular the chimpanzee may break off a branch and swing it vigorously as part of the display (Morris-Goodall). The animal does not try to strike the creature against whom the display is directed, but this might easily happen. Here then is a situation in which apes might repeatedly discover the effectiveness of striking with an object. As a part of the aggressive display the branch is effective whether it strikes another animal or not. Here is a relatively common situation in which the utility of a tool, both offensively and defensively, might be learned. I have always wondered about the first steps in the evolution of a weapon. Unless a stick is well-selected and skilfully used an ape's teeth are far more effective. The agonistic-display origin of weapons solves this dilemma because, if the display fails, the ape still may fight or flee. The selection pressure maintaining the large teeth would not be relaxed until after the swinging-branch display had evolved into effective behavior. If young apes incorporated this bipedal, object-using display into their play repertoire, a background for skilful adult use would be laid.

I see no conflict between the 'emotional' use of objects theory and continuing to stress the importance of even minor tool use in extending feeding habits. Surely the more different reasons objects are manipulated, the more likely it is that new uses will be found and skills developed. Future field observations and experiments, guided by Hall's clarification, may give us a much deeper understanding of the possible origins of human tool making.

By J. S. Weiner, London

Hall draws attention to and discusses the apparent paucity of evidence of 'tool-using' activities by non-human primates in the wild in contrast to the many instances recorded for captive animals. One of the two factors he puts forward to account for this discrepancy is simply that the systematic field evidence is missing and he mentions specifically here the ignorance of details on the feeding habits of *Cebus*. I claim no first-hand or special knowledge of this topic, but it seems to me that in the case of *Cebus fatuellus* the evidence for similar tool-using activities in the wild and in captivity is not so undocumented as Hall suggests. I had occasion to describe some of the 'hammering' activities of *Cebus fatuellus* at the Primate Symposium in London when making some comments on a film supplied by G. M. Vevers to show the use of a tool by a Capuchin monkey (Vevers and Weiner, 1963). I was interested to find fairly detailed references to rather similar activity in descriptions given by Romanes (1882) and by Osman Hill (1960) for both captive and wild monkeys. I would add that instances of this sort of tool-using in the wild, and of others mentioned by Hall, do not in any way refute the generalization for which I think he has made a very strong case, namely that the basis of the handling of various objects is to be found in the transfer of the 'emotional' repertoire of gesture to a different context. The importance of the *Cebus* example would be that it marks a particular case of such a transfer.

Reply

By K. R. L. Hall

Several very interesting points are made in these comments, and I shall select a few for more detailed discussion.

First, the question of terminology used in describing these, and other, performances is a recurrently difficult and important one. Čihák queries the use of 'homology' in the present context, but I think it is here appropriate because the point I was trying to emphasize was, to paraphrase Jerison's very clear expression of it, that tool-using has been a classificatory term for similar – unappearing performances the underlying bases of which may be radically different, but that the term has often been used with the *implication* of common origin. Analogies, therefore, they indeed are, but homologies they have been implied to be.

Carpenter deals with the terms used in describing the nature and status of the performances, and in drawing inferences from their description. Possibly 'elementary' or 'simple' would be less equivocal qualifiers of some of the instrumental acts under discussion, but I used the term 'primitive' in this context because, so far as I recall, it was the one Carpenter himself has used in describing branch-breaking or some other such emotional gesture. As to the status of these acts, it is still surely correct to apply the simplest kind of model that fits the evidence, and there is no denial of the possibility of purpose or insight or some other 'higher' conception being involved in some cases. The status of performances such as those of chimpanzees in using tools for food-getting is certainly more intelligent, and less emotional, than the display acts which these and other nonhuman primates show in the offensive–defensive kind of situation. But, as the theme of the paper tries to indicate, these more complex performances may be shown to derive, both ontogenetically and phylogenetically, from the simple emotional ones, in the kind of way Washburn has interestingly envisaged weapon-use might have developed.

A second major point that seems to me to arise out of several comments is the need for thorough comparative studies of behavior ontogeny. Scott indicates that such studies would be essential to substantiate, or otherwise, the suggestion that emotional gestures precede and form the basis for transfer to the more complex skills sometimes shown in food-getting. Scott also points out that only experimental studies could really distinguish between the status of tool-using performances by different types of animal, and these, I think, would have to be mainly developmental, and carried out under varying conditions that would test the limits of the animals' capacities.

Thirdly, and leading directly on from this, is the important point which Riopelle and Hewes discuss – how the skill involved in tool-using may be transmitted within a group, or from group to group in a population area. Hewes mentions the Japanese work on habit transmission in their Macaque groups, and, in my review elsewhere of this and other field and experimental data on imitation in monkeys and apes I thought that it was difficult clearly to show that anything more was occurring than a focusing of one animal's attention upon some object in the environment which, at least temporarily, it was ignoring. It seemed to me very doubtful whether anything new in the repertoire of skills of the observing animal ever has been convincingly shown to occur, and yet, at the same time, I feel that this whole fascinating problem of imitation needs perhaps a rather different research approach, particularly by exploring very thoroughly what it is that really goes on in the constant interactions of infant and mother and age-mates in the natural group situation of the animal. In watching sea otter pups with their mothers, one cannot fail to be impressed by the closeness of the relation and by the continual opportunity for the pup to observe what the mother is doing in her search for and manipulation of food objects. But with Scott I see no way of getting at the core of the problem except by experimental study.

A fourth point, concerning the nature of adaptability, is very well brought out in the comments of Andrew and Jerison. Jerison seems to me to go right to the heart of perhaps the major issue in modern comparative behavior studies in posing the question of how to define and measure adaptability. In terms of tool-using, chimpanzees seem easily to excel baboons. In terms of ability to make use of widely differing habitats and climatic zones, baboons, and perhaps vervets, are more successful than chimpanzees. Likewise, the sea otters might be considered the marine counterpart of the chimpanzee, and no doubt there is a Mustelid equivalent to baboons. In terms of laboratory measures, it seems clear that far too much emphasis has been placed upon performance scores which are not related to the sort of adaptability shown by the animal in the wild. Although there is obvious interest in seeing how an animal deals with a novel situation, it seems to me most likely that the animal studies that will give significant leads towards understanding some of the factors in human evolution will be planned to work out how the stresses of differing social and ecological settings affect the development of behavior. All this goes around the topic of tool-using, but I think it may put tool-using in the right perspective as possibly only a minor clue too close a look at which has stopped us seeing some of the major ones.

References

ANDREW, R. J. 1962. Evolution of intelligence and vocal mimicking. *Science* 137:585–9.

BEATTY, H. 1951. A note on the behavior of the chimpanzee. *Journal of Mammalogy* 32:118.

BIERENS DE HAAN, J. A. 1931. Werkzeuggebrauch und Werkzeugherstellung bei einem niedern Affen (*Cebus hypoleucus* Humb.). *Zeitschrift fur Physiologie* 13:639–95.

BIRCH, H. G. 1945. The relation of previous experience to insightful problemsolving. *Journal of Comparative Psychology* 38:367–83.

BISHOP, A. 1962. Control of the hand in lower primates. *Annals New York Academy Sciences* 102:316–37.

BOLWIG, N. 1959. A study of the behavior of the chacma baboon (*Papio ursinus*). *Behavior* 14:136–63.

BOLWIG, N. 1961. An intelligent tool-using baboon. *South African Journal of Science* 57:147–52.

BOULENGER, E. G. 1937. *Apes and monkeys.* New York: McBride.

BOWMAN, R. I. 1961. Morphological differentiation and adaptation in the Galapagos finches. *University of California Publications in Zoology* 58:1–326.

BREHM, A. E. 1916. *Tierleben, Band 4: Saugetiere.* Leipzig und Wien: Bibliographisches Institut.

CARPENTER, C. R. 1934. A field study of the behavior and social relations of howling monkeys. *Comparative Psychology Monographs* 10, No. 2.

——. 1935. Behavior of red spider monkeys in Panama. *Journal of Mammalogy* 16:171–80.

——. 1940. A field study in Siam of the behavior and social relations of the gibbon. *Comparative Psychology Monographs* 16:38–206.

CHANCE, M. R. A. 1960. Köhler's chimpanzees – how did they perform? *Man* 179:130–5.

CHISHOLM, A. H. 1954. The use by birds of 'tools' or 'instruments'. *Ibis* 96:380–3.

ČIHÁK, R. 1963. The development of the dorsal interossei in the human hand. *Ceskoslovenská morfologie* 11. In press.

COOPER, L. R., and H. F. HARLOW. 1961. Note on a Cebus monkey's use of a stick as a weapon. *Psychological Reports* 8:418.

DART, R. A. 1960. The bone tool-manufacturing ability of Australopithecus prometheus. *American Anthropologist* 62:134–43.

DEVORE, I. 1962. The social behavior and organization of baboon troops. Unpublished Ph. D. Thesis, University of Chicago, Chicago, Illinois.

DUERDEN, J. E. 1905. On the habits and reactions of crabs bearing actinians in their claws. *Proceedings of the Zoological Society of London* 2:494–511.

FISHER, E. M. 1939. Habits of the southern sea otter. *Journal of Mammalogy* 20:21–36.

FORSTER, A. 1916. Die Mm. contrahentes und interossei manus in der Säugetierreihe und beim Menschen. *Archiv für Anatomie und Entwickelungsge schichte* 101–378.

HALL, K. R. L. 1962a. Numerical data, maintenance activities, and locomotion in the wild chacma baboon, *Papio ursinus. Proceedings of the Zoological Society of London* 139:181–220.

——. 1962b. Sexual, derived social, and agonistic behavior patterns in the wild chacma baboon, *Papio ursinus. Proceedings of the Zoological Society of London* 139:284–327.

——. 1962c. Behaviour of monkeys to mirror-images. *Nature* 196:1258–61.

——. 1963. Variations in the ecology of the chacma baboon, *Papio ursinus. Symposium of the Zoological Society of London* 10:1–28

HALL, K. R. L., and GEORGE B. SCHALLER. 1964. Tool-using behavior of the California sea otter. *Journal of Mammalogy* 45:287–98.

173

HARINGTON, C. R. 1962. A bear fable? *The Beaver* No. 4 (winter): 4–7.

HEWES, G. W. 1961. Food transport and the origin of Hominid bipedalism. *American Anthropologist* 63:687–710.

HILL, W. C. O. 1960. *Primates.* Vol. 4. Cebidae, Part A. Edinburgh: University Press.

HINGSTON, R. W. G 1920. *A naturalist in Himalaya.* Boston: Small.

HORNADAY, W. T. 1922. *The minds and manners of wild animals.* New York: Scribner.

IMANISHI, K. 1960. Social organization of subhuman Primates in their natural habitat. *Current Anthropology* 1:393–407.

JOLÉAUD, L. 1933. Études de géographie zoologique sur la Berbérie. Les Primates: le Magot. Congrès International de Géographie, Paris 1931. Comptes rendus. Vol. II, part 2, pp. 851–63.

KAUFMANN, J. H. 1962. Ecology and social behavior of the coati, *Nasua narica,* on Barro Colorado Island, Panama. *University of California Publications in Zoology* 60:95–222.

KAWAMURA, S. 1959. The process of subculture propagation among Japanese macaques. *Journal of Primatology, Primates* (Japan Monkey Centre) 2 (No. 1):43–60.

KENYON, K. W. 1959. 'The sea otter', *Annual Report of the Smithsonian Institute, 1958.* Washington, D.C., The Smithsonian Institute, pp. 399–407.

KINNAMAN, A. J. 1902. Mental life of two *Macacus rhesus* monkeys in captivity. II. *American Journal of Psychology* 13:173–218.

KLÜVER, H. 1933. *Behavior mechanisms in monkeys.* Chicago: University of Chicago Press.

——. 1937. Re-examination of implement-using behavior in a *Cebus* monkey after an interval of three years. *Acta Psychologica* 2:347–97.

KORTLANDT, A., and M. KOOIJ. 1963. Protohominid behaviour in primates. *Symposium of the Zoological Society of London* 10:61–88.

KUMMER, H. 1957. Soziales Verhalten einer Mantelparian-Gruppe. *Beihandlung Schweizerisch Zeitschrift Psychologie* 33:1–92.

LACK, D. 1947. *Darwin's finches.* Cambridge: Cambridge University Press.

——. 1953. Darwin's finches. *Scientific American* (April) 188:66–72.

MARSHALL, A. J. 1960. Bower-birds. *Endeavor* 19:202–08.

MASSERMAN, J. H., and C. PECHTEL. 1953. Neuroses in monkeys. *Proceedings of the New York Academy of Science* 56:253–65.

McDOUGALL, W. 1923. *Outline of psychology.* New York: Scribner.

MERFIELD, F. G., and H. MILLER. 1956. *Gorilla hunter.* New York: Farrar.

MORGAN, C. L. 1900. *Animal behaviour.* London: E. Arnold.

MORRIS, D. 1962. *The biology of art.* New York: Alfred A. Knopf.

MORRIS-GOODALL, J. 1963. Feeding behaviour of wild chimpanzees. *Symposium of the Zoological Society of London* 10:39–48.

MURIE, O. J. 1940. Notes on the sea otter. *Journal of Mammalogy* 21:119–31.

NAPIER, J. R. 1960. Studies of the hands in living primates. *Proceedings Zoological Society London* 134:647–57.

——. 1962. The evolution of the hand. *Scientific American* 207:56–62 (No. 6).

——. 1963. Early man and his environment. *Discovery*, March, 12–18. *Newsweek*, 1963. *Tooling up.* May 27, p. 98f.

NISSEN, H. W. 1931. A field study of the chimpanzee. *Comparative Psychology Monographs* 8.

OAKLEY, K. P. 1951. A definition of man. *Science News* 20:69–81.

PECKHAM, G. W., and E. G. PECKHAM. 1898. On the instincts and habits of solitary wasps. *Wisconsin Geological and Nature History Survey*, II.

PITMAN, C. R. 1931. *A game warden among his charges*. London: Nisbet.

ROMANES, G. J. 1882. *Animal intelligence*. London: Kegan Paul Trench & Co.

SCHALLER, G. B. 1961. The orang-utan in Sarawak. *Zoologica* 46:73–82.

——. 1963. *The mountain gorilla: ecology and behavior*. Chicago: University of Chicago Press.

SCHILLER, P. H. 1957. 'Innate motor action as a basis of learning', in *Instinctive behavior* (Editor C. H. Schiller). New York: International University Press.

THORNDIKE, E. L. 1898. Animal intelligence, an experimental study of the associative processes in animals. *Psychological Review, Monograph Supplement* 2, no. 4 (whole no. 8).

THORPE, W. H. 1951. The learning abilities of birds. *Ibis* 93:1–52, 252–96.

——. 1956. *Learning and instinct in animals*. London: Methuen.

TINBERGEN, N. 1960. 'Behaviour, systematics, and natural selection', in *Evolution after Darwin* (Editor Sol Tax), vol. I: *The evolution of life*. Chicago: University of Chicago Press.

VEVERS, G. M. and WEINER, J. S. 1963. Use of a tool by a captive Capuchin monkey (*Cebus fatuellus*). *Symposium on Primate Biology*, Zoological Society, London.

WALLACE, A. R. 1902. 10th ed. *The Malay archipelago*. New York: Macmillan.

WASHBURN, S. L. 1950. The analysis of primate evolution with particular reference to the origin of man. *Cold Spring Harbor Symposium on Quantitative Biology* 15:67–78.

WASHBURN, S. L. and I. DEVORE. 1961. 'Social behavior of baboons and early man', in *Social life of early man*. Viking Fund Publications in Anthropology, No. 31, pp. 91–105.

WILLIAMS, J. H. 1950. *Elephant Bill*. New York: Doubleday.

WILLISTON, S. W. 1892. Notes on the habits of Ammophila. *Entomological News* 3:85–6.

ZUCKERMAN, S. 1932. *The social life of monkeys and apes*. London: Kegan Paul.

Part Four   GESTURES

There are many ways of evaluating the complexity of behaviour. Usually, performance is judged by its correctness or by its rapidity in the attainment of an objective. Spontaneously generated activity, as described in the brief abstract reprinted here, can also reveal the potential capacity of a species to solve problems which are beyond the capability of any single member. This report shows that one animal can solicit the aid of another to achieve a particular objective. Unfortunately, cinematographic analyses of this experiment cannot be reprinted in book form although they are more descriptive than the mere abstract. This paper nevertheless succeeds in suggesting the potentialities of a unique approach which is worthy of further study and exploitation.

13 M. P. Crawford

Further Study of Coöperative Behavior in Chimpanzee

M. P. Crawford, 'Further study of coöperative behavior in chimpanzee', *Psych. Bull.*, vol. 33 (1936), p. 809.

Young chimpanzees were trained in pairs to solve problems requiring teamwork or coöperation. The pulling in of a heavy box baited with food by two ropes was chosen for detailed study. The apparatus was controlled entirely from an observation booth where the experimenter was concealed from the subjects during an entire experimental session. Records consisted of verbal descriptions dictated while watching the animals, automatic recordings of amount and duration of pulls on the ropes, and moving picture films. The coöperative activity did not appear spontaneously, but was subject to training and developed through three stages. (1) The animals pulled together by responding simultaneously to an external cue. (2) Each animal learned to watch its partner and to join its pulling at the proper time. (3) Two of the chimpanzees developed gestures by which they solicited their partners' pulling. The gestures consisted in arm and hand movements, sometimes accompanied by vocalizations, specifically adapted to the needs of the situation. An animal was thus enabled to induce its partner to begin pulling, or to recall it to the task when its interest lagged. The animals which did any soliciting at all solicited every partner with whom they were paired, apparently having developed solicitation as a generalized method of problem solution. Animals who solicited sometimes did considerably less work than the partner whom they solicited. Those who learned to use gestures for solicitation in the pull-in-box problem also solicited in other problems requiring teamwork. Interesting consistencies in amount and style of pulling by individual animals when paired with different partners were discovered on analysis of graphic records.

Part Five LEARNING AND PROBLEM SOLVING

Two opposing viewpoints have shaped the development of the scientific study of complex behaviour. Both rely heavily on concepts which derive from the study of learning. Although these two do not exhaust the possibilities for theoretical frameworks, other viewpoints are in fact closely related to them. These two major approaches, one associationistic, the other cognitive, are represented in the first two papers of this group. The concept of 'learning sets' underlines a fundamental limitation of the earlier experimental work, namely that it concentrated on a naïve animal faced with an isolated problem. Learning set experiments emphasized that, to elucidate higher order learning, the proper unit for study is behaviour during a series of problem situations, in which the animal may transfer what he learns with an initial stimulus to new but related problems. The paper on chimpanzees examines the simultaneous learning of a number of problems; and the paper by Levine attempts to reformulate the Krechevsky approach and to apply it to learning set formation.

14 I. Krechevsky

'Hypothesis' Versus 'Chance' in the Pre-Solution Period in Sensory Discrimination-learning

I. Krechevsky, '"Hypothesis" versus "chance" in the pre-solution period in sensory discrimination-learning', *Univ. Calif. Publ. Psychol.*, vol. 6 (1932), pp. 27–44.

In a previous paper (3) it was pointed out that a re-examination of the data obtained from sensory discrimination experiments necessitates the adoption of a new description of learning. It was found that instead of considering the first part of 'learning' as consisting of random, haphazard behavior, we must recognize that the animal, during that period, is responding in an orderly, systematic manner. He is attempting various solutions and giving them up when they fail, until he hits finally upon the 'correct' one. The present paper presents part of the experimental evidence for such a thesis.

As originally planned and carried out, the experiment involved the setting up of two discrimination habits in each animal – a visual and a 'hurdle' habit – as well as a study of the general problem of transfer of training. The present report will concern itself, however, only with that part of the study relevant to this question of hypotheses. And for this purpose the results of the 'hurdle' discrimination only will be considered.[1]

In his *Brain Mechanisms and Intelligence*, Lashley made the first suggestion of a possible relationship between two often observed phenomena connected with the setting up of discrimination habits by the white rat – the peculiar shape of the learning curve and the tendency of the animal to form various position habits before mastering the problem. 'There are many indications,' he writes,

that . . . in the discrimination box, responses to position, to alteration, or to cues from the experimenter's movements usually precede the reaction to light and *represent attempted solutions* that are within the rat's customary range of activity. . . . The form of the learning curve is the more significant when considered in relation to such behavior . . . it suggests that the actual association is formed very quickly and that

1. A complete report of the experiment is on file at the graduate office of New York University.

both the practice preceding and the errors following are irrelevant to the actual formation of the association.[2]

In other words, even when the 'learning curve' appears to show 'random' behavior the animal may be responding in a wholly systematic manner. Lashley regrets, however, that 'there is no present way to record such behavior objectively and I can present the description only as an impression from the training of several hundred animals in these problems'. The data from the present experiment have been examined in the light of Lashley's suggestion and an attempt has been made to devise a method for the objective determination of the validity of that suggestion.

Procedure

Apparatus

The apparatus used was a modification of Stone's multiple-unit discrimination box (7). The box consisted of four equal units, each unit presenting to the animal one discrimination and each unit continuous with the other.

Figure 1 shows the ground plan for the whole apparatus. The animal is started from a small 'home' cage just outside the entrance to the first box. The door, operated by a gravity-string

Figure 1

arrangement, opens up into passageway *x–y*. *g1* and *g2* are metal guards serving to force the animal in a straight line toward the stimulus panel *a–e*. The mid-part of the box (*afle*) contains the two stimulus chambers. Triangle *po* is a metal partition which not only serves to separate the two chambers, *ab* and *ce*, but is also so constructed as to prevent any light rays, entering from the second unit through door *mn*, from reaching the animal in the vestibule *g1–g2*. It also serves to prevent the possibility of the animal's detecting the presence of the obstruction (*door d2*) in either of the two alleys.

Door *d2* swings on a pivot at *o*, so that, at the will of the experimenter, alley *ab* or *ce* can become the correct alley and the other,

2. Italics mine.

the cul-de-sac. In figure 1 the door is so arranged as to make *ab* the correct alley. When the animal enters the correct alley he is allowed to pass through pathway *mn* and into the next unit where he is presented with the very same situation as in the preceding unit. Immediately after entering the next alley, the door of the next box, corresponding to door *x–y*, is dropped so as to prevent any retracing.

For the most part the floor plan of this box is quite similar to Stone's apparatus except for a few insignificant differences in dimensions. In arranging the stimulus panel, however, a radical departure was made from Stone's apparatus. Figure 2 is a three-dimensional drawing of the stimulus chambers.[3]

In the hurdle discrimination set-up the only differentiating factor between both alleys was the presence of the hurdle. The animal actually had to climb this obstruction in order to gain entrance into the alley. The presence of the hurdle was meant to indicate the correct alley, i.e., the hurdle was the positive stimulus. While we are primarily interested here in the hurdle results, perhaps it would be appropriate to discuss this apparatus as used in setting up a brightness discrimination as well, since, in an experiment to be reported later and attacking the same general problem as here presented, brightness discrimination was used with this apparatus.

In making the correct choice (brightness discrimination) the animal is not only forced to go toward the light (as is the case in Stone's box) *but he is actually forced to go into and through the light as well.* This difference in procedure has some theoretical significance and one which, while it seems to be more and more recognized in actual practice, has not yet, by the very experimenters who make use of it, been explicitly acknowledged.[4]

The Gestaltists have been most forward with their criticisms of

3. The section labeled *abce* is in the same position as the section similarly labeled in figure 1. In figure 2, *afgb* and *ckle* are the two tunnels through which the rat must run. These tunnels are divided into an upper and lower part by a plate of translucent glass at *fg* running parallel with the floor of the box. The upper part contains the electric lights and the lower is the tunnel through which the animal runs. The tops of the two stimulus boxes are covered. Most of the light is directed through the translucent frosted glass plates over the tunnels *afgb* or *ckle*, as the case may be; i.e., when the apparatus is used for setting up a brightness discrimination or else, through both tunnels as in the hurdle discrimination. At points *h2, 3, 4* and *1*, holes were bored which permitted the insertion of a hurdle at the entrance to either alley, as is indicated in figure 2.

4. Since writing this section, a publication of N. L. Munn (6) has appeared which points out many of the considerations stated below.

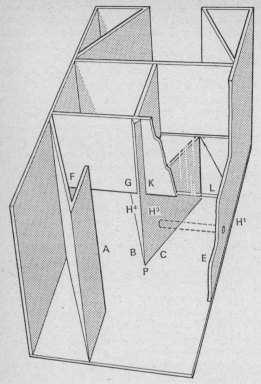

Figure 2

the usual experimental set-up used in studying animal learning on the ground that too often the animal is required to build up a wholly artificial connection between a given stimulus and a given response, with the result that the consequent performance does not give us a true picture of what the animal can do in a more 'natural' and reasonable problem situation. The stimulus, as in the case of the usual discrimination box and as is also the case in Stone's box, is not something that is *intrinsically* connected with either the animal's response or his 'reward', it is merely something the experimenter brings *ab extra* and imposes, or wishes the animal to impose, upon the situation. In discussing this very point, Köhler (2) writes,

186

The electric shock, for instance, applied to the legs, is not intimately connected to the task of getting a red spot as 'the negative stimulus'. There is only a very loose connection between them in space and time. If that spot *itself* would make a sudden movement against the animal and so frighten it . . . we should certainly have a situation much nearer the animal's learning in common life and a more efficient one.

In other words the stimulus, the response, and the consequence should all be intrinsically bound together; the whole should make a meaningful combination. We have some actual experimental evidence to bear out this assertion. Hubbard (1) found that while it took a group of animals an average of 99·3 trials and 29·7 errors to set up a light–dark discrimination when the animals were forced *through* the stimulus, it took another group of animals an average of 174 trials and 56·9 errors to set up a similar habit when the animals could merely travel *toward* the light. Unfortunately the results of that experiment are partly vitiated by the experimenter's failure to control other differences in stimulation between the two groups, such as tactual stimulation, etc., however much the same suggestion is implied in the surprising efficiency of Lashley's new technique for setting up form discrimination habits (5). Here, also, the animal is required to jump *through* the stimulus pattern. This very fact may account for the ability of Lashley to demonstrate form discrimination in the white rat where previous experimenters have failed.

The results of this experiment also tend to support Köhler's point. It took the 40 animals an average of but 13 trials and 21 errors to set up a visual discrimination.

It is also apparent that in the hurdle discrimination set-up we have the same desirable situation. Here the animal must not only see the hurdle and travel toward it, but he must also actually *do* something with it. Hurdling the obstacle is an intrinsic and necessary part of the response. The set-up, in general, is one which should encourage rapid discrimination learning.

Animals

Forty previously untrained male albino rats, about three months of age, were used as subjects.

Method

No animal was used for experimental purposes until three weeks had elapsed from the time he had been received in the laboratory. Thus every animal was given a period in which to adapt himself to the general laboratory conditions. During these three weeks of acclimatization the animals were fed once a day, at about the same hour that their training series was to be run, in a special feeding cage. Their diet consisted of 'McCullum's Mixture' plus a semi-weekly ration of lettuce. Fresh water was always available.

All runs were made at night. A night's work consisted of ten trials per animal. This program was adhered to until the animal satisfied the established norm for learning.

During the runs the experimenter was seated away from the apparatus and was able to observe the behavior of the animal through a series of mirrors which allowed a full view of the box and its contents from one point of observation. The only light in the room, during experimentation, came from within the apparatus itself. Since the top of the apparatus was covered with a fine mesh wire, it would have been almost impossible for the animal to be able to see anything outside of the box. The mirror arrangement also obviated the necessity for the experimenter to move about during the run.

Special care was taken in drawing up the order of presentation of stimuli, to avoid introducing any but chance orders. It will be seen that the situation in this discrimination box is more complicated in this respect than it is in the single-unit discrimination box. In the latter case it is merely necessary that the positive stimulus be on the right as often as on the left, but in the present case it is not only necessary that the total number of stimuli be equated for their position, but also that each unit be equated for that factor. The order of presentation for ten trials is given below.

Trials	1	2	3	4	5	6	7	8	9	10
Unit 1	r	l	l	l	r	r	r	l	r	l
Unit 2	r	l	r	r	l	l	r	l	l	r
Unit 3	l	l	r	r	l	r	l	r	l	r
Unit 4	r	r	l	r	l	l	r	l	r	l

This order sufficed for ten trials or for one day's runs. Every day the same order was repeated. It is highly improbable that the rats learned this order, since the series contains 40 items and in no case was any rat presented with the series more than 12 times. Every rat was, of course, given the same series.

At the end of each trial the animal found in his food box a cube of milk-soaked bread. This cube was cut to a predetermined standard size which helped to equate somewhat the reward received by the different animals and the reward received by the same animal from trial to trial. The animal, however, did not depend upon this diet for maintenance. After he had completed his day's work he was transferred to his feeding cage in the animal room where he was allowed to feed on the balanced ration of 'McCullum's Diet' for an hour.

In keeping records of the performance, the following factors were considered: (*1*) ERRORS. An error was counted if the animal inserted his head into the wrong chamber. Complete entry was not necessary.[5] (*2*) POSITION RESPONSES. Not only was a record made of the animal's response on the basis of the 'correct' stimulus, i.e., whether he entered a blind or a true alley, but the side of the box (left or right) was also noted. (*3*) NORM FOR LEARNING. The problem was considered mastered when the animal completed five errorless runs, that is, twenty consecutive errorless discriminations.

Results and Discussion

In order to obtain significant data in attacking our problem, namely, the relation of the shape of the curve to the various 'interfering' position habits, we could not content ourselves with plotting the usual type of curve. The method we finally adopted, and the reasons therefore have been stated in detail in the previous paper (3), but for convenience we might briefly sum up the process here.

After the animals had mastered the discrimination problem the entire performance of each animal was individually analyzed, and the resulting learning curves were individually plotted. For each rat the following items were determined: (*1*) the number of 'errors' the animal made each day; (*2*) the number of turns to the left; (*3*) the number of turns to the right; (*4*) the number of turns which were in keeping with an 'alternating' scheme; and (*5*) the number of turns in keeping with a 'perseverance' scheme.

In considering the resulting curves one must be certain that the locus of any point on any one curve is a significant one. That is,

5. Stone (7) in working with his apparatus isolated three different kinds of errors: (*1*) advancing into the wrong alley; (*2*) entering the correct alley, but instead of continuing on into the next unit, retracing back into the same unit; (*3*) entering the wrong alley but retracing before actually coming into contact with the obstruction. Stone states that he found this third type not definite enough or objective enough to be of any value as different from the first type, and that errors of the second type were so infrequent (another instance of the rapidity with which an animal can build up a general forward-going tendency) as to be of little value. While these three types of errors were also observed in this study the same objections to their consideration were found to hold as in Stone's study.

since we are graphing almost every response of the animal it is imaginable that by a certain combination of circumstances some one curve will always appear to show systematic behavior yet actually be a chance fluctuation. To meet this criticism, the extreme limits beyond which chance alone would very rarely send any one curve were determined by the use of the formula $\sigma = \sqrt{\dfrac{PQ}{N}}$. That is, if chance were the sole determining influence for any one curve, that curve should never go beyond 50 per cent $\pm$ 3σ. Doing this we find the σ for 40 chances (one day's work) to be 7·8 per cent, which would give, for the extreme limits of chance fluctuations 50 $\pm$ 21·4 per cent, or 28·6 and 71·4 per cent. The graphs have so been constructed as to concern only the upper limit, i.e., 71·4 per cent. This limit, to facilitate inspection of the curve, has been indicated by drawing a line at the proper point across each graph.

Now, if any of the resulting curves should go beyond this limit we can be fairly certain that such a change is owing to some systematic cause. If, therefore, any of the 'position' curves go beyond their chance zone limit, while the 'error' curve remains on the 50 per cent line we would be justified in saying that, during that period, the animal is responding to the situation in a *systematic spatial* manner; then, if that spatial curve goes back to the 50 per cent line and the 'hurdle' curve goes beyond the chance limit and finally reaches 100 per cent efficiency, we have a perfectly objective demonstration of Lashley's suggestion.

We are now ready for a discussion of the actual graphs. Out of the 40 graphs, figures 3 to 6 represent samples of the most clear-cut curves.

In figure 3 we find the rat, for perhaps the first five days, running according to 'chance', that is, his 'error' score remains well within the pure chance zone; then, during the sixth and seventh days he very rapidly brings his error score down, indicating complete mastery of the problem. A consideration of the broken-line curve, however (the curve representing the animal's turns to the right side of the box), shows that such a description is misleading and entirely untrue. The animal, during the first five days was *not* running by 'chance'; the animal, during that period was behaving in a definite, systematic manner, *but on a spatial basis*. During the so-called 'chance' period the animal adopted, brought to near-perfection, and then surrendered a perfectly legitimate and unified 'attempt at solution'. His choices on the basis of the presence or absence of the hurdle represent a second

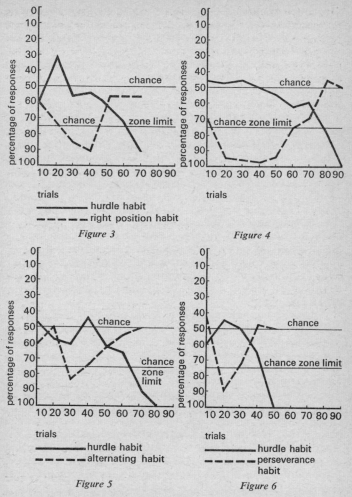

Figure 3

Figure 4

Figure 5

Figure 6

hurdle habit
right position habit

hurdle habit
alternating habit

hurdle habit
perseverance habit

systematic series of responses, which was preceded by a different, but nevertheless just as unified series of responses.

In this specific case then, learning did not consist of haphazard chance responses which finally (through the action of the various Laws of Learning) became systematic, but learning consisted of one systematic series of responses followed by another.

Figure 4 represents the performance of another animal who also happened to show, as a previous 'attempt at solution', a right position habit. The implications here are also clear and need no further discussion.

In figures 5 and 6 the 'attempted' solutions are an 'alternating' and 'perseverance' habit respectively.[6]

A more detailed analysis of these curves strengthens the suggestion that the interpretation here proposed is a valid one.

A point that should be noticed in these curves is the close similarity between the rapidity with which the animal builds up his position habit and that with which he builds up his hurdle habit. Thus in figure 3 it took the animal four days to bring his right position habit to the point of greatest efficiency, and it also took him four days to bring the hurdle habit to the same degree of efficiency. (It is obvious that this is so only when we consider the hurdle curve as beginning where the position curve leaves off.) The same is true for the other curves. This striking fact is a further substantiation of the assumption that the adoption of the various position habits is a real phenomenon of the learning act and not some 'chance' epi-phenomenon; as real, at any rate, as is the adoption of the hurdle discrimination by the rat, the same organism showing in either behavior the same characteristics of speed and efficiency.

Another point to be made is in relation to the 'difficulty' of a discrimination problem and the resulting shape of the learning curve. It may be pointed out that the 'typical' discrimination curve is obtained only where the discrimination involved is a more or less difficult one; where the problem is 'easy' no such curve results. We can see, from our proposed relationship between the shape of the curve and the animals' adoption of the various position habits, why one should expect that very thing. We call that discrimination problem 'easy' for the animal which requires but a few trials for its establishment. In order to establish any sensory discrimination habit rapidly the animal must 'pay attention to' ('react to') the correct stimulus from the very outset. That would mean that the experimental situations were of such

6. The chance zone for these two habits will, of course, differ slightly from the chance zone for the left or right position habits, because that for the latter habits is based on 40 choices, and that for the former habits on but 30 choices, since the animal's first choice at every trial could neither be considered as 'alternating' nor 'perseverance'. Only the last three choices of each trial were therefore considered. This difference in number of choices gives, as the σ for the last two habits 9 per cent with the limit as 77 per cent instead of 71·4 per cent.

nature as to make outstanding and most obvious the 'correct' stimulus. This would further mean that the animal's first 'attempted solution' was the correct one and therefore an analysis of his performance would reveal no other systematic 'attempted solutions', with the result that his 'error' curve would never remain on the 50 per cent line, but would show the same characteristics as the maze-learning curve, i.e. steady improvement.

Figure 7 shows a concrete example of the argument proposed above. Here the curve for the hurdle habit is atypical, it does not show the usual picture, but rather resembles more closely the curve obtained from the light–dark discrimination (see fig. 9), the 'easy' discrimination. It appears that here the animal 'hit upon' the correct stimulus from almost the very beginning with the result that he solved the problem with extreme rapidity. This would mean, according to the interpretation suggested above, that the animal did not at first attempt other 'wrong' solutions as, for example, spatial solutions. That is exactly what happened. The two curves representing the four possible position habits stay very close to the 50 per cent line, although they are not forced to do so by virtue of the locus of the hurdle curve. In other words it would have been possible, statistically considered, for the two position curves to go well beyond the 50 per cent line at the same time that the hurdle curve was at the 70 per cent line; nevertheless

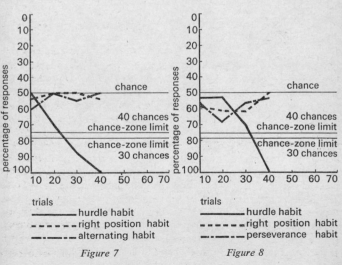

Figure 7   Figure 8

193

they failed to do so, the animal was not attempting a position solution.

It was remarked above, when introducing our curves, that we were reproducing only some of the most clear-cut ones. Not all of the remaining curves show quite the same things as those which we have reproduced. Out of the 40 curves, perhaps 15 are of the very same type as illustrated in figures 3 to 6 inclusive. The others are more confusing in implications. In figure 8 we have an example of a curve which does not fit in with our description of the others. While this curve is of the positively accelerated type,

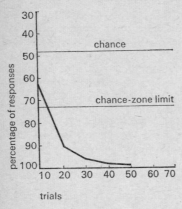

Figure 9

and in that respect shows a similarity to the others, nevertheless the curves representing the *position habits* for this animal do not show the same characteristics as the other curves; none of the four possible position habits going beyond a chance fluctuation. This curve, and it must be admitted there are a number of them, need not be interpreted however as contradictory to our general thesis. As a matter of fact, a close analysis of these very curves strengthens our hypothesis. Regarding figure 8 more closely it will be seen that while neither the right position habit nor the perseverence habit ever get beyond the chance zone, the two curves do depart a little from the 50 per cent line, and depart from that line at the same time. On the second day both curves reach their maximum together. This suggests that at any one time (that is, over the space of one day's trials) the animal was responding not to one position habit, but to two, alternately. Further analysis proves this to be quite a tenable view. Upon inspecting the animal's individual responses more closely it was found that of *the ten responses* (on the second day) *which did not fit in with the perseverance scheme eight were choices to the right*! Every time the animal departed from his perseverance scheme he went to the right side of the box. Only two times out of all 40 possibilities did he make a response which fitted in with neither 'hypothesis'.[7] This vacillation on the part of the rat, between a perseverance habit and a right position habit, would prevent the curve representing either habit from reaching a point outside the chance zone. Such behavior, however, is not different from the other behavior we have analyzed. In this case the animal, instead of making but one systematic attempt at solution before hitting upon the correct one, tries several, and each for a short period of time only. Even in these curves then, we fail to find room for haphazard and non-unified behavior patterns existing at many points of the learning process.

An analysis such as has just been made lays itself open to serious statistical criticisms. Essentially what we have done, the argument may be, is that by considering *every* response as part of some systematic form of behavior, we have of course eliminated, *ipso facto*, the possibility of finding any 'chance' responses. Such a criticism is difficult to meet here. All our learning curves are so short as to make it impossible to deal with our data in the statistical manner required in order to prove that our *combinations* of these various position habits do not lead to artifacts, but are statistically justified. In another experiment, the set-up was one which gave us longer learning curves and more data with the result that we were able to demonstrate quite definitely the validity of our method of combining the responses.

Throughout this paper we have been forced to present the data of individual animals only. Nowhere have we been able to call upon group results. The reason for this is obvious. An analysis such as we have made here would be impossible if we were to content ourselves with obtaining hypothetical averages of the hypothetical average rat and draw hypothetical learning curves. We feel that real and valid information in reference to the behavior of organisms can be obtained only by studying the actual individual *as* an individual. Such a method however has the obvious drawback of appearing non-quantitative in nature. We have attempted to devise some manner of presenting these results

7. For the use of the term 'hypothesis' to describe these various 'attempts at solution' see our introductory paper 'Hypotheses in Rats' (3).

as group results. The value of such procedure is to suggest that the behavior, of which up to now we have merely given samples, is universal for the white rat.

The evidence is shown in table 1. This table was constructed in the following manner: The curve for each rat was surveyed, noting for each position habit the lowest point on the curve.

Table 1

Percentages of Maximal Efficiency Reached by Animals in Building Up Position Habits

Habit	71–75	76–80	81–85	86–90	91–95	95–100
Right	2	5	3	4	—	1
Left	3	1	1	—	—	—
Perseverative	4	2	—	1	—	—
Alternating	3	2	4	—	—	—
Total	12	10	8	5	—	1

(Thus for rat #810-C, figure 6, the lowest point for the perseverance habit would be 87 per cent; for the rat 51-D, figure 8, the lowest point for the right position habit would be 62 per cent and for the perseverance habit, 67 per cent, and so forth.) In table 1 are presented the frequency of occurrences of these points for the four possible position habits. Thus, five curves (from all 40) reached the 76–80 per cent line of efficiency for the right position habit, etc. *It will be seen that in all there are 36 cases of position-habit-curves going beyond the line allowed by chance (73 per cent);* twelve of these reaching an efficiency between 71 and 75 per cent; ten, between 76 and 80; and 14 between 81 and 100 per cent. In other words, *the tendency to build up a systematic series of responses during the so-called period of chance is characteristic of most of the rats studied in this experiment.*

Conclusions

The characteristic form of the learning curve obtained in setting up discrimination problems was investigated in relation to the animal's tendency to form various position habits prior to mastery of the discrimination habit. Objective and quantitative evidence is presented of Lashley's suggestion that such position habits represent 'attempted solutions' on the part of the rat, and it is shown quite definitely that during that part of the learning performance, which is represented on the usual curve by an almost horizontal line at the 50 per cent point indicating no improvement, the animal is engaged in bringing to perfection various attempted solutions. After each 'wrong' solution is discarded in turn, the animal attempts another until he finally hits upon the 'correct' one. Four different such spatial 'attempts' at solution were isolated, a right-going habit, a left-going habit, a perseverance habit, and an alternating habit. The 40 animals used as subjects showed a total of 36 such habits before finally adopting the 'correct' response, a hurdle discrimination.

In the light of all the evidence presented here it is suggested that helter-skelter unorganized trial and error response as a description of the early part of the learning process is invalid, and that we must change our description of the learning process so as to recognize the existence of organized and systematic responses at *all* stages of the process.

References

1. HUBBARD, R. M. 1927. 'The Stimulus for the Visual Discrimination Habit.' *Jour. Comp. Psychol.*, 7:75.
2. KÖHLER, W. 1925. Intelligence in Apes. Psychologies of 1925 (Clark University Press).
3. KRECHEVSKY, I. 1932. 'Hypotheses' in Rats. MS.
4. LASHLEY, K. S. 1929. *Brain Mechanisms and Intelligence* (University of Chicago Press, Chicago, Ill., 1929).
5. LASHLEY, K. S. 1930. 'The Mechanisms of Vision.' *Jour. Genet. Psychol.*, 37:453.
6. MUNN, N. L. 1931. 'An Apparatus for Testing Visual Discrimination in Animals.' *Jour. Genet. Psychol.*, 39:342.
7. STONE, C. P. 1928. 'A Multiple Discrimination Box and Its Uses in Studying the Learning Ability of White Rats.' *Jour. Genet. Psychol.*, 35:559.

15 K. W. Spence

Gradual versus Sudden Solution of Discrimination Problems by Chimpanzees

K. W. Spence, 'Gradual versus sudden solution of discrimination problems by chimpanzees', *J. comp. Psychol.*, vol. 25 (1938), pp. 213–24.

Introduction

The occurrence of sharp rises in the learning curves of animals at or just preceding the solution of a problem has led to the critical view that the learning process, at least in such instances, is not aptly described or explained in terms of the building up of associative connections between stimuli and responses by means of appropriate rewards and punishments. Instead, a picture of learning is offered in terms of such concepts as 'insight', 'seeing into' or 'reorganization of the sensory field'. The Gestalt psychologists, in particular, have insisted upon the necessity of viewing the learning process in these terms and they have placed considerable stress upon the instances of sudden solution in the learning of animals as evidence of its insightful nature (1, 3). Thus Perkins and Wheeler (4), American proponents of the Gestalt views, concluded, on the basis of the sudden jumps in the learning curves they obtained with goldfish, that these animals learned a brightness discrimination in an insightful manner and not through changes effected by repetition and satisfaction.

Köhler, in his 1925 Powell lectures (2), likewise considered sudden solutions in the learning of discrimination problems. While he pointed out that discrimination learning is usually a slow, gradual process even in the anthropoids, he nevertheless claimed the learning is probably quite different in cases in which the solution is sudden. The occurrence of such sudden solutions is, moreover, evidence to him that the learning involves more than mere associative processes or, to quote him: 'We do not well describe experiments of this type by saying, as we usually do, that an animal in such a situation learns to connect certain stimuli with certain reactions and that the connection is "stamped in". This formulation of the process gives too much importance to the memory or association side of the problem, and it neglects another side of it which may be even more important and more difficult' (2). This neglected aspect of the problem, according to him, is the process by which the sensory field becomes organized, or rather reorganized, during learning, and it is this part that is responsible for the sudden solutions or insights in learning.

But are such instances of sudden jumps in the learning curves of animals evidence either for the existence of an insightful factor in learning, or for the inadequacy of the view that learning consists in the formation of stimulus response connections by a repetitive process of reinforcement and non-reinforcement? In the opinion of the writer, both parts of the question are, as yet, to be answered in the negative. To say, as the Gestalt psychologists do, that such learning involves the development of insight is merely to restate the problem in new terms. No satisfactory theoretical account of how such an insight factor operates to produce such sudden learning in discrimination problems, or for that matter any other type of problem, has ever been given by its Gestalt proponents. The association theorists, of course, are in exactly the same position, for they have never given a satisfactory theoretical account of this phenomenon. It does not logically follow, however, that an adequate theory cannot be developed on association principles.

The writer recently presented a theory of the nature of discrimination learning, based on association or conditioning principles, which was shown to be capable of explaining the various phenomena known to be characteristic of the presolution period of learning (5). Quite in contrast to the Gestalt or configuration interpretation, this theory conceives discrimination learning as a cumulative process of building up the strength of the excitatory tendency of the positive stimulus cue (i.e., the tendency of this stimulus to evoke the response of approaching it) by means of the successive reinforcements of the response to it, as compared with the excitatory strength of the negative stimulus, responses to which receive no reinforcements. Learning is completed when the difference between the excitatory strengths of the two cue stimuli is sufficiently large to offset always any differences in strength which may exist between other aspects of the stimulus situation that happen to be allied in their action with one or other of the cue stimuli; for example, such differences as may exist between the excitatory strengths of the food boxes on which the cue stimuli are placed. In the presentation of this theory, no consideration was given to the problem of the occurrence of sudden solution in discrimination learning. It is proposed in the present paper to examine the relation of the theory to this problem. Our discussion will be based largely on the results of an analysis of discrimination learning curves of chimpanzees.

Description of Experiment

The experimental data employed were obtained from an investigation with chimpanzees which was designated to test certain aspects of our theory of discrimination learning (6). The subjects were required to learn a series of discrimination problems involving four different stimulus forms, which may be designated A, B, C, D respectively. Each subject was first taught two preliminary discriminations: A (+) versus B (−) and, after the completion of this, C (+) versus D (−). Following the learning of these problems the animals were presented with five tests consisting of five new learning problems in which the same stimuli were used in new combinations. Table 1 shows the sequence of the problems, including the two preliminary habits.

According to our theory of discrimination learning, a definite relationship should have been found between the learning of each of these test problems (both the initial response and the total learning score, e.g., number of errors) and the relative number of reinforcements and non-reinforcements the stimuli had in previous problems. Thus, in the case of a particular subject, if the positive stimulus of a particular test has received a greater number of reinforcements and fewer non-reinforcements in the learning of previous problems than the negative stimulus, the excitatory strength of the former should be greater than that of the latter and the animal should respond from the first predominantly to it; possibly even choosing it exclusively if the difference is sufficiently great for complete learning. On the other hand, if the negative stimulus has had a greater number of reinforcements than the positive in previous problems, it should have the greater excitatory strength and, consequently, the animal should at first tend to respond predominantly to it. In such cases a greater amount of time (number of trials and errors) should be required to complete the learning, as this difference in strength of the excitatory tendencies must first be reduced to zero through non-reinforcement of the response to the negative stimulus, and a difference developed in favor of the positive stimulus.

The results of the experiment were in substantial agreement with the theoretical expectations. It was found that the learning of form discrimination problems by our chimpanzee subjects was directly dependent on the relative excitatory strengths of the positive and negative stimuli as determined by the relative

Table 1

Showing the Sequence of Discrimination Problems

(The animals were divided into two groups, the A group and the C group, on the basis of the stimulus, A or C, that was made positive in the first test problems. These two groups are each divided again in the third test problem according to the stimulus made positive.)

Sequence of problems	Group	Stimulus	
		Positive	Negative
Preliminary habits	Total group {	A	B
		C	D
Test 1 {	A	A	C
	C	C	A
Test 2 {	A	D	B
	C	B	D
Test 3 {	A-1	A	D
	A-2	D	A
	C-1	C	B
	C-2	B	C
Test 4 and 5	Total group {	B	A
		D	C

number of reinforcements and non-reinforcements each had received in previous problems. This relationship held not only for the initial response of the animal in each new problem, but also for the entire learning period. The data of the experiment are of particular interest in the present connection because of the fact that a number of the learning curves of the chimpanzee subjects, which began at chance or, because of a greater amount of training in earlier problems to the negative stimulus, less than chance, showed sudden jumps to solution.

Discussion of Results

The twelve chimpanzee subjects were presented in all with 76 discrimination problems. In twenty of these cases there was little or no learning involved as the subjects had previously had a greater number of reinforcements on the positive than on the negative stimulus. Consequently they responded from the beginning predominantly to the correct stimulus. Table 2 presents the numerical data for the fifty-six remaining cases. It shows the sharpness with which the curves of learning rise to solution in terms of the size of the increase in the percentage of correct responses from the period of twenty trials preceding to the period of twenty trials in which the criterion of learning (90 per cent correct) is satisfied. The larger the size of this increase the more sudden is the learning. An increase of 40 per cent or more, as will be seen, represents a jump from a chance score to completed learning.

Examination of the data contained in this table reveals several interesting facts. First of all, arbitrarily adopting an increase of 40 per cent as a criterion of sudden or 'insightful' learning, there were 19 instances in which this criterion was met and 37 in which the learning was more or less gradual. The question immediately arises as to whether the cases involving sudden solution were the result of some novel process, *insight*, and as such, *quite independent of associative changes resulting from selective reinforcements and non-reinforcements*. If this is true there should not be in these instances any relationship between the learning or solution of the discrimination problem and the relative excitatory strengths of

Table 2

Showing the Suddenness with which the Curves of Learning Rise to Solution in Terms of the Size of the Increase in the Percentage of Correct Responses from the Period of Trials Preceding to the Period in which the Learning Criterion was Attained

Subject	Preliminary problems		Test problems				
	P-1	P-2	T-1	T-2	T-3	T-4	T-5
1. Mimi	15	30	50	45	A	40	A
2. Lia	30	15	A	45	60	40	A
3. May	25	60	80	A	60	70	A
4. Jack	25	30	30·	A	A	40	40
5. Pan	35	15	40	20	A	50	A
6. Bokar	40	25	25	A	40	90	A
7. Mona	30	25	30	A	A	25	30
8. Nana	20	20	A	15	25	20	A
9. Wendy	20	10	30	A	A		
10. Josie	20	10	A	25	45		
11. Cuba	25	15	30	A			
12. Nira	10	30	30	30	25	40	
Mean	24·6	23·7	38·3	30	42·5	44·0	

A = Little or no learning involved because of initial preference for positive stimulus.

the stimuli as determined by cumulating the number of reinforcements and non-reinforcements each had previously received. As was reported in our previous paper (6), however, the learning of the test problems (tests 1, 3, 4 and 5) was very closely related to

Table 3

Showing the Relative Excitatory Strengths of the Positive and Negative Stimuli at the Beginning and End of the Experimental Period Preceding Solution

Test	Subject	20 trials preceding solution	20 trials on which solution	Relative excitatory strengths of positive and negative stimuli (P–N)	
				Beginning	End
1	Mimi	50	100	+21	+41
1	May	15	95	+24	+44
1	Pan	55	95	+10	+30
3	May	35	95	−2	+18
3	Bokar	60	100	−14	+6
3	Josie	50	95	−1	+19
3	Lia	40	100	−20	0
4	Mimi	55	95	−67	45
4	May	20	90	−16	+4
4	Jack	60	100	−4	+16
4	Pan	50	100	−14	+6
4	Bokar	60	100	−14	+6
4	Nira	55	100	−3	+17
4	Lia	50	90	−10	+10
5	Jack	50	90	+14	+34

the relative excitatory strengths of the stimuli, as determined by the number of past reinforcements and non-reinforcements.[1] The fact that the cases of sudden solution constituted a part of these data suggests that they were not altogether independent of these associative processes. This conclusion is further strengthened by

1. The stimuli of test 2 have received no previous reinforcements as they were the negative stimuli of the two preliminary problems. No relationship was found between the number of non-reinforcements these stimuli had received and the learning of this test. A more extended discussion of this result is given in the previous report (6).

the observation that this relationship was greatest in test problems 4 and 5, in which the proportion of cases showing sudden solution was also greatest.

In table 3 is presented a further analysis of the cases of sudden learning in test problems 1, 3, 4 and 5. The first two columns of this table show the number of the test and the subject. The third and fourth columns give, respectively, the percentage of responses to the positive stimulus in the period of 20 trials preceding and the period of 20 trials in which the learning criterion was attained. The final two columns show the relative excitatory strengths of the positive and negative stimuli at the beginning and at the end of the period of 20 trials preceding that on which the learning occurred.

The first point to be observed in the table (see final column) is the fact that at the point of solution, the excitatory strength of the positive stimulus, in terms of previous reinforcements and non-reinforcements, was greater than that of the negative stimulus in all but one instance (Mimi, test 4). Moreover, in ten of eleven cases which involved the reversal of an initial preference, the learning occurred *immediately* following a shift in the relative strengths of the stimuli, the positive stimulus becoming stronger than the negative, as shown by the fact that the P–N values shifted from negative to positive. The probability of a large number of such cases resulting from chance is extremely remote.

Still another indication of a definite relationship between the learning of the discrimination in these cases and the relative associative strengths of the two stimuli is the rank order correlation of $-\cdot 79$ between the number of errors made in learning and a measure of the relative excitatory strengths ($R = P - N$) of the stimuli at the beginning of the learning. This coefficient compares favorably with similar correlations obtained with all of the subjects, which, as reported in the previous study (6), were $-\cdot 65$ for test 1, $-\cdot 79$ for test 3 and $-\cdot 96$ for combined tests 4 and 5.

The above evidence strongly indicates, then, that sudden learning *in discrimination problems* is not to be distinguished from gradual learning by the presence of a novel factor or process (insight), which is independent of associative changes effected by repeated satisfactions and frustrations. The sudden solutions, just as the gradual ones, occurred only after the positive stimulus had attained greater excitatory strength than the negative, and the time taken to learn (number of errors) was closely correlated with the original relative excitatory strengths of the two stimuli as determined by previous training. Again, the curves of discrimination learning of our subjects (see table 2) reveal no evidence of discontinuity, but range all the way from very gradual to very sudden learning. Our criterion of 40 per cent was a purely arbitrary one, and in no sense marked off two different types of functions. Apparently the learning in both cases was of the same kind.

We turn now to a consideration of the relation of the theory of discrimination learning which we have proposed to the experimental facts presented in this paper. According to this theory (5) the animal responds, other things being equal, to the cue stimulus which has the greater excitatory strength. The discrimination situation is complicated, however, by the fact that there are other stimulus aspects present, some of which, on any particular trial, are allied in their action (i.e., their excitatory tendencies lead to the same response) with one of the cue stimuli, and some of which are allied to the other. The stimulus or food boxes are two such stimuli which are always present. Further, depending upon the extent to which the experimental conditions cannot be rigidly controlled, there may be other variable (chance) factors, or stimulating agents, which coincide in their action with one or other of the cue aspects. When the excitatory strengths of the cue stimuli do not differ greatly, the subject responds sometimes to one and sometimes to the other (approximately 50 per cent), depending on which has the greater excitatory support from other stimuli. With training (reinforcement of responses to positive cue and non-reinforcement of those to the negative cue) the difference between the excitatory strengths of the cue stimuli gradually increases until it becomes sufficiently great to offset always the effects of differences in the excitatory strengths of other stimulus aspects. At such a point the learning is completed, that is, the subject responds consistently (100 per cent) to the positive stimulus aspect.

Now whether the subject's response will shift suddenly or gradually from a chance performance to the consistent choice of the positive stimulus will depend upon several factors. First is the extent to which variable stimulus factors (both environmental and internal or physiological) are operative in the situation. Irregular control of such factors will lead to a more or less gradual and irregular curve of learning, for some of these irrelevant (distracting) stimuli will by chance favor the incorrect, negative stimulus, with the result that the subject will respond to it despite the fact that the positive cue aspect, *per se*, is stronger than the negative.

As the difference between the excitatory strengths of the stimuli increases with training, however, the interfering effect of this factor of variability gradually lessens, until it finally ceases altogether.

A second and more fundamental factor determining the slope of the discrimination learning curve is the rapidity with which the *difference* in the excitatory strengths of the cue stimuli develop. This, in turn, may be a function of several factors. One very important determiner is the excitatory strength of the cue stimuli, for according to the postulates of the theory, the amount of increase in strength of an excitatory tendency (S–R connection) with each reinforcement and the amount of weakening with each non-reinforcement, varies according to its strength. This relationship in the case of the positive stimulus is assumed to be similar in shape to the normal probability curve, the increment of strength being relatively small for a weak excitatory tendency, increasing to a maximum, and finally becoming small again as the limiting, maximum strength of the excitatory tendency is approached. In the case of the negative stimulus the amount of weakening is assumed to be directly proportional to the excitatory strength of the stimulus with no effect occurring below a certain minimum strength (5, p. 433). If the subject has had little or no previous experience with either of the cue stimuli, we should expect the learning to be gradual, for the increment of reinforcement is small and there is little or no weakening effect from non-reinforcements. On the other hand, if the cue stimuli have previously been reinforced, the effects of both reinforcement and non-reinforcement should be greater, with the result that the difference between them should develop more rapidly and the learning of the discrimination should be more sudden. Experimental evidence supporting this theoretical implication is provided in the final row of figures of table 2, which gives the average increase in the percentage of correct responses for the several tests. Thus it will be seen that there is a definite tendency for the learning to be more gradual, as shown by the smaller average increase under the condition of the two preliminary problems and test problem no. 2, in which the excitatory tendencies of the stimuli were presumably very slight since the subjects had little or no previous positive experience with them. In tests 1, 3, 4 and 5, the learning was more sudden, which is in accord with the fact that either one or both of the cue stimuli had been previously reinforced.

Another factor determining the rate with which differences in

Table 4

Showing the Relationship between the Rate of Learning of the Two Preliminary Discriminations and the Percentage of Sudden Solutions in Test Problems 1, 3, 4 and 5

Group	Trials		Percentage of sudden solutions		
	Mean	Range	Tests 1 and 3	Tests 4 and 5	Total
Quick learners	65	50–85	6/8 or 75%	7/7 or 100%	13/15 or 86%
Slow learners	135·8	130–150	1/7 or 14·2%	1/4 or 25%	2/11 or 18%

the strengths of the cue stimuli develop, is that of individual differences in the effects of reinforcements and non-reinforcements. A subject whose rate of acquisition of excitatory tendencies with successive reinforcements is relatively slow, or one in whom inhibitory tendencies from non-reinforcement are relatively slight, is not likely to exhibit sudden jumps from chance to solution. It follows from this that individuals who learn slowly are not likely to learn suddenly, i.e. jump abruptly from chance to solution, while, on the other hand, quick learners should tend to show such sudden solutions. Evidence in support of this implication is shown in the results presented in table 4. The twelve subjects were divided into two groups according to the mean number of trials required to learn the two preliminary discriminations. It will be seen from the table that the rapid learners showed a markedly greater tendency to learn the subsequent test problems suddenly than did the slow learners; whereas the former learned 13 out of 15 (86 per cent) of the test problems suddenly the latter learned only 2 of 11 (18 per cent) in this manner. No such logical connection between rapid learning and the tendency to learn suddenly has ever been demonstrated by any type of insight theory.

In concluding this part of our discussion attention is directed to the contrast provided by the 'insight' account of these sudden solutions and that offered by the present theory. The former, in so far as it attempts to be explanatory, does little more than introduce us to a new set of terms. When an animal learns a discrimination problem suddenly there undoubtedly occurs a 'reorganization of its sensory field'. But such a statement may with equal applicability be made of gradual learning. The problem still remains as to why the reorganization appears suddenly in certain instances and not in others. The theory of discrimination

207

learning we have proposed, on the other hand, is able, in some degree at least, to state the conditions which determine the occurrence of sudden solutions and to indicate how these factors differ from those which lead to more gradual learning of this type of problem.

Summary

Analysis of the learning curves of chimpanzees for discrimination problems indicates that sudden learning, like gradual, is closely correlated with the relative associative strengths of the cue stimuli as determined by the number of their previous reinforcements and frustrations. This result fails to support the interpretation that sudden solutions in the case of discrimination learning are marked by the presence of a novel process (insight) which is independent of these associative changes.

As alternative to the insight interpretation an attempt has been made to show how the occurrence of these sudden solutions may be accounted for in terms of a theory of discrimination learning based on association principles of reinforcement and non-reinforcement. This theory, which permits a description of the circumstances under which sudden learning should and should not occur, is supported by the experimental results.

References

1. KÖHLER, W.: The mentality of apes. (Trans. by E. Winter.) New York: Harcourt Brace, 1925. Pp. viii and 342.
2. KÖHLER, W.: Intelligence in apes. Jour. Genet. Psychol., 1925, **32**, 674–690.
3. KOFFKA, K.: The growth of the mind. London: Kegan Paul, 1924. Pp. 382.
4. PERKINS, F. T., AND WHEELER, R. H.: Configurational learning in goldfish. Comp. Psychol. Monog, 1930, **7**, no. 1, 50.
5. SPENCE, K. W.: The nature of discrimination learning in animals. Psychol. Rev., 1936, **43**, 427–449.
6. SPENCE, K. W.: Analysis of the formation of visual discrimination habits in chimpanzee. Jour. Comp. Psychol., 1937, **23**, 77–100.

The Formation of Learning Sets

H. F. Harlow, 'The formation of learning sets', *Psychol. Rev.*, vol. 56 (1949), pp. 51–65.

In most psychological ivory towers there will be found an animal laboratory. The scientists who live there think of themselves as theoretical psychologists, since they obviously have no other rationalization to explain their extravagantly paid and idyllic sinecures. These theoretical psychologists have one great advantage over those psychological citizens who study men and women. The theoreticians can subject their sub-human animals, be they rats, dogs, or monkeys, to more rigorous controls than can ordinarily be exerted over human beings. The obligation of the theoretical psychologist is to discover general laws of behavior applicable to mice, monkeys, and men. In this obligation the theoretical psychologist has often failed. His deductions frequently have had no generality beyond the species which he has studied, and his laws have been so limited that attempts to apply them to man have resulted in confusion rather than clarification.

One limitation of many experiments on subhuman animals is the brief period of time the subjects have been studied. In the typical problem, 48 rats are arranged in groups to test the effect of three different intensities of stimulation operating in conjunction with two different motivational conditions upon the formation of *an isolated* conditioned response. A brilliant Blitzkrieg research is effected – the controls are perfect, the results are important, and the rats are dead.

If this *do and die* technique were applied widely in investigations with human subjects, the results would be appalling. But of equal concern to the psychologist should be the fact that the derived general laws would be extremely limited in their application. There are experiments in which the use of naive subjects is justified, but the psychological compulsion to follow this design indicates that frequently the naive animals are to be found on both sides of the one-way vision screen.

The variety of learning situations that play an important rôle in determining our basic personality characteristics and in changing some of us into thinking animals are repeated many times in similar form. The behavior of the human being is not to be understood in terms of the results of single learning situations but rather in terms of the changes which are affected through multiple, though comparable, learning problems. Our emotional, personal, and intellectual characteristics are not the mere algebraic summation of a near infinity of stimulus-response bonds. The learning of primary importance to the primates, at least, is the formation of learning sets; it is the *learning how to learn efficiently* in the situations the animal frequently encounters. This learning to learn transforms the organism from a creature that adapts to a changing environment by trial and error to one that adapts by seeming hypothesis and insight.

The rat psychologists have largely ignored this fundamental aspect of learning and, as a result, this theoretical domain remains a *terra incognita*. If learning sets are the mechanisms which, in part, transform the organism from a conditioned response robot to a reasonably rational creature, it may be thought that the mechanisms are too intangible for proper quantification. Any such presupposition is false. It is the purpose of this paper to demonstrate the extremely orderly and quantifiable nature of the development of certain learning sets and, more broadly, to indicate the importance of learning sets to the development of intellectual organization and personality structure.

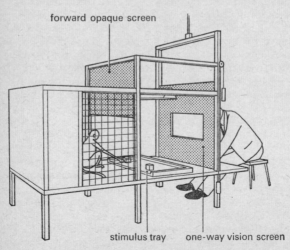

forward opaque screen

stimulus tray   one-way vision screen

Figure 1 Wisconsin general test apparatus.

The apparatus used throughout the studies subsequently referred to is illustrated in Fig. 1. The monkey responds by displacing one of two stimulus-objects covering the food-wells in the tray before him. An opaque screen is interposed between the monkey and the stimulus situation between trials and a one-way vision screen separates monkey and man during trials.

The first problem chosen for the investigation of learning sets was the object-quality discrimination learning problem. The monkey was required to choose the rewarded one or two objects differing in multiple characteristics and shifting in the left-right positions in a predetermined balanced order. A series of 344 such problems using 344 different pairs of stimuli was run on a group of eight monkeys. Each of the first 32 problems was run for 50 trials; the next 200 problems for six trials; and the last 112 problems for an average of nine trials.

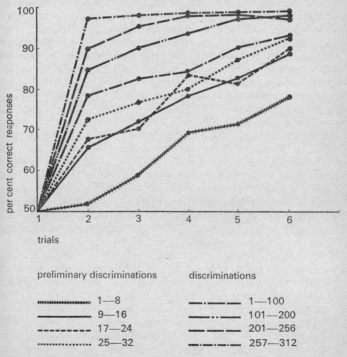

Figure 2 Discrimination learning curves on successive blocks of problems.

In Fig. 2 are presented learning curves which show the per cent of correct responses on the first six trials of these discriminations. The data for the first 32 discriminations are grouped for blocks of eight problems, and the remaining discriminations are arranged in blocks of 100, 100, 56, and 56 problems. The data indicate that the subjects progressively improve in their ability to learn object-quality discrimination problems. The monkeys *learn how to learn* individual problems with a minimum of errors. It is this *learning how to learn a kind of problem* that we designate by the term *learning set*.

The very form of the learning curve changes as learning sets become more efficient. The form of the learning curve for the first eight discrimination problems appears S-shaped; it could be described as a curve of 'trial-and-error' learning. The curve for the last 56 problems approaches linearity after Trial 2. Curves of similar form have been described as indicators of 'insightful' learning.

We wish to emphasize that this *learning to learn*, this *transfer from problem to problem* which we call the formation of a learning set, is a highly *predictable*, *orderly* process which can be demonstrated as long as controls are maintained over the subjects' experience and the difficulty of the problems. Our subjects, when they started these researches, had no previous laboratory learning experience. Their entire discrimination learning set history was obtained in this study. The stimulus pairs employed had been arranged and their serial order determined from tables of random numbers. Like nonsense syllables, the stimulus pairs were equated for difficulty. It is unlikely that any group of problems differed significantly in intrinsic difficulty from any other group.

In a conventional learning curve we plot change in performance over a series of *trials*; in a learning set curve we plot change in performance over a series of *problems*. It is important to remember that *we measure learning set in terms of problems* just as *we measure habit in terms of trials*.

Figure 3 presents a discrimination learning set curve showing progressive increase in the per cent of correct responses on Trials 2–6 on successive blocks of problems. This curve appears to be negatively accelerated or possibly linear.

Discrimination learning set curves obtained on four additional naive normal monkeys and eight naive monkeys with extensive unilateral cortical lesions, are shown in Fig. 4. Brain-injured as well as normal monkeys are seen to form effective discrimination learning sets, although the partial hemidecorticate monkeys are

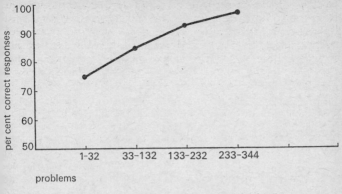

Figure 3 Discrimination learning set curve based on Trial 2–6 responses.

less efficient than the normal subjects. Improvement for both groups is progressive and the fluctuations that occur may be attributed to the small number of subjects and the relatively small number of problems, 14, included in each of the problem blocks presented on the abscissa.

Through the courtesy of Dr Margaret Kuenne we have discrimination learning set data on another primate species. These animals were also run on a series of six-trial discrimination problems but under slightly different conditions. Macaroni beads

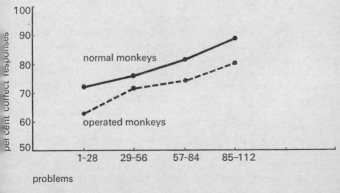

Figure 4 Discrimination learning set curves based on Trial 2–6 responses: normal and operated monkeys.

and toys were substituted for food rewards, and the subjects were tested sans iron-barred cages. The data for these 17 children, whose ages range from two to five years and whose intelligence quotients range from 109 to 151, are presented in Fig. 5. Learning set curves are plotted for groups of children attaining a prede-

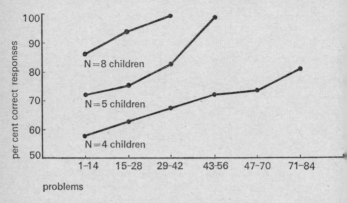

Figure 5 Discrimination learning set curves based on Trial 2-6 responses: children.

termined learning criterion within differing numbers of problem blocks. In spite of the small number of cases and the behavioral vagaries that are known to characterize this primate species, the learning set curves are orderly and lawful and show progressive increase in per cent of correct responses.

Learning set curves, like learning curves, can be plotted in terms of correct responses or errors, in terms of responses on any trial or total trials. A measure which we have frequently used is per cent of correct Trial 2 responses – the behavioral measure of the amount learned on Trial 1.

Figure 6 shows learning set curves measured in terms of the per cent correct Trial 2 responses for the 344-problem series. The data from the first 32 preliminary discriminations and the 312 subsequent discriminations have been plotted separately. As one might expect, these learning set curves are similar to those that have been previously presented. What the curves show with especial clarity is the almost unbelievable change which has taken place in the *effectiveness of the first training trial*. In the initial eight discriminations, this single paired stimulus presentation brings the Trial 2 performance of the monkeys to a level less than three per cent above chance; in the last 56 discriminations, this first training trial brings the performance of the monkeys to a level *less than three per cent* short of perfection. Before the formation of a discrimination learning set, a single training trial

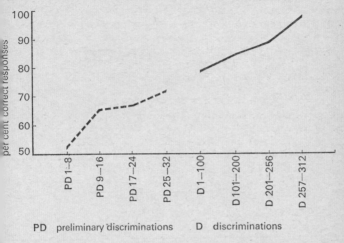

Figure 6 Discrimination learning set curve based on Trial 2 responses.

produces negligible gain; after the formation of a discrimination learning set, *a single training trial constitutes problem solution.* These data clearly show that *animals can gradually learn insight.*

In the final phase of our discrimination series with monkeys there were subjects that solved from 20 to 30 consecutive problems with no errors whatsoever following the first blind trial – and many of the children, after the first day or two of training, did as well or better.

These data indicate the function of learning set in converting a problem which is initially difficult for a subject into a problem which is so simple as to be immediately solvable. The learning set is the mechanism that changes the problem from an intellectual tribulation into an intellectual triviality and leaves the organism free to attack problems of another hierarchy of difficulty.

For the analysis of learning sets in monkeys on a problem that is ostensibly at a more complex level than the discrimination problem, we chose the discrimination reversal problem. The procedure was to run the monkeys on a discrimination problem for

7, 9, or 11 trials and then to reverse the reward value of the stimuli for eight trials; that is to say, the stimulus previously correct was made incorrect and the stimulus previously incorrect became correct.

The eight monkeys previously trained on discrimination learning were tested on a series of 112 discrimination reversal problems. Discrimination reversal learning curves for successive

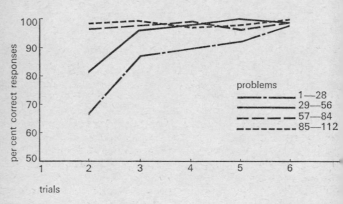

Figure 7 Discrimination reversal learning curves on successive blocks of problems.

blocks of 28 problems are shown in Fig. 7. The measure used is per cent of correct responses on Reversal Trials 2 to 6. Figure 8 presents data on the formation of the discrimination reversal learning set in terms of the per cent of correct responses on Reversal Trial 2 for successive blocks of 14 problems. Reversal Trial 2 is the first trial following the 'informing' trial, *i.e.*, the initial trial reversing the reward value of the stimuli. Reversal Trial 2 is the measure of the effectiveness with which the single informing trial leads the subject to abandon a reaction pattern which has proved correct for 7 to 11 trials, and to initiate a new reaction pattern to the stimulus pair. On the last 42 discrimination reversal problems the monkeys were responding as efficiently on Reversal Trial 2 as they were on complementary Discrimination Trial 2, *i.e.*, they were making over 97 per cent correct responses on both aspects of the problems. The eight monkeys made from 12 to 57 successive correct second trial reversal responses. Thus it becomes perfectly obvious that at the end of this problem the monkeys possessed sets both to learn and to reverse a reaction tendency.

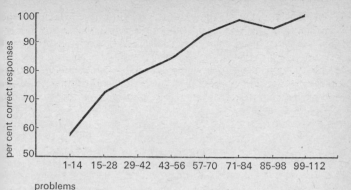

Figure 8 Discrimination reversal learning set curve based on Trial 2 responses.

and that this behavior could be consistently and immediately elicited with hypothesis-like efficiency.

This terminal performance level is likely to focus undue attention on the one-trial learning at the expense of the earlier, less efficient performance levels. It should be kept in mind that this one-trial learning appeared only as the end result of an orderly and progressive learning process; insofar as these subjects are concerned, the insights are only to be understood in an historical perspective.

Although the discrimination reversal problems might be expected to be more difficult for the monkeys than discrimination

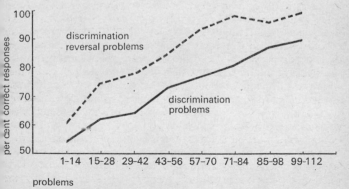

Figure 9 Discrimination reversal and discrimination learning set curves based on Trial 2 responses.

problems, the data of Fig. 9 indicate that the discrimination reversal learning set was formed more rapidly than the previously acquired discrimination learning set. The explanation probably lies in the nature of the transfer of training from the discrimination learning to the discrimination reversal problems. A detailed analysis of the discrimination learning data indicates the operation throughout the learning series of certain error-producing factors, but with each successive block of problems the frequencies of errors attributable to these factors are progressively decreased, although at different rates and to different degrees. The process might be conceived of as a learning of response tendencies that counteract the error-producing factors. A description of the reduction of the error-producing factors is beyond the scope of this paper, even though we are of the opinion that this type of analysis is basic to an adequate theory of discrimination learning.

Suffice it to say that there is reason to believe that there is a large degree of transfer from the discrimination series to the reversal series, of the learned response tendencies counteracting the operation of two of the three primary error-producing factors thus far identified.

The combined discrimination and discrimination reversal data show clearly how the learning set delivers the animal from Thorndikian bondage. By the time the monkey has run 232 discriminations and followed these by 112 discriminations and reversals, he does not possess 344 or 456 specific habits, bonds, connections or associations. We doubt if our monkeys at this time could respond with much more than chance efficiency on the first trial of any series of the previously learned problems. But the monkey does have a generalized ability to learn *any* discrimination problem or *any* discrimination reversal problem with the greatest of ease. Training on several hundred specific problems has not turned the monkey into an automaton exhibiting forced, stereotyped, reflex responses to specific stimuli. These several hundred habits have, instead, made the monkey an adjustable creature with an *increased capacity* to adapt to the ever-changing demands of a psychology laboratory environment.

We believe that other learning sets acquired in and appropriate to the monkey's natural environment would enable him to adapt better to the changing conditions there. We are certain, moreover, that learning sets acquired by man in and appropriate to his environment have accounted for his ability to adapt and survive.

Before leaving the problem of discrimination reversal learning we submit one additional set of data that we feel merits attention. Nine of the children previously referred to were also subjected to a series of discrimination reversal problems. The outcome is partially indicated in Fig. 10 which shows the per cent of correct Reversal Trial 2 responses made on successive blocks of 14 problems. It can be seen that these three to five-year-old children clearly bested the monkeys in performance on this series of

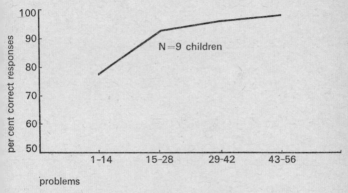

Figure 10 Discrimination reversal learning set curve based on Trial 2 responses: children.

problems. Trial 2 responses approach perfection in the second block of 14 discrimination reversal problems. Actually, over half of the total Trial 2 errors were made by one child.

These discrimination reversal data on the children are the perfect illustration of set formation and transfer producing adaptable abilities rather than specific bonds. Without benefit of the monkey's discrimination reversal set learning curves we might be tempted to assume that the children's data indicate a gulf between human and subhuman learning. But the *extremely rapid* learning on the part of the children is not unlike the *rapid* learning on the part of the monkeys, and analysis of the error-producing factors shows that the same basic mechanisms are operating in both species.

Following the discrimination reversal problem the eight monkeys were presented a new series of 56 problems designed to elicit alternation of unequivocally antagonistic response patterns. The first 7, 9, or 11 trials of each problem were simple object-quality discrimination trials. These were followed immediately by ten right-position discrimination trials with the same stimuli continuing to shift in the right-left positions in predetermined orders. In the first 7 to 11 trials, a particular object was correct regardless of its position. In the subsequent 10 trials, a particular position – the experimenter's right position – was correct, regardless of the object placed there. Thus to solve the problem the animal had to respond to object-quality cues and disregard position cues in the first 7 to 11 trials and, following the failure of reward of the pre-

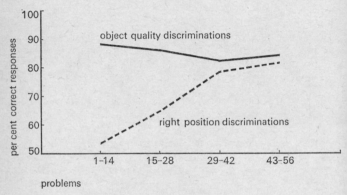

Figure 11 Learning set curves for problem requiring shift from object-quality discrimination to right-position discrimination.

viously rewarded object, he had to disregard object-quality cues and respond to position cues.

The learning data on these two antagonistic tasks are presented in Fig. 11. It is to be noted that the object-quality curve, which is based on Trials 1 to 7, begins at a very high level of accuracy, whereas the position curve, plotted for Trials 1 to 10, begins at a level little above chance. This no doubt reflects the operation of the previously well-established object-quality discrimination learning set. As the series continues, the object-quality curve shows a drop until the last block of problems, while the position curve rises progressively. In the evaluation of these data, it should be noted that chance performance is 50 per cent correct responses for the object-quality discriminations and 45 per cent for the position discriminations, since each sequence of 10 position trials includes an error 'informing' trial. It would appear that the learning of the right-position discriminations interferes with the learning of the object-quality discriminations to some extent. In spite of this decrement in object-quality discrimination performance for a time, the subjects were functioning at levels far beyond chance on the antagonistic parts of the problems during the last half of the series. We believe that this behavior reflects the formation of a right-position learning set which operates at a high degree of independence of the previously established object-quality discrimination learning set.

The precision of the independent operation of these learning sets throughout the last 14 problems is indicated in Fig. 12. Since

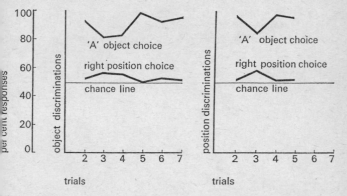

Figure 12 Object and position choices following initial errors on both phases of object-position shift series, based on problems 42–56.

the right-position part of the problem was almost invariably initiated by an error trial, these data are limited to those problems on which the first trial object-quality discrimination response was incorrect. The per cent of correct Trial 7 responses to the 'A' object, the correct stimulus for the object-quality discriminations, is 98. The initiating error trial which occurs when the problem shifts without warning to a right-position problem, drops this per cent response to the 'A' object to 52 – a level barely above chance. The per cent of Trial 7 responses to the right position during the object-quality discriminations is 52. The single error trial initiating the shift of the problem to a right-position discrimination is followed by 97 per cent right-position responses on the next trial. In other words, *it is as though* the outcome of a single *push of an object* is adequate to switch off the 'A'-object choice reaction tendency and to switch on the right-position choice reaction tendency.

The cue afforded by a single trial produces at this point almost complete discontinuity of the learning process. The only question now left unsettled in the controversy over hypotheses in sub-human animals is whether or not to use this term to describe the behavior of a species incapable of verbalization.

Again, it should be remembered that both the object-quality discrimination learning set and the right-position discrimination learning set developed in a gradual and orderly manner. Only after the learning sets are formed do these phenomena of discontinuity in learned behavior appear.

Further evidence for the integrity of learning sets is presented in an additional experiment. Six monkeys with object-quality discrimination learning experience, but without training on reversal

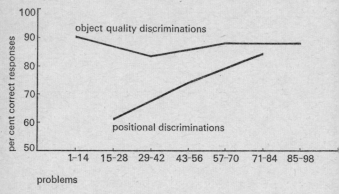

Figure 13 Learning set curves for problem series with alternating object-quality and positional discriminations, based on total trial responses.

problems or position discriminations, were given seven blocks of 14 problems each, starting with a block of 25-trial object-quality discriminations, followed by a block of 14 25-trial positional discriminations composed of right-position and left-position problems presented alternately. The remaining five blocks of problems continued the alternate presentation of 14 object-quality discrimination problems and 14 right-left positional discrimination problems. Figure 13 presents curves showing the per cent of correct responses on total trials on these alternate blocks of antagonistic discriminations. The complex positional discrimination learning set curve shows progressive improvement throughout the series, whereas the object-quality discrimination curve begins at a high level of accuracy, shows decrement on the second block and subsequently recovers. By the end of the experiment the two basically antagonistic learning sets had 'learned' to live together with a minimum of conflict. These data are the more striking if it is recalled that between each two blocks of object-quality discriminations there were 350 trials in which no object was differentially rewarded, and between each two blocks of 14 positional discriminations there were 350 trials in which no position was differentially rewarded.

In Fig. 14 we present additional total-trial data on the formation of the positional learning set. These data show the change in performance on the first and last seven positional discriminations in each of the three separate blocks of positional discriminations. The interposed object-quality discrimination problems clearly

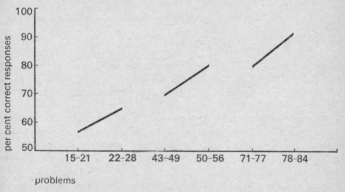

problems

Figure 14 Right-left positional discrimination learning set curve based on total trial responses. (Data on antagonistic object-quality discrimination problems omitted.)

produced interference, but they did not prevent the orderly development of the positional learning sets, nor the final attainment of a high level of performance on these problems.

We have data which suggest that the educated man can face arteriosclerosis with confidence, if the results on brain-injured animals are applicable to men. Figure 15 shows discrimination learning set curves for the previously described groups of four normal monkeys and eight monkeys with very extensive unilateral cortical injury. The upper curves show total errors on an initial series of 112 six-trial discriminations. The lower curves show total errors on an additional group of 56 discriminations presented one year later. In both situations the full-brained monkeys

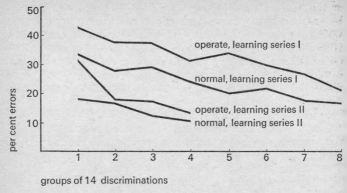

Figure 15 Discrimination learning set curves based on total error responses: normal and operated monkeys.

make significantly better scores, but one should note that the educated hemidecorticate animals are superior to the uneducated unoperated monkeys. Such data suggest that half a brain is better than one if you compare the individuals having appropriate learning sets with the individuals lacking them.

More seriously, these data may indicate why educated people show less apparent deterioration with advancing age than uneducated individuals, and the data lend support to the clinical observation that our fields of greatest proficiency are the last to suffer gross deterioration.

Although our objective data are limited to the formation of learning sets which operate to give efficient performance on intellectual problems, we have observational data of a qualitative nature on social-emotional changes in our animals. When the monkeys come to us they are wild and intractable but within a few years they have acquired, from the experimenter's point of view, good personalities. Actually we believe that one of the very important factors in the development of the good personalities of our monkeys is the formation of social-emotional learning sets organized in a manner comparable with the intellectual learning sets we have previously described. Each contact the monkey has with a human being represents a single specific learning trial. Each person represents a separate problem. Learning to react favorably to one person is followed by learning favorable reactions more rapidly to the next person to whom the monkey is socially introduced. Experience with additional individuals enbles the monkey to learn further how to behave with human beings, and eventually the monkey's favorable reactions to new people are acquired so rapidly as to appear almost instantaneous.

The formation of social-emotional learning sets is not to be confused with mere stimulus generalization, a construct applied in this field with undue freedom. Actually a learning set once formed determines in large part the nature and direction of stimulus generalization. In the classic study in which Watson conditioned fear in Albert, the child developed a fear of the rat and generalized this fear, but failed to develop or generalize fear to Watson, even though Watson must have been the more conspicuous stimulus. Apparently Albert had already formed an affectional social-emotional learning set to people, which inhibited both learning and simple Pavlovian generalization.

Our observations on the formation of social-emotional learning sets have been entirely qualitative and informal, but there would appear to be no reason why they could not be studied experimentally.

The emphasis throughout this paper has been on the rôle of the historical or experience variable in learning behavior – the forgotten variable in current learning theory and research. Hull's Neo-behaviorists have constantly emphasized the necessity for an historical approach to learning, yet they have not exploited it fully. Their experimental manipulation of the experience variable has been largely limited to the development of isolated habits and their generalization. Their failure to find the phenomenon of discontinuity in learning may stem from their study of individual as opposed to repetitive learning situations.

The field theorists, unlike the Neo-behaviorists, have stressed insight and hypothesis in their description of learning. The impression these theorists give is that these phenomena are properties of the innate organization of the individual. If such phenomena appear independently of a gradual learning history, we have not found them in the primate order.

Psychologists working with human subjects have long believed in the phenomenon of learning sets and have even used sets as explanatory principles to account for perceptual selection and incidental learning. These psychologists have not, however, investigated the nature of these learning sets which their subjects bring to the experimental situation. The determining experiential variables of these learning sets lie buried in the subjects' pasts, but the development of such sets can be studied in the laboratory as long as the human race continues to reproduce its kind. Actually, detailed knowledge of the nature of the formation of learning sets could be of such importance to educational theory and practice as to justify prolonged and systematic investigation.

In the animal laboratory where the experiential factor can be easily controlled, we have carried out studies that outline the development and operation of specific learning sets. We believe that the construct of learning sets is of importance in the understanding of adaptive behavior. Since this is our faith, it is our hope that our limited data will be extended by those brave souls who study *real* men and *real* women.

Concurrent Discrimination Learning in Chimpanzees

K. J. Hayes, R. Thompson and C. Hayes, 'Concurrent discrimination learning in chimpanzees', *J. comp. physiol. Psychol.*, vol. 46 (1953), pp. 105–7.

One of the most unique characteristics of human behavior is the extent to which it utilizes large numbers of arbitrary associations concurrently, despite the possibilities of mutual interference among them. Language provides the most obvious example of this feature, but man's cultural way of life involves much more general use of a large 'information-handling capacity'. This aspect of behavior has received little attention from comparative psychologists.

It appears reasonable that the amount of information which can be stored in a mechanism of a given type would be limited by the size of that mechanism. Since the chimpanzee's brain has about one-third the mass of man's, its capacity for concurrent learning (and retention) may well be smaller. This is only an inference, however, since the associative abilities of laboratory primates have commonly been tested only in terms of isolated, individual items.

Actual measurement of information capacity, in this sense, is presumably impossible; and the closeness of an approximation might well be limited by such practical matters as the S's life span, and the nature of the sensory channels through which information can be transmitted. However, it is not unreasonable to assume that the ultimate capacity of a species would be reflected in its ability to handle a smaller amount of information, of limited variety, in a short period of time. The present investigation was based on this assumption, and was designed to explore the experimental possibilities of concurrent learning, using the object-discrimination technique.

Method

Our principle Ss were six chimpanzees that had recently served in a study of discrimination learning set (1) and had attained a high level of proficiency in the learning of individual object-discrimination problems. Except for the differences noted below, our general procedure was the same as that used in the preceding study.

Concurrent discrimination procedure. In this experiment, a *problem* involved not one pair of objects, but 5, 10, or 20 pairs. A *trial* consisted of the presentation of all the pairs in a given problem, in succession. One trial followed another immediately, with no break in procedure, the beginning of the second trial being distinguished from the end of the first only by the reappearance of an old pair of objects. The order of presentation of pairs within a problem was ordinarily held constant from trial to trial; however, this was merely a matter of convenience, for the serial position of a pair provides no cue to correct choice. (We have occasionally scrambled the order on successive trials, without affecting the *S*'s performance.)

Five-pair problems were run for 5 trials; 10- and 20-pair problems were run for 3 trials. Subjects were given one problem at a session, which thus involved 25, 30, or 60 choices. From 25 to 60 of these multi-pair problems were used with various *S*s. In general, the shorter problems were used first and the longer ones last, but there were numerous exceptions to this order.

Although our purpose was to vary only the number of concurrent associations being learned in the three sizes of problem, our procedure introduced a related variation in the time interval between successive presentations of a given pair of objects. This interval ranged from about 90 sec. for 5-pair problems to approximately 6 min. for 20-pair problems. We have some data which indicate that trial spacing of this order has no great effect on the learning of single-pair problems, and we will tentatively assume that this factor is not important in the present work.

The discriminanda were 600 previously described objects (1) plus 100 more of the same general type. No two of them were enough alike to be difficult to distinguish when seen at the same time, but there were many similarities which provided possibilities for confusion among them in memory. Because more than five hundred *pairs* of objects were used with some *S*s, it was often necessary to recombine previously used objects into new pairs, and use them again. Control tests have indicated that such re-use has no appreciable effect on performance.

Our procedure will be recognized as very similar to that referred to by Riopelle *et al.* (2) as 'serial discrimination'. (We have not adopted this terminology because it emphasizes an essentially incidental feature of the procedure, and because it has occasionally been applied to maze learning and to the multi-unit discrimination apparatus often used with rats.)

Results

Figure 1 shows how problems consisting of 1, 5, 10, and 20 pairs of objects were solved by four *S*s toward the end of their training. (The data for single-pair problems are from an earlier investiga-

1. Later work indicates that an inter-trial delay of 60 sec. may cause an appreciable reduction in second-trial accuracy. It would have been better, therefore, to have kept the time interval constant in the present study.

tion [1].) The relative difficulty of problems containing various numbers of pairs is shown in Figure 2, in terms of second-trial accuracy.

Our data do not provide a clear picture of the development of a learning set for this kind of work – largely, no doubt, because our

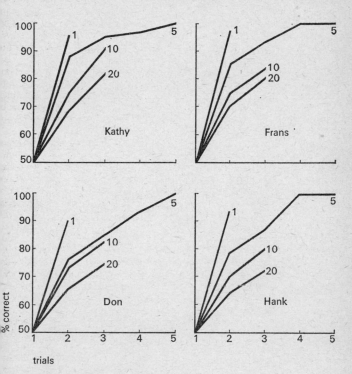

Figure 1 Concurrent discrimination learning curves for the last 50 single-pair problems, the last 10 five-pair and ten-pair problems, and the last 5 twenty-pair problems.

procedure was not designed for that purpose. There was some indication of improvement during early training on 5-pair problems, but much less during later 10-pair problems, and none during the 20-pair work. The superior performance of the home-raised chimpanzee, Viki, may be due to a pre-experimental learning set.

229

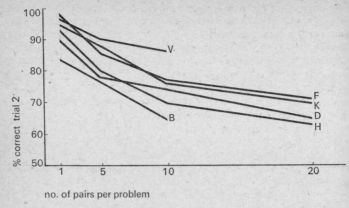

Figure 2 Second-trial accuracy as a function of problem size. Individual subjects are indicated by their initials. Their ages, in years, were: Viki 4½, Frans 6, Kathy 2½, Don 17, Hank 7, Bokar 26.

Supplementary work with Naive Chimpanzees

Dehn (7 yr) and Dag (7 yr) were each tested on two ten-pair problems without having previously been trained on single-pair discrimination. These problems were run to a criterion of two successive errorless trials (20 consecutive correct choices). The criterion was attained after from 10 to 14 trials. An average learning curve for the total of four problems would reach the 80 per cent level at about trial 10. This performance is not greatly different from that of naive chimpanzees on single-pair problems.

Although training on each of these problems extended over three or four days, there was little evidence of forgetting between sessions.

Discussion

It is apparent from Figure 1 that the number of discrimination solutions a chimpanzee can retain simultaneously is a function of the amount of training given. Our problems were limited to a maximum of 20 pairs so that each one could be completed (if not mastered) in a single work session. However, since our two naive *S*s showed little inter-session forgetting, it would apparently be quite practical to use problems of 50 or more pairs, with one trial per session. Extrapolation of the curves of Figures 1 and 2 suggests that a 50-pair problem might be learned to the 90 per cent level in something on the order of 20 trials.

Performance on concurrent problems would undoubtedly be a function of the type of discriminanda used. In the case of spectral hues, for instance, a limited number of discriminable stimuli would be available, and the interference among many of them would be extreme. In the present experiment, one test object might resemble another one in the same problem quite close in color (*or* size, form, texture, etc.), but there was never simultaneous similarity in *all* visual characteristics, nor in the total configuration.

It seems unlikely that the sensory acuity of our Ss was overtaxed by these objects, but their perceptual organization may have been. An S that learned only that the baited object was red might be confused on encountering another red (but unbaited) object, before the reappearance of the first one. This would be much less troublesome for an S that learned these objects as a large, rectangular, red one, and a small, round, red one. If the objects could be perceived as a brick and a rubber ball, there would be very little basis for interference. Utilization of this last type of perception may have been responsible for the superior performance of Viki, our home-raised chimpanzee. After four and one-half years in a human environment, she was quite familiar with many of the things used as test objects, or with the parts and materials of which they were made

Figure 2 shows that our Ss tended to maintain the same rank order in concurrent learning as they had previously attained in the learning of individual pairs. This suggests that concurrent discrimination learning may be thought of as demanding a higher degree of the same basic skills or abilities as are involved in simple discrimination learning. In the latter case, an object need be learned only well enough to distinguish it from the other member of the pair; in the former case, it must be distinguished from all the other objects in the multi-pair problem. Both cases are subject to proactive inhibition from the preceding problems, but concurrent learning is subject, in addition, to retroactive inhibition within each problem.

Summary

Chimpanzees were trained on discrimination problems in which 5, 10, or 20 pairs of stimulus objects were presented in rotation. Accuracy as high as 80 per cent was attained on the third presentation of the 20-pair problems.

References

1. HAYES, K. J., THOMPSON, R., & HAYES, CATHERINE. Discrimination learning set in chimpanzees. *J. comp. physiol. Psychol.*, 1953, **46**, 99–104.

2. RIOPELLE, A. J., HARLOW, H. F., SETTLAGE, P. H., & ADES, H. W. Performance of normal and operated monkeys on visual learning tests. *J. comp. physiol. Psychol.*, 1951, **44**, 283–289.

A Model of Hypothesis Behavior in Discrimination Learning Set

M. Levine, 'A model of hypothesis behavior in discrimination learning set', *Psych. Rev.*, vol. 66 (1959), pp. 353–66.

In discrimination learning, or learning-set experiments, one typically measures the percentage of correct responses on a given trial (or block of trials, or, in learning set, on a block of problems) and ignores the changes in other systematic response patterns. An alternative approach was taken by Krechevsky (1932) who first measured position preferences, position alternation, and light-going tendencies in the white rat in a discrimination problem. He described each tendency as a 'hypothesis' (H), which may be defined as a specifiable pattern of response to a selected stimulus set. Harlow (1950) demonstrated other Hs by the monkey in the discrimination learning-set experiment, and Goodnow and several co-workers (Goodnow & Pettigrew, 1955; Goodnow & Postman, 1955; Goodnow, Shanks, Rubinstein, and Lubin, 1957) demonstrated patterns of response in humans.

While these researchers have found that such analyses provide useful insights into the nature of the learning process, the methods of measurement were selected for the specific demonstration at hand. No comprehensive picture of H behavior was available to suggest the total set of Hs which existed, to ensure a lack of confounding in the measurement of various Hs, and to show the proportion of behavior under the control of each H. The purpose of this paper is to provide such a picture, to describe a mathematical model of H behavior which permits an analysis having the following characteristics: (*a*) The operation of a large number of Hs can be analyzed simultaneously. As many as nine will be so analyzed, although this number is by no means an upper limit. (*b*) The relative strength of each H, i.e., the proportion of responses controlled by each H, can be demonstrated at successive stages of the experiment. (*c*) The measure of a given H is uninfluenced by the presence of other Hs. (*d*) The analysis is independent of the particular reward and stimulus sequences employed. For example, the correct stimulus may be permitted to perseverate on one side for three consecutive trials, or not, or

233

may alternate from side to side as frequently as it perseverates, or may not, etc.

This model will be applied to the behavior of the rhesus monkey in a discrimination learning-set experiment in which each problem is presented for only three trials. The stimuli in this experiment consist of two objects per problem, response to one object producing a reward (a rasin or peanut), response to the other going unrewarded. Every three trials the problem is changed by introducing two new objects, and several hundred problems are typically presented in this manner. A more detailed description of the learning-set procedure is given by Harlow (1949).

No analysis will be made in this paper of data beyond the third trial of any problem. The analysis may be applied to learning-set experiments utilizing longer problems simply by ignoring all trials past the third trial. The description of the behavior in such cases applies only to the first-three-trial sets. Attempts are currently being made to generalize the model in a more satisfactory way. Work is now in progress, for example, extending the model to oddity learning-set data in which each problem is presented for 12 trials and to single discrimination problems several hundred trials in length.

Assumptions and Definitions

The first assumption is that if an H is appearing, its occurrence will be manifested over all three trials of a given problem. Suppose, for example, that an S has a position preference on one problem. The only acceptable manifestation of this preference will be response to one position for the three trials. Response to this position for two out of the three trials will not serve as an instance of this H.

The second assumption is that the stimuli determining a response go no further back than the immediately preceding trial. A double-alternation H, for example, will not be considered, since the response on Trial n requires residual stimulation from the response on Trial n-2.

Given these two restrictions, the definition of a few symbols will provide sufficient background for describing the set of Hs which are considered in this paper. In any learning-set experiment the E decides in advance the sequence of positions which the reward (and rewarded object) will take. The reward sequence may go LLR on the first problem, RRR on the second problem, etc. He records the outcome for the three trials as $+ + -$, $- + -$, etc., and from the combination of L, R, and $+$, $-$ sequences can deduce the S's responses. There are then three sets of symbols that are necessary: The reward sequences, the response sequences, and the outcome sequences. For any three-trial problem there are eight possible reward sequences. These may be paired into symmetrical pairs of (LLL, RRR), (LLR, RRL), (LRL, RLR), and (LRR, RLL). From the standpoint of the subsequent analysis the pairs may be combined. That is, the important property is how the reward varies rather than the particular side on which it appears on a given trial. If the sequence goes LLL, the important fact is that the food was on one side for three trials. The additional fact that it was the left side is here irrelevant. This consideration reduces the reward sequences to four: AAA, AAB, ABA, and ABB, where A is defined as the location of the reward on the first trial, and B is defined as the other position. A similar combining applies to the S's responses. The four resulting response sequences will be symbolized by III, IIO, IOI, IOO, where I is the position responded to on the first trial, and O is the other position. Whereas the reward and response sequences reduce to four, the $+$, $-$ outcome sequences will not be combined so that all eight of these will be used.

The manifestation of the Hs considered in this paper may now be specified. These Hs, their general definition, and rationale for selection are listed below. In parentheses, following the definition, is the manifestation of the H as it appears in the raw data.

1. Position Preference: consistent response to one position. This H has been frequently observed in monkey and in rat behavior (III).

2. Position Alternation: alternating between positions from trial to trial. While this H has been noted only rarely in the monkey, Gellermann (1933) felt that it might occur in sufficient degree to control for it. It is a common phenomenon in rats (IOI).

3. Stimulus Preference: consistent response to one of the stimulus objects irrespective of reinforcement. This too has been commonly found in the primate and other orders ($+++$ or $---$).

4. Stimulus Alternation; alternating between stimuli from trial to trial. This, like its position analogue, is uncommon in the monkey. It has, however, been shown to occur in other orders ($+-+$ or $-+-$).

5. Win-stay-Lose-shift (with respect to position): repetition of a response to a position which has just been rewarded and alternating away from a position not rewarded. This type of H has been noted in human behavior by Goodnow and Pettigrew (1955), and in monkey behavior by Harlow (1950) in a slightly different form under the name 'differential cue' ($I + I$ or $I - O$).

6. Lose-stay-Win-shift (with respect to position): repetition of a

response to a position not rewarded on the preceding trial, and alternation away from a position just rewarded. This is the reverse of the H above, and would not be expected to occur except in Ss with special experimental histories. It was included in order to provide an H which one would expect to have zero strength ($I - I$ or $I + O$).

7. (Problem-solution behavior)$_2$ or Win-stay-Lose-shift (with respect to the object): repetition of a response to an object which has just been rewarded, and alternation away from an object not rewarded. This H yields maximum reward in the learning-set situation, since correct responding begins on the second trial of the problem ($+ + +$, or $- + +$).

8. (Problem-solution behavior)$_3$: manifestation of the correct response on the third trial although not on the second trial. This H is required by the well-known fact that the correct response may suddenly appear on later trials ($+ - +$ or $- - +$).

9. Random Responding: this H, while it has a single form of manifestation, may be produced in any one of three ways: (*a*) The determinants of a response may fluctuate nonsystematically from trial to trial, in which case all sequences would be expected to occur with approximately the same frequency. (*b*) The S may be systematically responding to stimulus changes which are unrecorded and which are randomly related to the position sequence of the rewarded object. In this case, again, all response sequences would have equal expected frequencies. (*c*) Under certain special conditions Hs which have been ignored will contribute to this Random Responding H without affecting the estimation of any other H. These conditions are described elsewhere (Levine, 1959). For now it is sufficient to note that the Random Responding measure is conceptualized as an estimate of both nonsystematic responding and residual sequence strength. (This H is manifested in all sequences.)

These nine Hs, their definitions, and manifestations are summarized in Table 1. In the last column of this table are the symbols which will be used to represent the probability of occurrence of an H or the proportion of problems showing the H in a set of data. For example, the result $a = 0.5$ means that Ss show Position Preference on 50% of the problems. The first goal of this paper is to demonstrate a technique for evaluating these probabilities.

Two further assumptions will be useful in attaining this goal. The first is that the Hs are mutually exclusive. The occurrence on a single problem of the sequence $+ + +$ may mean, among other possibilities, that either Stimulus Preference or (Problem-solution)$_2$ has taken place, not both. In general, if a sequence may be attributed to two or more Hs and several instances of the sequence have occurred, different Hs may have been operating on different problems, but two Hs never combine on the same problem. The

Table 1
Definition of the Hs Evaluated in the Present Paper

H	Definition	Manifestation	Probability symbol
Position Preference	Sequence of response to one side	*III*	*a*
Position Alternation	Alternating between positions on consecutive trials	*IOI*	*b*
Stimulus Preference	Sequence of responses to one of the relevant stimuli	$+++$ or $---$	*c*
Stimulus Alternation	Alternating between the relevant stimuli on consecutive trials	$+-+$ or $-+-$	*d*
Win-stay-Lose-shift (pos.)	Response to the position rewarded on the preceding trial	$I+I+I$ or $I+I-O$ or $I-O+O$ or $I-O-I$	*u*
Lose-stay-Win-shift (pos.)	Response to the position not rewarded on the preceding trial	$I+O+I$ or $I+O-O$ or $I-I+O$ or $I-I-I$	*v*
(Problem-solution)₂ or Win-stay-Lose-shift (obj.)	Learning manifested on the second trial of a problem	$+++$ or $-++$	p_2
(Problem-solution)₃	Learning first manifested on the third trial of a problem	$+-+$ or $-++$	p_3
Random Responding	Responses uncorrelated with recorded stimulus changes	All sequences	*R*

second assumption is that the above set of Hs includes all Hs whose probability is greater than zero. These two assumptions permit the following statement:

$$a + b + c + d + u + v + p_2 + p_3 + R = 1 \cdot 00 \qquad [1]$$

The Evaluation of the H Strengths

The assumptions outlined above determine the relationship between a set of data and the probabilities of the Hs. Figure 1 shows a set of 32 cells, each one of which represents one of the 32 possible sequences which can occur in a three-trial problem. The 32 cells are organized into two blocks of 16 each, the block on the left containing those sequences with a first trial minus, the other containing those sequences with a first trial plus. The rewarded position sequences are on the rows and the response sequences are on the columns.

Any one sequence may be a manifestation of some Hs and not

237

of others. For example, $A - {}_1A - {}_2A - {}_3$ may be interpreted as Position Preference, Stimulus Preference, Lose-stay-Win-shift (with respect to position), or Random Responding, but not as any of the other five Hs. If, when E presents AAA, any of the

reward sequence ↓

	III	IIO	IOI	IOO
A A A	a c v r	p_3 r	b d r	u p_2 r
	-1 -2 -3	-1 -2 +3	-1 +2 -3	-1 +2 +3
A A B	a v p_3 r	c r	b p_2 r	d u r
	-1 -2 +3	-1 -2 -3	-1 +2 +3	-1 +2 -3
A B A	a d r	v p_2 r	b c u r	p_3 r
	-1 +2 -3	-1 +2 +3	-1 -2 -3	-1 -2 +3
A B B	a p_2 r	d v r	b u p_3 r	c
	-1 +2 +3	-1 +2 -3	-1 -2 +3	-1 -2 -3

response sequence

reward sequence ↓

	III	IIO	IOI	IOO
A A A	a c u p_2 r	r	b d p_3 r	v r
	+1 +2 +3	+1 +2 -3	+1 -2 +3	+1 -2 -3
A A B	a u r	c p_2 r	b r	d v p_3 r
	+1 +2 -3	+1 +2 +3	+1 -2 -3	+1 -2 +3
A B A	a d p_3 r	u r	b c v p_2 r	r
	+1 -2 +3	+1 -2 -3	+1 +2 +3	+1 +2 -3
A B B	a r	d u p_3 r	b v r	c p_2 r
	+1 -2 -3	+1 -2 +3	+1 +2 -3	+1 +2 +3

response sequence

Figure 1 Thirty-two cells representing the 32 possible sequences which can occur in a three-trial problem. The symbols in each cell represent the Hs which can produce the associated response sequence.

other five Hs should be occurring, then $-_1 -_2 -_3$ cannot occur. In the $A - {}_1A - {}_2A - {}_3$ cell are listed the probability symbols associated with the four possible Hs. In general, each cell contains the symbols for the Hs which may produce the indicated sequence. The only new symbol is r. This is used here instead of R to represent Random Responding, and is defined by $r = R/4$. The justification for this change of variable is that the Random Responding H enters into four times as many cells as any of the other Hs. If $a = 1$, for example, a's influence is felt in only eight cells whereas if $R = 1$ its influence is distributed over 32 cells. Its effect on any one cell would be $\frac{1}{4}$ the corresponding effect of any of the other Hs.

In a three-trial-per-problem learning-set experiment the data may be analyzed into the frequencies with which each of these 32 sequences occurs in a block of problems, and these frequencies may be used to estimate certain conditional probabilities. In particular, the probability of the outcomes on trials two and three given the reward sequence and the outcome on trial one may be estimated. For the $A - {}_1A - {}_2A - {}_3$ sequence, such a probability is symbolized as $P(-_2 -_3 | A - {}_1AA)$, where the vertical line is defined as the word 'given'. These probabilities may be obtained from the data by use of a few elementary probability theorems (Feller, 1957). To continue with the example selected,

$$P(-_2 -_3 | A - {}_1AA)$$
$$= \frac{P(A - {}_1A - {}_2A - {}_3)}{P(A - {}_1AA)} = \frac{\dfrac{n(A - {}_1A - {}_2A - {}_3)}{N}}{\dfrac{n(A - {}_1AA)}{N}}$$

where $n(A - {}_1A - {}_2A - {}_3)$ and $n(A - {}_1AA)$ mean the number of times that $A - {}_1A - {}_2A - {}_3$ and $A - {}_1AA$, respectively, have occurred, and N is the total number of problems presented. The statement may be simplified to yield

$$P(-_2 -_3 | A - {}_1AA) = \frac{n(A - {}_1A - {}_2A - {}_3)}{n(A - {}_1AA)} \qquad [2]$$

From the assumptions, it follows that on a certain proportion of the problems Position Preference may occur, producing $(-_2 -_3 | A - {}_1AA)$, on a certain proportion of the problems Stimulus Preference may occur, producing the same sequence, and so on, for the four Hs which can produce this sequence. Because the Hs are mutually exclusive the $P(-_2 -_3 | A - {}_1AA)$ is

239

equal to the sum of the probabilities of each of the associated Hs, i.e.,

$$P(-_2 -_3 | A -_1 AA) = a + c + v + r \qquad [3]$$

From Equations [2] and [3] it follows that

$$a + c + v + r = \frac{n(A -_1 A -_2 A -_3)}{n(A -_1 AA)} \qquad [4]$$

Now, $n(A -_1 A -_2 A -_3)$ is the frequency with which $A -_1 A -_2 A -_3$ has occurred in the experiment and $n(A -_1 AA)$ may be obtained from the left-hand matrix of Fig. 1 as the row total of the row containing $n(A -_1 A -_2 A -_3)$. That is,

$$\begin{aligned}
n(A -_1 AA) = \ & n(A -_1 A -_2 A -_3) \\
& + n(A -_1 A -_2 A +_3) \\
& + n(A -_1 A +_2 A -_3) \\
& + n(A -_1 A +_2 A +_3)
\end{aligned}$$

The right side of [4] is, therefore, a number obtainable from the data, and Equation 4 is an equation in four unknowns.

With nine unknowns to be evaluated, nine such equations are required for simultaneous solution. These equations may be obtained from any nine cells yielding nonparallel equations. If the assumption is made that a given H has the same strength no matter in which cell it appears, then the solutions from the nine equations will give estimates of the nine H strengths for the block of problems considered. The first problem, then, that of evaluating the strengths of the various Hs, has been solved. In general, the solution may be summarized by the following:

Theorem: The probabilities associated with a set of m independently specifiable Hs may be obtained from the solution of m equations of the form

$$(j + k + \ldots)_i = \frac{\text{(frequency of the } i\text{th sequence)}}{\text{(frequency of the corresponding row total)}}$$

where $(j + k + \ldots)_i$, represents the sum of the probabilities of the Hs which may produce the ith sequence.

A Test of the Model

It is now possible to apply the analysis to data from a learning-set experiment and to determine, for each block of problems, the relative strength of the Hs. Using the technique outlined above, one could solve three sets of nine equations based on 27 different sequences and obtain three estimates of each H. If the 27 sequences were carefully selected, the remaining five sequences could contribute another estimate of five of the Hs. Averaging the estimates for each H would yield a mean estimate of each of the H probabilities based on all the data. There is, however, one important objection to this procedure: application of the method without some prior testing of the model would leave the validity of the estimates in question. Some indication is first required that the estimates are a product of the behavior, and not simply of the mathematical machinery.

The present section deals with such validation. The test consists in estimating the probabilities from some of the sequences and then in predicting, on the basis of these estimates, the frequencies with which each of the remaining sequences should occur. These frequencies may be predicted from Equation 4 once the H probabilities are known. This frequency prediction was applied to four sets of data, with a slightly different treatment for each. Each of these sets will be discussed in turn.

The first application was to the first block of three-trial-per-problem data from Levine, Levinson, and Harlow (1959). Eighteen sequences were selected in order to have two estimates of each H. The criterion for selection of each sequence was that it be based on no more than three Hs. Both sequences based only on Random Responding (i.e., $A + {}_1A + {}_2A - {}_3$ and $A + {}_1B + {}_2A - {}_3$), all eight sequences based only on two Hs, and eight of the sequences based on three Hs were selected. Averaging the solutions from the two sets of nine equations yielded:

$$a = 0.08, \qquad b = 0.03, \qquad c = 0.16,$$
$$d = 0.02, \qquad u = -0.02, \qquad v = -0.01,$$
$$p_2 = 0.20, \qquad p_3 = 0.07, \qquad R = 0.44$$

A few interesting aspects of these results may be noted. First, the Lose-stay-Win-shift H was included with the prediction that $v = 0$, and a close estimate of zero was obtained. Second, b, d, u, and v all appear to be estimates of zero. This finding is not of special significance here, but will be referred to later because of its consistent emergence. Third, Equation 1 was not used in obtaining these estimates and may serve as a prediction. The sum of the obtained estimates is 0.97.

The values for these nine Hs were substituted into the equations for each of the remaining 14 sequences, and the predicted frequency for each sequence was obtained. The observed and predicted frequencies are plotted in Fig. 2 with each axis in the same

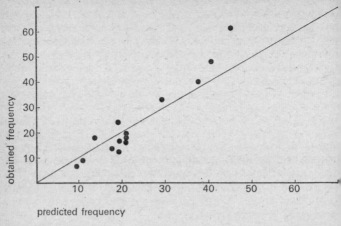

Figure 2 Sequence frequencies from Block I (Problems 1–96) of the Levine et al. experiment.

units, so that perfect prediction would yield 14 points lying along the 45° line. It will be seen that the points distribute themselves in reasonable fashion along this line.

In order to quantitatively describe the accuracy of prediction, a statistic describing the proportion of variance explained (PVE) by the predicted frequencies was devised. This is given by:

$$\text{PVE} = 1 - \frac{\sigma_{o.p}^2}{\sigma_o^2} \qquad [5$$

where σ_o^2 is the variance of the observed values, and $\sigma_{o.p}^2$ is the variance around the 45° line, i.e., $\sigma_{o.p}^2 = \sum_{}^{n} (o - p)^2/n$. The symbols o and p represent the observed and predicted frequencies, respectively, and n represents the number of points. For these data, PVE = 0·85.

The second set of data to which this test was applied was from the first 100 problems of a learning-set study by Harlow, Harlow, Rueping, and Mason (1960). A new criterion was used in selecting the sequences for solution. The H probabilities were obtained primarily from sequences with a third trial minus, and predictions were made primarily for the sequences ending in third trial plus. To accomplish this, it was convenient to use eight Hs and so here it was assumed that $v = 0$. Twelve sequences ending

242

in a third trial minus, and two sequences with a third trial plus (the two based only on p_3 and r) were selected to solve for all Hs but p_2. This H was then obtained from Equation 1. As a result, predictions could be made for 14 third-trial-plus sequences, and four third-trial-minus sequences. These 18 points are plotted in Fig. 3, where the PVE = 0·84. The specific probability values are:

$$a = 0·13 \qquad b = 0·00, \qquad c = 0·19,$$
$$d = -0·03, \qquad u = 0·02, \qquad p_2 = 0·13,$$
$$p_3 = 0·12, \qquad R = 0·44$$

Again b, d, and u appear to be estimates of zero. This finding, along with the assumption that $v = 0$, repeats the earlier finding.

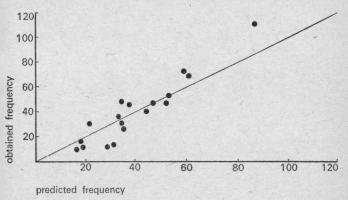

Figure 3 Sequence frequencies from Block I (Problems 1–100) of the Harlow et al. *experiment.*

The test was next applied to the first block of problems from a study by Schrier (1958). The same method of selection used in the preceding study was employed here in determining the sequences for solution, i.e., as many third-trial-minus sequences as necessary, two third-trial-plus sequences and Equation 1 were used. There was one minor difference, however. Schrier did not permit the reward to perseverate on one side for three consecutive trials. In this experiment, therefore, the top row of eight cells (see Fig. 1) does not exist, leaving only 24 sequences. In order to increase the number of sequences for which predictions could be made, it was assumed that $b = 0$, $v = 0$. This permits prediction for 12 sequences: 10 third-trial-plus and 2 third-trial-minus sequences. The results are shown in Fig. 4. Here the PVE = 0·91.

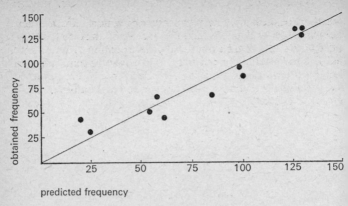

Figure 4 Sequence frequencies from Block I (Problems 1–80) of Schrier's experiment.

The specific H probabilities are: $a = 0.13$, $c = 0.07$, $d = 0.00$, $u = -0.01$, $p_2 = 0.32$, $p_3 = 0.14$, $R = 0.36$. Again, d and u are estimates of zero, and the assumption that $b = 0$, $v = 0$ did not serve to reduce the PVE.

The PVE, in fact, is somewhat larger in this study than in the preceding two sets of data. The difference is not so great as to warrant extensive speculation, but it was also noted that in the Schrier data R was lower than in the preceding sets. A check on

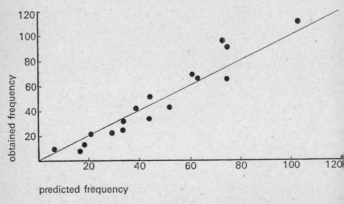

Figure 5 Sequence frequencies from Block VI (Problems 501–600) of the Harlow et al. experiment.

244

whether variance and Random Responding were related entailed applying the analysis to another block of data, the last 100 problems of the learning-set study described above by Harlow *et al.* This block of problems was selected because it became known in subsequent work that its R value was 0·20. Precisely the same analysis was applied as with the first 100 problems for this group. The results are shown in Fig. 5. The resulting PVE was

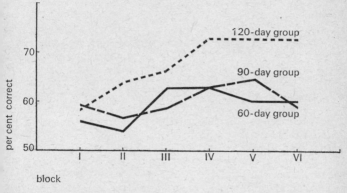

Figure 6 Performance of the three groups in the Harlow et al. *experiment as measured by the percentage of correct responses on Trial 2 for each 100-problem block.*

0·91 which bears out the possibility of the relationship. More relevant to the present topic, it provides another confirmation of the applicability of the model by this test, and suggests, along with the finding that R decreases throughout an experiment (to be described in the next section), that the PVEs would have been even higher had the test been applied to last blocks rather than first blocks of problems.

An Analysis of Learning-Set Functions into H Components

Now that the model has been described and its correspondence to behavior has been indicated, the analysis may be applied to demonstrate its value in describing behavioral processes. Harlow, Rueping, and Mason (1960) have performed a learning-set experiment with young rhesus monkeys in which they compared the effects of age upon the acquisition of learning set. Three groups of 10 Ss each received 600 problems starting at 60, 90, or 120 days. The learning-set functions showing percentage correct on Trial 2 for blocks of 100 problems are plotted in Fig. 6. By *t* test, the 60- and 90-day groups are not significantly different but the 120-day group is significantly different from both of these.

The H analysis was applied to each block for each of the three groups, producing 18 separate analyses. Each analysis was based on all the nine Hs listed in Table 1. A detailed description of the analysis is given elsewhere by the author (Levine, 1959).

In the preceding section it was found either empirically or by assumption that b, d, u, and v could consistently be regarded as having zero strength. It might be predicted that in the 18 blocks of problems considered here these four Hs would yield 72 estimates of zero. These 72 estimates ranged from -0.05 to $+0.05$. The mean was at -0.002 with $\sigma = 0.02$. This finding further validates the model by confirming an expected finding, and simplifies the Harlow *et al.* data by eliminating four of the Hs from consideration.

The remaining Hs are plotted in Fig. 7. The p_2 and p_3 values have been added together to depict the number of problems manifesting a learning H, and are plotted in the upper left-hand quadrant. The differences here reflect the differences seen in Fig. 6, that the 120-day group shows more problem-solution behavior throughout than the 60- and 90-day groups.

Consideration of the remaining three Hs suggests some of the sources of these differences. The Position Preference H, plotted in the lower left-hand quadrant, is striking in that this H has the same strength for the three groups. Thus, the difference in over-all performance between the 120-day and the 60- and 90-day groups is not attributable to this H. The basis for the difference between the learning-set functions may be seen in the right-hand side of Fig. 7. This difference is attributable specifically to the differences in Stimulus Preference and Random Responding.

In addition to providing more detail about the differences among the three groups, Fig. 7 shows the various behavioral processes which underlie the learning-set functions. Position Preference is again unique in that it does not decrease but has a constant strength at about 0.18. A comparison of this H with the other two nonsolution Hs shows that Hs do not extinguish simultaneously or at the same rate. Also, the $p_2 + p_3$ plot shows the progress of learning 'purified' of the other behavior patterns. It may well be, although this is clearly conjecture at present, that the formulae describing these elementary processes will have greater simplicity and universality than the formulations of what is here seen as a complex, composite function: *the* learning curve.

Since it is clear that these processes underlie the learning-set

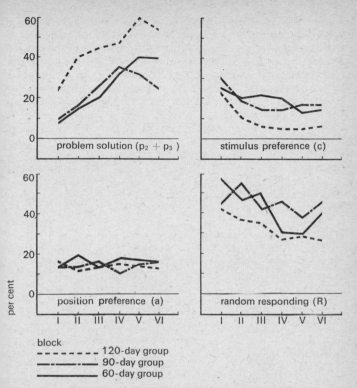

Figure 7 Analysis of the three Harlow et al. *groups. Each quadrant shows the percentage of problems in which the behavior was determined by the indicated H.*

function, it should be possible to synthesize this function by proper combination of the H values. Two classes of learning-set functions may be considered. One is the class described in Fig. 6, percentage correct on Trial 2; the other is percentage correct on Trial 3. Percentage correct on Trial 2 may be synthesized from the following considerations: whenever (Problem-solution)$_2$ occurs, the S is rewarded on Trial 2; when (Problem-solution)$_3$ occurs, the S is never rewarded on Trial 2; and whenever any of the other Hs occurs, the S is rewarded half of the time on Trial two. Percentage correct on Trial 2 would then be estimated by

$$\% \text{ Correct} = \left[p_2 + \frac{1 - (p_2 + p_3)}{2} \right] \times 100 \qquad [6]$$

247

The estimates for each block of problems, as well as the conventional learning-set functions, are plotted in Fig. 8, where it will be seen that there is a good fit with two kinds of deviations. The first is that the synthesized values consistently underestimate the conventional values by about 2%; the other is that the synthesized curve tends to be a more regular learning function. For example, the strange decrements seen in the empirical functions

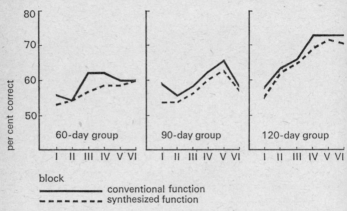

Figure 8 Conventional learning-set functions and synthesized learning-set functions for the Trial-2 data of the three Harlow et al. groups.

for the 60- and 90-day groups are either eliminated or decreased. Whether either or both of these characteristics are reliable is, for the present, an empirical question. It has not been proved that they must appear.

The trial-three learning-set functions may be synthesized by considering that each time (Problem-solution)$_2$ or (Problem-solution)$_3$ occurs the S is rewarded on Trial three, and whenever any of the other Hs occurs the S is rewarded half the time. Percentage correct on Trial 3 would then be estimated by

$$\% \text{ Correct} = \left[p_2 + p_3 + \frac{1 - (p_2 + p_3)}{2} \right] \times 100 \qquad [7]$$

The synthesized and conventional Trial-3 learning-set functions are plotted in Fig. 9, where it will be seen that the two functions are identical. This identity does not have the status of a verified prediction since it has been demonstrated (Levine, 1959) that the operations employed in obtaining the two sets of functions are

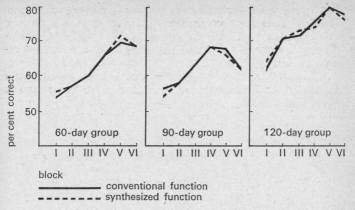

Figure 9 Conventional learning-set functions and synthesized learning-set functions for the Trial-3 data of the three Harlow et al. *groups.*

virtually identical. However, the correspondence indicates that the assumptions of the model are reasonable in that they do lead to these operations.

Discussion

The model presented here has a few useful features. Primarily, it provides a technique for evaluating the strengths of a variety of Hs. This method follows directly from certain relatively simple assumptions concerning the appearance of response patterns. Secondly, almost all of the variance of the frequencies of response sequences occurring in a block of problems may be explained by the model (Figs. 2–5). Then, evaluation of H strengths at successive stages of learning shows that Hs follow regular functions (Fig. 7). Finally, the conventional learning-set functions may be synthesized by appropriate combination of the Hs (Figs. 8–9).

While the data are, for the most part, in accord with predictions from the model, two intriguing systematic discrepancies are to be noted. The most obvious discrepancy is seen in Fig. 8 in which percentage correct on Trial 2 is always consistently underestimated. The other is illustrated in Figs. 2–5 where the points typically organize themselves around a line whose slope is slightly larger than the 45° line. Although insufficient analysis has been performed to determine the source of these discrepancies, a promising lead is that the sequences $-+-$ and $++-$ are

249

occurring somewhat more frequently than would be predicted by the model. It may be shown that both discrepancies would follow if this were the case. These discrepancies may mean that some H has been overlooked or that some of the other assumptions require revision.

Assuming that the model in its current form is approximately correct, it provides interesting implications for some current psychological problems. The central property of the model is that it takes as the dependent variable unit the H, defined as a pattern of responses to selected stimuli. The specification of a behavior pattern means that this pattern as a whole is susceptible to the traditional effects of reinforcement operations, i.e., it is possible to reinforce some Hs and extinguish others. Thus, one may reinforce Position Alternation, Stimulus Alternation, or various kinds of stay-shift combinations. This idea of the reinforcement of a response pattern has specific relevance for understanding the phenomenon of learning-to-learn as seen in the discrimination learning-set situation. Since Harlow's (1949) demonstration that Ss show progressive improvement on Trial-2 performance in successive problems the question of the nature of this improvement has provided a challenge to theory. Two types of explanations have been proposed. The first, by Riopelle (1953) and Harlow and Hicks (1957), attributes the increasing interproblem transfer to the weakening of interfering response tendencies. Riopelle demonstrated that negative transfer from preceding problems decreased over problem blocks, and described the phenomenon as 'transfer suppression'. Harlow and Hicks described learning-set development as a 'uni-process' which, they suggested, is an inhibition of incorrect behaviors. These interpretations omit the conception of reinforcement as directly strengthening any response.

The second explanation, by Restle (1958), accepts the strengthening of a response via reinforcement during the experiment, but requires no assumption about the character of the response. Restle, rather, postulates a class of stimuli 'Type-a cues', responses to which are always rewarded, and which become conditioned to the correct response during the course of the learning-set experiment.

The explanation of learning-set development suggested by the present paper is consonant with this aspect of Restle's theory. The explanation results from assuming that the S is capable of responding in terms of Hs, and that Hs may be reinforced. One of the Hs, Win-stay-Lose-shift (with respect to the object), is the H which the *E* chooses to reinforce. There is nothing unique about this H. It has the same formal status as responses to one position or any of the other Hs. Learning-set development then is the gradual strengthening, via 100% reinforcement, of this H, and the gradual extinction, because of 50% reinforcement, of the other Hs. Thus, this example of learning-to-learn is amenable to treatment by any conventional reinforcement theory, so long as a *pattern* of response is taken as the dependent variable. Note that 'Win' and 'Lose' are analogous to Restle's Type-a cues, and that the responses are staying and shifting (with respect to the object), respectively.

The model provides description not only of the H which is reinforced but also of other Hs. An important empirical finding presented in this paper is that these Hs may not all extinguish at the same rate. This finding creates a problem for current learning theories, which make no provision for several extinction processes. It is, of course, too soon to know how many different extinction processes must be postulated and to develop theories about the nature of the differences. The analysis described herein should make a contribution toward solving these problems.

References

FELLER, W. *An introduction to probability theory and its applications.* (2nd ed.) New York: Wiley, 1957.

GELLERMANN, L. W. Chance orders of alternating stimuli in visual discrimination experiments. *J. genet. Psychol.*, 1933, **42**, 207–208.

GOODNOW, JACQUELINE J., & PETTIGREW, T. F. Effect of prior patterns of experience upon strategies and learning sets. *J. exp. Psychol.*, 1955, **49**, 381–389.

GOODNOW, JACQUELINE J., & POSTMAN, L. Learning in a two-choice probability situation with a problem-solving setting. *J. exp. Psychol.*, 1955, **49**, 16–22.

GOODNOW, JACQUELINE J., SHANKS, BETTY, RUBINSTEIN, I., & LUBIN, A. What is the human subject responding to in a two-choice task? *WRAIR Problem-Solving Proj. Memo.*, 1957, No. 3.

HARLOW, H. F. The formation of learning sets. *Psychol. Rev.*, 1949, **56**, 51–65.

HARLOW, H. F. Analysis of discrimination learning by monkeys. *J. exp. Psychol.*, 1950, **40**, 26–39.

HARLOW, H. F., & HICKS, L. H. Discrimination learning theory: Uniprocess *vs.* duo-process. *Psychol. Rev.*, 1957, **64**, 104–109.

HARLOW, H. F., HARLOW, M. K., RUEPING, R. R., & MASON, W. A. Performance of infant rhesus monkeys on discrimination learning, delayed response, and discrimination learning set. *J. comp. physiol. Psychol.*, 1960, **53**, 113–121.

KRECHEVSKY, I. 'Hypotheses' versus 'chance' in the pre-solution period in sensory discrimination learning. *Univer. Calif. publ. Psychol.*, 1932, **6**, 27–44.

LEVINE, M. A model of hypothesis behavior in discrimination learning set. Unpublished doctoral dissertation, Univer. of Wisconsin, 1959.

LEVINE, M., LEVINSON, BILLEY, & HARLOW, H. F. Trials per problem as a variable in the acquisition of discrimination learning set. *J. comp. physiol. Psychol.*, 1959, **52**, 396–398.

RESTLE, F. Toward a quantitative description of learning set data. *Psychol. Rev.*, 1958, **65**, 77–91.

RIOPELLE, A. J. Transfer suppression and learning sets. *J. comp. physiol. Psychol.*, 1953, **56**, 108–114.

SCHRIER, A. M. Comparison of two methods of investigating the effect of amount of reward on performance by monkeys. *J. comp. physiol. Psychol.*, 1958, **51**, 725–731.

Part Six FLEXIBILITY OF RESPONSE

An important factor in efficient problem solving is flexibility of response; that is, the ability rapidly to discard unsuccessful responses and to attempt new ones, until the correct one is found. An animal which repeats an erroneous response many times is scarcely showing intelligent behaviour. The characteristics of repetitive responses and their role in hindering problem solving are discussed in the first two papers of this group. The remaining papers deal with the opposite characteristic of maximal flexibility as shown in the capacity rapidly to reverse a response which is no longer rewarded or to keep track of multiple conflicting conditions which determine the final solution to a problem.

19 G. V. Hamilton

A Study of Trial and Error Reactions in Mammals

G. V. Hamilton, 'A study of trial and error reactions in mammals'
J. animal Behav., vol. 1 (1911), pp. 33–66.

I. Introduction; Description of Apparatus; Description of Method

The literature of animal behavior contains considerable experimentally obtained evidence that among the mammalia there are marked differences of ability to profit by experience, but these differences have been analysed almost exclusively in terms of sensory equipment and of quantitative measurements of reaction time and reactive errors. The trial and error mode of adjustment has thus come to serve the student of behavior as a conceptional unit in his analyses of mammalian reactions, and has been dealt with as genetically variable only with reference to the degree of rapidity with which it leads to the formation of associations appropriate to given situations, and to the elimination of useless activities. We speak of qualitatively different instinctive adjustments, but not of qualitatively different 'try-try-again' (trial and error) efforts to meet a situation for which there is no specifically appropriate instinct, no opportunity for imitation of any kind, and no rational equipment.

The present investigation seeks to collect facts of behavior which may lend themselves to qualitative interpretations of trial and error activities. In other words, it is concerned with the following problem: *What, if any, are the qualitative differences of reactive tendency that account for the fact that some mammals learn slowly, and with many errors, to meet situations which their fellows of superior age or race learn to meet quickly and with but few errors?*

We cannot know how to attack this problem, nor specifically what to look for, until we gain a general orientation concerning the facts relevant to it. With this in mind I have made use of the apparatus and method described below.

Description of apparatus. The reader will more clearly understand the purpose of the apparatus by picturing to himself a room which may be entered by a door capable of giving entrance only, and which may be gotten out of by means of a constantly varying one of four possible doors of exit. Let us then imagine that from within the room one may see on each of the five doors a distinctive inscription, as follows:

Entrance door: cannot be used for exit.
Exit door No. 1: push against it; will afford exit unless it is locked.
Exit door No. 2: (same inscription).
Exit door No. 3: (same inscription).
Exit door No. 4: (same inscription).

The apparatus differs from this imaginary room in that its various doors are not labelled at all, and are all alike in appearance, so that a subject seeking exit from the apparatus must gain by experience the information that the above inscriptions would have afforded.

The floor of the apparatus is of wood, and the top of wire netting, and both are of the form shown in Fig. 1. The narrow, rectangular part of this figure represents the *entrance hall* (EH, Fig. 1). This hall can be entered by way of an *entrance door* (Ent. D, Fig. 1), which will swing in the inward direction only, and which fits so snugly within its frame that, once it is closed, it cannot be opened from within the apparatus. It is hung a little out of plumb, so that it will always swing to the closed position when not actually held open by the subject.

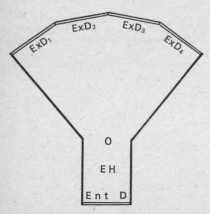

Figure 1 Floor plan of apparatus. Ent D, Entrance Door; O, point of equidistance from exit doors; ExD 1, ExD 2, ExD 3, ExD 4, Exit Door number 1, Exit Door number 2, etc.

At the opposite, broader end of the apparatus are four *exit doors* (Ex D-1, Ex D-2, Ex D-3, Ex D-4, Fig. 1). Each of these exit doors opens outward only, and when released from pressure swings to the closed position. Like the entrance door, the exit doors are hung out of plumb.

The *exit doors* just described are equidistant from point O in Fig. 1.

Figure 2 is intended to show the manner in which the various exit doors can be 'locked' or 'unlocked' without the subject's knowledge. It represents the outer aspect of an exit door, set within its frame, and equipped with a *button* (B, Fig. 2) and two *strings* (S¹, S², Fig. 2). When the experimenter pulls the string attached to the inner end of the button (S¹, Fig. 2) the latter is

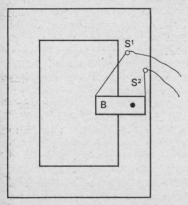

Figure 2 An exit door set within its frame, and equipped with button an button strings. B, Button, S¹, String number 1; S², String number 2.

brought to the vertical position and the door is thus unlocked. When the string attached to the outer end of the button (S², Fig. 2) is pulled, the button assumes the horizontal position, thus locking the door. The subject has nothing to do with the manipulation of these strings, which are carried in metal eyes to the under surface of the apparatus, whence they are carried in grooves, thoroughly concealed, to any part of the laboratory from which the experimenter can operate them without the subject's knowledge. Each of the four exit doors is thus equipped with a button and two strings.

The sides of the apparatus are of wire netting. The inner

surfaces of the exit doors are painted greyish-white, whilst the remainder of the interior of the apparatus is dark green. The exit doors have no individually distinctive marks.

The dimensions of the apparatus are determined according to the following general rule: the subject's length being '1', the uniform inside height of the apparatus is '3'; the height of the entrance and exit doors is '2·9' and their width '2'. From point O (Fig. 1) to the mid-point of each exit door's lower margin is '6'. The various doors are sand-papered to prevent binding.

In order to meet special conditions I have made various unimportant modifications of the apparatus just described. The human subjects, by reason of their upright position in walking, required a relatively higher apparatus. For the horse an apparatus was provided which had 'exit doors' merely wide enough to enable him to thrust his head and neck into a food box just beyond; after a trial he was led out of the entrance end of the apparatus. The monkeys so resented handling that their apparatus had to be built within a larger enclosure which, in turn, adjoined their living rooms. In every case the following essential condition was met: the subject, once within the apparatus, was unable to discover whether a given exit door was locked or unlocked except by actually pushing against it.

Description of method. (1) *Preliminary training.* It was found to be desirable to give the animal subjects thorough familiarity with the apparatus before their formal trials were begun, hence, a subject's first experience with the apparatus was merely that of entrance into it, with all the doors propped open and with food scattered about on the floor. After he had eaten he was coaxed out of one of the entrance doors. This was repeated until the subject was thoroughly familiar with the interior of the apparatus as a feeding ground, and with the open exit doors as the most convenient avenues of approach to a desirable locality. In the case of the horse this differed in that the feeding ground was, from the start, a place just beyond any of the exit doors.

The next step in training the subject for the experiment was to close the entrance door as soon as he had entered the apparatus. As soon as this had ceased to produce any evidence of uneasiness the four exit doors were left partially closed, so that the subject was compelled to exert some pressure against any of the exit doors through which he sought to escape. As the training advanced the exit doors were left more and more nearly closed until they were quite closed, although still unlocked. The subject was considered 'trained' as soon as he had learned to seek the exit doors for escape from the apparatus, and to push against them without hesitation.

(2) *Formal trials*. The description of these trials, which constitute the experiment proper, will be facilitated by speaking of the various exit doors as if they were numbered '1', '2', '3' and '4', in order, from left to right. For the *first formal trial* of any subject three of the exit doors were locked by the experimenter, who pulled the appropriate button strings without the subject's knowledge. The remaining exit door, *and only that one door* was left unlocked. From within the apparatus, therefore, all four exit doors looked alike, i.e., closed. With the apparatus thus prepared, the subject was placed within it for his first trial, and was allowed to choose his own time for effecting his escape. As soon as he found the one unlocked exit door and effected his escape he was rewarded with food.

For the *second formal trial* the one unlocked door of the first trial was locked, and another of the exit doors was unlocked. Thus, if door 4 were the unlocked door for the first trial, it would be one of the three *locked* doors for the second trial. Each succeeding trial in a total series of 100 trials differed from the trial immediately preceding it according to the same principle: the unlocked exit door of the immediately preceding trial was always one of the three locked exit doors during the present trial.

A second condition of the formal trials was this: during each subject's 100 trials, each exit door was left unlocked for twenty-five trials and locked for seventy-five trials, and care was taken by the experimenter to avoid a discoverable sequence in selecting an ever-varying exit door to be left unlocked. Even the most sophisticated human subject was thus left in ignorance as to which of three inferentially possible doors of exit would open when pressed against until he had actually tried one or more of these doors. Ten consecutive trials were given each subject daily for ten successive days.

The older human subjects were given no preliminary training, but were frankly told that no tricks would be played, and that they were expected to leave the apparatus by way of an exit door. The human infant was given essentially the same training that the animals received, except that in his case toys were substituted for food when my commendation proved insufficient as a motive for reaction.

Before we enter into a discussion of results, two obvious defects of the above method must be taken into account: (1) The situations may have had different sensory values for the different subjects. For example, the dogs of my experiment were unmistakably guided by local odor signs in their discrimination of one exit door from another, whilst these signs were of no value to the human subjects, and probably of but little value to the cats and monkeys. On the other hand, the monkeys may have detected fine differences of visual appearance of the inner surfaces of the exit doors, whereas these doors certainly presented no such differences for the human subjects, and may have been visually indistinguishable to the cats, dogs, and horse.

A fairly satisfactory solution of this difficulty was effected by the preliminary training, which taught the subjects to discriminate among the various exit doors by their differences of spatial position.

(2) There was no adequate measurement of the reactive value of the motives supplied to the various subjects for escaping from the apparatus with the greatest possible speed and accuracy. Yerkes' and Dodson's (1) discoveries concerning the relation of strength of stimulus to rapidity of habit formation impose on the student of behavior a scientific obligation to regulate as accurately as possible the strength of motive-stimuli. Unfortunately, the easily regulated painful stimuli (electric shock) that proved so useful in their work with the Dancing Mouse cannot be applied where one seeks comparable results from subjects who differ so widely in emotional responsiveness to frequently recurring discomfort as do, for example, dogs and monkeys. Even in the case of my naive human subjects, the possibility that the size of the reward or the degree of my approbation might be affected by stupidity or cleverness of reaction had to be ruled out in order to obtain uniform results.

By observing, for each individual, the relation between strength and kind of motive on the one hand, and uniformity of reaction on the other hand, I was able to secure results which I believe to be quite safely comparable for the purposes of the present exploratory investigation. The animal subjects were never used for experiment until their hunger was partially appeased, and if they chose to lie down and sleep while within the apparatus they were merely urged to return to me for a bit of extra-tempting food. With cats and dogs an atmosphere of lazy comradeship with their master greatly favored a steady, apparently unemotional quest of the unlocked door. The horse's natural habit of seeking food over prolonged periods of time rendered him an excellent subject. The monkeys would doubtless have given more uniform results had there been any way of overcoming their natural distractibility, but the food seeking aspect of the experiment proved to be most helpful in reducing the effects of their tendency to shift their attention from the apparatus to fortuitous sights and sounds.

II. Description of Subjects

The selection of subjects for experiment was made with reference to the desirability of covering considerable ontogenetic and phylogenetic ranges without thereby impairing the value of the results for comparison. Since it was more relevant to the purpose of the investigation to explore for different kinds of adjustment than to make an intensive study of any particular mode of adjustment, no effort was made to obtain averages for large numbers of individuals belonging to a given age or species.

The many gaps in the age and phyletic series are due to the fact that the results obtained from many of my subjects had to be rejected for various reasons. Some of the subjects were stolen and some died before their trials were completed; in some cases I could not be reasonably sure that a possible difficulty in discriminating one exit door from another did not exist; and many unavoidable interruptions rendered it impossible to make use of all the subjects that were available for experiment. It is much to be regretted that the list given below includes no human subjects between the ages of twenty-six months and eight years; the writer's wholly undeserved local reputation as a vivisectionist seemed to create a stubborn unwillingness on the part of parents to supply young children for experimental work.

Human Subjects

Man 1. Age, 34 years. Native (Spanish-Indian) Californian. Ranch laborer in the experimenter's employ. A man of limited education, but of average intelligence for his class. He went through his trials in the stolid, unemotional manner that characterised his work in the fields. The 'boss' wanted him to walk into and out of an enclosure 100 times, and he did so without asking questions or shirking his task.

Boy 7. Age, 15 years. American, of original English descent. Grocer's boy. Country school education. He was shy and nervous at the beginning of the experiment, and always seemed to be more or less affected by a fear of appearing stupid.

Boy 6F1. Age, 13 years. Father Italian, mother Swedish.

Country schoolboy. He was less alert, mentally, than were his brothers, who are described below.

Boy 5F1. Age, 11 years. Brother of Boy 6F1. Country schoolboy. Volatile, alert, and rather distractible.

Boy 4F1. Age, 10 years. Brother of Boys 6F1 and 5F1. Country schoolboy. Relatively precocious, and an excellent subject.

Boy 3. Age, 10 years. Native (Spanish-Indian) Californian. Country schoolboy. Bright, but rather shy, and too nervously eager to please the experimenter.

Girl 1. Age, 10 years. American of Scotch descent. Until recently a student in the public schools of Cambridge, Mass. Her superiority of school training, and her very considerable degree of mental precocity, gave her a decided advantage over all the other human subjects, including, even, the adult Man 1.

Boy 7. Age, 26 months. American of mixed descent (son of the experimenter). At the time of the experiment he could walk; had a limited vocabulary of words, which he did not put into sentences; was able to find his way about the house; and understood many simple commands. Very quick to form new associations.

Defective Man A. Age, 45 years. Native (Spanish-Indian) Californian. Ranch laborer in the experimenter's employ. Limited school education, but had read history and uncritical works on socialism. He was a nervous, suspicious, 'muddled' person, with a grievance against society in general, and a surprising fund of self-acquired misinterpretations relating to his social environment. He expressed a belief that my experiment was dangerous meddling with the human mind, and that it had some occult power of 'making people crazy'. His curiosity and his desire to argue matters rendered him available, but he seemed to be in constant dread of the apparatus, and always labored under a suspicion that it was not the simple structure that it pretended to be.

Defective Boy A. Age, 11 years. English. With the exception of occasional perfunctory lessons from a governess, his education was practically *nil*. He was barely able to read simple words, was unable to respect the conventions of conversation usually recognized by a child of six years, and manifested an inordinate fondness for asking questions. His cooperation varied: at times he gave attention to the experiment, and did well enough; and at times he behaved in a dull, mechanical manner. His reactions are of considerable interest.

Monkeys

Monkey 6.[1] Age, 15 years (estimated). *Macacus cynomolgus.* About 10 years in captivity. Tame, and an excellent subject.

Monkey 4. Age, 1·5 years (estimated). *Macacus rhesus.* About 6 months in captivity. Very tame. After his 20th trial his vision became defective, so that he had difficulty in finding his way about the apparatus. His results do not appear in any of the averages.

Monkey 3. Age, 5 years (estimated). *Macacus rhesus.* About 3 years in captivity. A truculent, untamable animal, but a fairly good subject.

Monkey 2. Age, 1·5 years (estimated). *Macacus —— (species undetermined). About 1 year in captivity. Timid, but exceptionally resourceful in meeting outdoor situations when he was given the freedom of the ranch. His timidity doubtless affected his behavior.

Monkey 1. Age, 1·5 years (estimated). *Macacus rhesus.* About 1 year in captivity. A comparatively stupid animal, but uniform in behavior during the experiment.

Dogs

The sixteen dogs of the following list range in age from thirty-six days to three years. With the exception of the two adults (Dogs 1 and 2), they are all descended from a common sire, the subject of my previously published 'An Experimental Study of an Unusual Type of Reaction in a Dog'. (3) This sire was a Boston terrier of impure breed. The six puppies that are designated 'F2' in the list below were from a mongrel bitch of the small hound type. Their mother was unavailable for experiment. The eight puppies of the 'F1' group were from an English setter bitch, 'Dog 1' of the list.

Dog 1. Age, 3 years. English setter. Mother of dogs 3, 7, 8, 9, 11, 12, 14 and 18 (one litter). She was untrained, hence a study of her behavior under natural conditions was easily possible. It was found that whenever she sighted or scented her prey she would inhibit every visible movement of her body but a slight tremor and a wagging of her tail, and would stand thus, in a rigid attitude, for several minutes before making a final dash to seize the object of her attention. A tendency to inhibit, *momentarily*, all active movements when prey is first discovered is not limited to

1. The writer has followed Professor Yerkes' (2) method of designating male subjects by even numbers, and female subjects by odd numbers.

any special breed of dogs: it is the prolongation of this momentary inhibition that so marks the behavior of the English setter. This reactive tendency of the mother of my puppies is of much interest for the present investigation.

Dog 2. Age, 1 year (estimated). Great Dane-mongrel. His tendency to look to his master for cues to action marked him as characteristically different from all the other dogs of my experiment. The other dogs sought cues to action in the situation, and were not so much affected by my presence.

Dog 4F2. Age, 116 days. Boston terrier–mongrel.
Dog 6F2. Age, 109 days. Boston terrier–mongrel.
Dog 3F1. Age, 102 days. Boston terrier–English setter.
Dog 8F1. Age, 95 days. Boston terrier–English setter.
Dog 5F2. Age, 88 days. Boston terrier–mongrel.
Dog 7F1. Age, 81 days. Boston terrier–English setter.
Dog 10F2. Age, 74 days. Boston terrier–mongrel.
Dog 9F1. Age, 67 days. Boston terrier–English setter.
Dog 11F1. Age, 60 days. Boston terrier–English setter.
Dog 12F1. Age, 53 days. Boston terrier–English setter.
Dog 14F1. Age, 46 days. Boston terrier–English setter.
Dog 13F2. Age, 43 days. Boston terrier–mongrel.
Dog 16F2. Age, 43 days. Boston terrier–mongrel.
Dog 18F1. Age, 36 days. Boston terrier–English setter.

Cats

Cat 1. Age, 1 year. Manx. This animal was reared in the Harvard Psychological laboratory, and enjoyed the further distinction of having been one of Doctor Berry's (4) subjects in his studies of imitation. Although my apparatus has no technical resemblance to that used by Doctor Berry, Cat 1 explored it carefully, and for several trials persisted in her efforts to claw at imaginary loops of string beyond the meshes of the wire netting. Her close attention to the apparatus situation, and her remarkable intelligence (as compared with that of common cats) was of much interest.

Cat 2. Age, 1 year. Common house cat. Co-operated well.
Cat 3. Age, 1 year. Same as Cat 2 except in sex.
Cat 5. Age, 56 days. Common cat. Co-operated well.
Cat 7. Age, 70 days. Common cat. Timid and sluggish.

Horse

Horse 2. Age, 8 years. Gelding of western breed. Carriage horse. In view of the very poor showing made by this animal, the stableman's belief in his 'smartness' is of some interest. On one occasion the writer was driving this horse at night, over an unfamiliar network of roads. The horse was guided in a wrong direction on the way home, and the writer became quite disoriented. When the horse was given a loose rein he traced the way back without error, although he had been over the various roads involved less frequently than had his master.

III. Tabulation and Preliminary Analysis of Results

It will be remembered that each of the subjects was given 100 trials, and that during each of these trials one, but only one, of the four exit doors was capable of being opened. It will be further remembered that this 'unlocked' door varied from trial to trial. Thus, if Door 3 were unlocked for any present trial it would surely be locked for the next trial. It is apparent, therefore, that any subject who avoided, during each present trial, the unlocked door of the immediately preceding trial, was apt to effect his escape during his 100 trials by trying the various exit doors 200 or 201 times: 200 times if he did not try all four doors during his first trial, otherwise, 201 times.

Again, any subject who tried the various doors without reference to the ever varying one impossible door as such, or as a preferable door to try on account of its having just afforded the escape, would be apt to effect his escape from the apparatus necessary 100 times by trying the various exit doors 250 times.

The 'average' number of efforts to open exit doors would be affected by any of the following factors:

(1) This number would be decreased by a tendency to try first, on entering the apparatus for a trial, the exit door that had been most remotely (in time, with reference to the present trial) an unlocked door. This, in spite of the fact that the experimenter followed an irregular order in selecting exit doors for unlocking.

(2) It would be increased by a tendency to prefer, as first choice of door to be tried during a given trial, the unlocked door of the immediately preceding trial.

(3) It would be increased by a tendency to make more than one separate effort to open the same exit door during a given trial.

In table 1, I have tabulated the total number of separate efforts to open exit doors manifested by each of the various subjects during his 100 trials. In making current observations of my subjects' behavior I recorded as a separate effort to open an exit door the total activity of a subject from the time he attacked an exit door until he left its immediate vicinity. For example, during his second trial Dog 18F1 went to Door 4 and clawed it for several minutes, then turned away from this door and wandered about the apparatus; one effort to open an exit door was recorded. Then he returned to Door 4 and again spent some time in alternately clawing and barking at it; when he left the door a second time a second effort was recorded. He returned to it, tried it and left it a third and a fourth time before attacking another door, hence his first four separate activities, all of which were definitely directed against the same unyielding door, were recorded as four separate efforts to open exit doors.

With the above in mind the reader will be able to obtain a general orientation concerning the value of the situations for each of the various subjects.

Discussion of table 1. In the light of analyses that are to follow, this table has a largely negative value. It shows how misleading a single objective measure of ability to profit by experience may be. For example, the three-year-old mother of the F1 puppies (Dog 1) made 324 separate efforts to open exit doors during 100 trials, whilst her fifty-three-days-old puppy (Dog 12 F1) has a record of only 307 efforts to open doors. Her record is also greater than that of three of the other puppies (Dogs 3F1, 5F2, and 13F2). Table 1 also shows that immature Monkey 2 has a lower record than either of the two adult monkeys; and that the record of mature Cat 2 exceeds that of fifty-six-days-old Cat 5 by ten efforts to open doors. In the case of the monkeys, the apparent inconsistency of ontogenetic findings becomes all the more striking when we take into account the fact that at 1.5 years of age the Macacque is scarcely half-grown, and sexually immature.

When we enter upon a discussion of the different modes of searching for unlocked doors, and attempt to isolate the specific reactive tendencies to which these may be attributed, it will be seen that a genetically superior reactive tendency may lead, in some of its manifestations, to an actual increase in number of efforts to open doors. For the present, however, it is desirable to subject the data contained in table 1 to further analysis in order to discover whether or not there is a general tendency for increasing age and phyletic position to decrease the number of efforts to open doors. To this end the various subjects will be divided into age and phyletic groups, and the averages for each of these groups will be compared.

Since the results obtained from the normal human subjects whose ages range from eight to thirty-four years do not present individual variations from their general average which can be clearly traced to age differences, these eight subjects will be in-

Table 1

Subject	Age	No. of efforts to open exit doors
Man 1	34 years	200
Boy 7	15 years	193
Boy 6F1	13 years	201
Boy 5F1	12 years	216
Boy 4F1	10 years	194
Boy 3	10 years	211
Girl 1	10 years	183
Boy 2F1	8 years	216
Boy 1	26 months	315
Man A	45 years	217
Boy A	11 years	237
Monkey 6	15 years	275
Monkey 4	1·5 years	291
Monkey 3	5 years	278
Monkey 2	1·5 years	272
Monkey 1	1·5 years	278
Dog 1	3 years	324
Dog 2	1 year	302
Dog 4F2	116 days	346
Dog 6F2	109 days	329
Dog 3F1	102 days	284
Dog 8F1	95 days	378
Dog 5F2	88 days	304
Dog 7F1	81 days	357
Dog 10F2	74 days	427
Dog 9F1	67 days	389
Dog 11F1	60 days	358
Dog 12F1	53 days	307
Dog 14F1	46 days	413
Dog 13F2	43 days	314
Dog 16F2	43 days	376
Dog 18F1	36 days	438
Cat 1	1 year	358
Cat 2	1 year	378
Cat 3	1 year	320
Cat 7	70 days	406
Cat 5	56 days	368
Horse 1	8 years	461

cluded in a single group. The two defective human subjects – Man A and Boy A – cannot properly be classed together, hence their individual results will appear separately in the table of averages (table 2, below). The human infant (Boy 1), the monkey whose failing vision affected his behavior (Monkey 4), and the horse should, for obvious reasons, appear separately in a table of averages. The mature dogs and mature cats each form an age group, as do also the kittens. In the case of the puppies, their considerable number enables us to form two age groups: the thirty-six-to-seventy-four-days-old puppies and the eighty-one-to-one hundred and sixteen-days-old puppies.

Table 2

Groups of subjects	No. of subjects in each group	Average age for entire group	Average number of efforts to open exit doors
8-to-34-years-old normal human	8	14 years	201·75
Defective man A	1	45 years	217·00
Defective boy A	1	11 years	237·00
Infant Boy 1	1	26 months	315·00
Mature monkeys	2	10 years	276·50
Immature monkeys	2	1·5 years	275·00
Defective monkey	1	1·5 years	291·00
Mature dogs	2	2 years	313·00
81-to-116-days-old puppies	6	98·50 days	333·00
36-to-74-days-old puppies	8	52·75 days	377·75
Mature cats	3	1 year	352·00
Kittens	2	63 days	387·00
Horse	1	8 years	461·00

Ontogenetic aspects of table 2. The normal humans, the dogs and the cats manifest a tendency toward increase in number of efforts to open doors with decrease in age. This is especially prominent in the case of the human infant, whose record exceeds that of the average for the older normal human subjects by 56·13 per cent. Defective Man A, whose record appreciably exceeds that of the eight-to-thirty-four-years-old normal human subjects, would doubtless have presented a much higher record had he not manifested a marked tendency to make first choice of the most remotely unlocked door during each present trial. It may be said, indeed, that his total modes of adjustment to the situations of the experiment were, on the average, of a lower type than those manifested by defective Boy A, whose record places him below Man A in the table 2 list. This additional evidence of the unreliability of the findings of tables 1 and 2 as measures of intelligence will be brought out more explicitly in sections IV and V.

A general knowledge of the marked differences that obtain between the behavior of an adult monkey and that of a half-grown one would lead the student of behavior to expect that under similar conditions no year-and-a-half-old macacque would find the unlocked door one hundred times with fewer efforts than an adult macacque. The but slightly lower record of the two half-grown monkeys is, therefore, of some interest. Here, too, an explanation is to be found in differences of reactive tendency which require, for genetic evaluation, more than a single standard of measurement.

Phylogenetic aspects of table 2. A comparison of the various adult groups shows that in order of ability to avoid useless efforts to open exit doors the older normal human subject stands first, the mature monkeys second, the dogs third, the cats fourth, and the horse fifth. Table 1 shows that the horse has the highest individual record of efforts to open doors that is manifested by any subject, regardless of age.

It is of some interest that twenty-six-months-old-Boy 1 made a greater number of efforts to open exit doors than did any of the following subjects: All other human subjects, all of the monkeys, and dogs 2, 3F1, 5F2, 12F1, 13F2. If mere ability to avoid useless activities were a measure of intelligence, this finding would imply that my son was less intelligent at twenty-six months than was one of my forty-three-days-old puppies (Dog 13F2). In view of the fact that at the time of the experiment Boy 1 gave unmistakable evidence of having 'free ideas' (5), this is an absurd implication.

IV. Determination of the Different Modes of Adjustment Manifested

It will be remembered that the conditions of the experiment require the subject who seeks escape from the apparatus merely to search for an unlocked door until he finds one. The present chapter seeks to classify the different modes of searching for this ever-varying unlocked door.

In order to facilitate the descriptions that follow, the value of each of the four exit doors in a given trial-situation will be designated by one of the following terms:

The impossible door. For any present trial this is the unlocked door of the immediately preceding trial; hence it is an inferentially impossible door of exit during the present trial for any subject who is able to appreciate that no one door is ever an unlocked door in two successive trials.

The possible doors. No subject is able, during a given trial, to tell with certainty which one of three exit doors will yield to pressure until he tries it. Of these three inferentially possible doors of exit, two are actually locked, and one is unlocked. We shall speak, therefore, of 'locked possible doors' and an 'unlocked possible door'.

The intention of our investigation requires a division of all the reactions of the subjects into two groups, only one of which can enter into the tables. These groups are:

(1) *Unclassified reactions.* This group includes all reactions which led to the discovery of the unlocked door before all three possible doors were tried, and which did not include more than a single effort to open any given door during the trial. I have rejected from the tables as 'unclassified' all reactions which met the above conditions, even though such a reaction included an effort to open the impossible door. This is justified, I believe, by the fact that none of the animal subjects seemed to have a consistent awareness of the impossible door as such. The description of classified reactions will disclose an additional reason for this exclusion.

(2) *Classified reactions.* To fall within this group a reaction must meet one of the following conditions: (*a*) Efforts to open each of the three possible doors; (*b*) more than one separate continuous effort to open a given door during the trial. For example, if during a present trial, door 3 were the unlocked door of the immediately preceding trial and door 2 the unlocked door of the present trial, a reaction which could be tabulated according to any of the following formulae would fall within the classified group: Efforts to open exit doors 4, 1, 2 in the order given; or exit doors 1, 4, 1, 2; or exit doors 4, 4, 1, 2, etc.

The classified modes of searching for the unlocked door were found to belong to five objectively different general types, which may be described as follows:

Type A. All three possible doors tried, *once each*; no effort made to open the impossible door.

This is the most adequate possible type of classified reactions.

Type B. All four exit doors are tried, once each, and in an irregular order.

Type C. This reaction can occur only when the door to the extreme right (Door 4), or the one to the extreme left (Door 1) is the unlocked door. It involves trying each of the four exit doors once, and in order from left to right or from right to left, according as Door 4 or Door 1 is the unlocked door. Thus, if Door 1 be unlocked, the subject tries the doors in the following order: 4, 3, 2, 1.

Type D. More than a single continuous effort to open a given door during the trial; but between separate efforts to open the same door there must be an effort to open some other door. Thus, the subject tries doors in the following order: 4, 1, 4, 3; or 4, 1, 2, 4, 3, etc.

Type E. This type includes various highly inappropriate modes of seeking escape from the apparatus which might be classed as separate types of reaction were it not that when collectively treated as a unit in the distribution curve they are seen to belong to a single general type. The various forms of Type E reactions are, – (*a*) during a given trial the subject tries a door, leaves it, then returns to it and tries it a second time *without having tried any other door*; (*b*) during a given trial the subject attacks a group of two or three locked doors two or more times in a regular order; (*c*) during a given trial the subject, without falling into either of the above two errors of reaction, persistently avoids an exit door, so that he makes at least seven separate efforts to open exit doors before effecting his escape.

It is especially important to gain a clear understanding of the objective characteristics of the classified types of reaction described above, since they will appear as units in all of the analyses that are to follow. Table 3, given below, contains characteristic examples.

Table 3

Examples of Classified Reactions

Type A	Type B	Type C	Type E	Type E
4, 2, 1	4, 2, 3, 1	4, 3, 2, 1	4, 3, 4, 1	3, 3, 1 (sub-type a)
2, 4, 1	3, 4, 2, 1	1, 2, 3, 4	2, 3, 4, 3, 2, 1	4, 2, 2, 2, 2, 1 (sub-type a)
	2, 3, 4, 1		2, 4, 3, 2, 1	4, 2, 4, 2, 1 (sub-type b)
				3, 4, 2, 3, 4, 2, 3, 4, 2, 1 (sub-type b)
				4, 3, 2, 4, 2, 3, 1 (sub-type c)
				3, 4, 2, 4, 3, 2, 3, 4, 1 (sub-type c)

EXPLANATION OF TABLE 3 – Each horizontally arranged group of figures describes a single trial; and each figure in such a group refers to an exit door tried. Thus, '4, 2, 3, 1' is descriptive of a trial during which the subject tried first to open door 4, following which he tried doors 2, 3 and 1 in the order given. The last figure in each horizontally arranged group refers to the exit door which afforded escape when the subject pushed against it.

The examples under Type A obtain their true significance only when we assume that they describe trials during which door 3 was the impossible door.

Discussion of table 4. The arrangement of the subjects in phyletic groups, and their arrangement within these groups according to age, enable us to gain from table 4 a general idea of the behavior of individuals as conforming to or varying from that which might be expected to obtain at a given position in the ontogenetic and phylogenetic scales. The highest percentage for each subject is marked by an m in the table in order to render it easy for the reader to tell at a glance the type of reaction most frequently manifested by any subject.

The older normal human subjects and defective Boy A are seen to have 'preferred' Type A reaction. Defective Man A preferred Type B, and the infant Boy 1 preferred Type E.

The mature monkeys and one of the immature monkeys (No. 4) have their highest percentages in the Type D column, whilst immature Monkeys 2 and 1 have their highest percentages in Type C and Type B columns respectively. In view of the fact that reactions of Types B and C are more adequate modes of adjustment than is the Type D reaction, this finding is of considerable interest, as will be shown in the next chapter, where a psychological interpretation of these types of reaction is attempted.

Of the twenty-two animal subjects below the primates, only five preferred any other type of reaction to Type E. These exceptional cases require the following explanation. Dogs 2 and 3F1 were obviously more intelligent in meeting the situations of everyday life than were their fellows. Dogs 5F2 and 11F1, who manifested a preference for Type C reactions, seem to have fixed upon this systematic mode of searching for the unlocked door much earlier in the experiment than is usually the case with dogs: after a variable number of trials (usually from 300 to 600) the average dog will manifest 100 per cent of Type C reactions.

Cat 1, who manifested a preference for Type B reactions, has already been described as an exceptionally intelligent animal (p. 264).

Table 4

Distribution of Classifiable Reactions Manifested by each Subject During His Series of 100 Trials

Subject	Age	No. of classified reactions	Distribution of classified reactions in percentages of each subject's total number of the same				
			Type A %	Type B %	Type C %	Type D %	Type E %
Man 1	34 years	28	m82·14	17·86	0·00	0·00	0·00
Boy 7	15 years	27	m70·37	25·92	0·00	0·00	3·70
Boy 6F1	13 years	26	m69·23	23·08	7·69	0·00	0·00
Boy 5F1	12 years	33	m84·85	15·15	0·00	0·00	0·00
Boy 4F1	10 years	26	m76·92	23·08	0·00	0·00	0·00
Boy 3	10 years	31	m70·97	19·35	3·23	6·45	0·00
Girl 1	10 years	21	m85·71	14·29	0·00	0·00	0·00
Boy 2F1	8 years	34	m70·59	17·65	5·88	5·88	0·00
Boy 1	26 months	38	15·79	5·26	18·42	26·32	m34·21
Man A	45 years	29	48·28	m51·72	0·00	0·00	0·00
Boy A	11 years	40	m62·50	7·50	30·00	0·00	0·00
Monkey 6	15 years	36	19·44	22·22	19·44	m27·78	11·11
Monkey 3	5 years	39	23·08	23·08	20·51	m30·77	2·56
Monkey 4	1·5 years	39	17·95	15·38	12·82	m28·21	25·64
Monkey 2	1·5 years	34	14·71	14·71	m41·18	14·71	14·71
Monkey 1	1·5 years	37	16·22	m29·73	21·62	21·62	10·81
Dog 1	3 years	40	12·50	12·50	0·00	30·00	m45·00
Dog 2	1 year	42	11·90	30·95	0·00	m38·10	19·05
Dog 4F2	116 days	43	11·63	16·28	16·28	18·60	m37·21
Dog 6F2	109 days	48	16·67	27·08	20·83	6·25	m29·17
Dog 3F1	102 days	31	25·81	m38·71	12·90	0·00	22·58
Dog 8F1	95 days	42	4·76	16·67	0·00	26·19	m52·38
Dog 5F2	88 days	42	7·14	16·67	m28·57	19·05	28·57
Dog 7F1	81 days	51	17·65	9·80	9·80	29·41	m33·33
Dog 10F2	74 days	48	16·67	10·42	2·08	33·33	m37·50
Dog 9F1	67 days	52	15·38	9·62	13·46	23·08	m38·46
Dog 11F1	60 days	45	20·00	4·44	m33·33	13·33	28·89
Dog 12F1	53 days	35	11·43	20·00	31·43	0·00	m37·14
Dog 14F1	46 days	53	7·55	11·32	5·66	30·19	m45·28
Dog 13F2	43 days	41	17·07	24·39	12·20	17·07	m29·27
Dog 16F2	43 days	42	14·29	0·00	11·90	35·71	m38·10
Dog 18F1	36 days	48	12·50	4·17	6·25	25·00	m52·08
Cat 1	1 year	49	12·24	m30·61	10·20	18·37	28·57
Cat 2	1 year	42	4·76	11·90	0·00	33·33	m50·00
Cat 3	1 year	36	8·33	13·89	0·00	33·33	m44·44
Cat 7	70 days	53	7·55	1·89	0·00	22·64	m67·92
Cat 5	56 days	51	5·88	19·61	0·00	5·88	m68·63
Horse 1	8 years	50	8·00	4·00	2·00	24·00	m62·00

The evidences of marked individual differences contained in table 4 must be looked upon, of course, as a serious obstacle to any effort to deal with the results in terms of age and phyletic averages. It is obvious that such averages, to be available for conclusive interpretations, would have to be obtained from a far greater number of subjects for experiment than could be practically used in an exploratory investigation. However, since the averages obtainable from the above table may serve to attract attention to some interesting possibilities in genetic psychology, the writer is justified, I believe, in presenting them.

Table 5

Distribution of Classified Reactions According To Age and Phyletic Averages

Subjects	Average age	Total classi- fied reac- tions	Distribution of classified reactions in percentage of same				
			Type A %	Type B %	Type C %	Type D %	Type E %
Older human (8)	14 years	226	76·11	19·47	2·21	1·77	0·44
Man A (1)	45 years	29	48·28	51·72	0·00	0·00	0·00
Boy A (1)	11 years	40	62·50	7·50	30·00	0·00	0·00
Infant (1)	26 months	38	15·79	5·26	18·42	26·32	34·21
Mature monkeys (2)	10 years	75	21·33	22·67	20·00	29·33	6·67
Immature monkeys (2)	1·5 years	71	15·49	22·53	30·99	18·31	12·68
Mature dogs (2)	2 years	82	12·20	21·95	0·00	34·15	31·71
Older puppies (6)	98·50 days	357	13·61	19·84	14·79	17·51	34·24
Younger puppies (8)	52·75 days	364	14·26	10·16	13·74	23·08	38·76
Mature cats (3)	1 year	127	8·66	19·68	3·94	27·56	40·16
Kittens (2)	63 days	104	6·73	10·58	0·00	14·42	68·27
Horse (1)	8 years	50	8·00	4·00	2·00	24·00	62·00

Discussion of table 5. The significance of the findings of the table becomes more apparent when they are plotted in distribution curves, as shown in figure 3. Reference to these curves will disclose the following facts concerning the general effects of age and phyletic position on mode of adjustment:

(1) The curve for the older human subjects attains its greatest height at point A, whence it descends rapidly to point B, thence to point C, where it closely approximates the base (zero) line. From C to D to E the curve descends continuously.

(2) The infant's curve is relatively low at point A, whence it descends abruptly to point B, after which it ascends continuously and rather sharply until it reaches its maximum height at E.

(3) Defective Man A's curve *ascends* from A to B; from B it descends directly to the base line, with which it is coincident at points C, D and E.

(4) Defective Boy A's curve descends sharply from A to B, undergoes a marked secondary rise at C, and from there passes to the base line, with which it is coincident at D and E.

(5) The mature monkey's curve ascends slightly from A to B; descends slightly from B to C; attains its maximum height at D, from which point it descends sharply to E, where it is near the base line.

(6) The immature monkey's curve differs radically from that of the mature monkey's in that it ascends continuously and rather sharply from A to B to C, attaining its greatest height at C; the descent from C to D to E is likewise sharp and continuous. The curve is lower at A and higher at E than is the mature monkey's curve at these points.

(7) The mature dogs' curve makes a considerable ascent from A to B; drops to the base line at C, from which it ascends to its

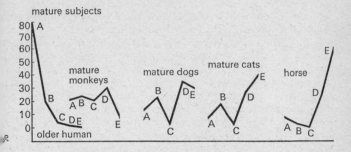

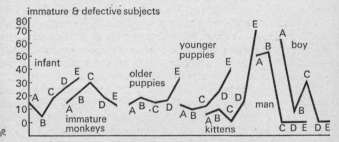

Figure 3 Curves showing the distribution of classified reactions. 'A', 'B', 'C', 'D' and 'E' refer to the types of classified reactions described in the text and the points marked by these letters indicate the percentages of the various reactions thus designated.

maximum height at D; and makes a slight descent from D to E. In view of the fact that with prolonged experience the dog tends to manifest C reactions only, the absolute absence of these reactions, as reflected by the position of C in their curve of distribution, is of considerable interest.

(8) The older puppies' curve ascends from A to B; descends slightly from B to C, after which it ascends slightly to D; and ascends sharply to attain its maximum height at E.

275

(9) The younger puppies' curve, when compared with that o the older puppies', affords us material of some value for onto genetic interpretations, since the averages for these two group include a considerable number of subjects. In both curves, A i relatively near the base line, but in the younger puppies' curv there is a descent from A to B, as compared with an A to B ascen in the older puppies' curve. From C to E both curves ascend con tinuously, but the younger puppies' curve makes a sharpe ascent, and is higher at E.

(10) The mature cats' curve bears a striking resemblance t that of the mature dogs', the only points in which they are essenti ally different being as follows: (a) The mature cats' curve i slightly above the base line at C, whilst in the case of the matur dogs' it is coincident with the base line at C; (b) the mature cat curve ascends from D to E, attaining its maximum height at E whilst the mature dogs' curve slightly descends from D to E. It i quite possible that averages for large number of cats and dog would efface these differences. It may be stated, however, that th writer's experience with these two classes of subjects leads him t believe that the average cat is more prone to manifest the Type reaction than is the average dog.

(11) The kittens' curve has many points of similarity with th older puppies' curve; it ascends from A to B; descends fro B to C, from which point it ascends to D; from D it ascends ver sharply to E, where it attains its maximum height.

(12) The horse's curve is near the base line until it reaches C from which it ascends sharply to D; from D it makes a st sharper ascent to E, the point of maximum height.

V. Interpretations of Results. Conclusions

It has been shown, I believe, that the higher mammals manife striking differences of modes of trial and error activity, and th these differences cannot be adequately expressed in terms rapidity of habit formation alone. The results indicate, also, th need of intensive behavior-studies along hitherto unexplored lin of investigation. The present chapter seeks to relate the types reaction that have been discussed in the foregoing to inferre reactive tendencies, and thus to assign psychological values to th curves of distribution shown in figure 3. This attempt must prefaced, however, by a statement of the viewpoints from whic the interpretations that follow have been undertaken.

While the Comparative Psychologist has been almost excl sively concerned with a single psychological value–associativ memory[2] – the field of Psychopathology has been revolutionized by a group of men who have shown that behavior is determined by a vast complexus of reactive tendencies which demand isolation and psychological estimation. These men, notably Freud (6), Jung (7), Bleuler (8), and Adolf Meyer (9), have opened up, by their activities along highly specialized lines of interest, new possibilities for the development of genetic psychology. They have shown, by implication, at least, that genetic psychology should not be solely concerned with the developmental history of the specifically adaptive instincts and of the mature human ability to think according to the traditional canons of logic. The dancing mouse's acquisition of a habit of selecting a spatially variable white labelled avenue of escape from pain, and the mathematician's solution of a problem in infinitesimal calculus are alike to be looked upon as end-products of reactive tendencies which have been variously subjected to the selective, suppressive, fixative and other corrective influences of experience. We must have knowledge, therefore, of the genetic relationships, not only of the adequately adaptive end-products in behavior, but of the reactive tendencies that lead to these end-products.

The present investigation becomes intelligible only when account is taken of the fact that it seeks to deal with the fundamental factors on which adaptation depends, rather than with the ultimate effects of experience on behavior. Figure 3 depicts, therefore, roughly determined curves of reactive tendency, and not curves of learning. Since their value as curves of reactive tendency will depend on the accuracy with which the objective facts are translated into terms of psychic entities, we are confronted by the difficult task of establishing an objective criterion of the subjective. How may we recognize a reactive tendency in the behavior of our subjects? During the interpretations that follow, a tentatively constructed criterion will be adhered to: *A mode of adjustment which appears, disappears and reappears consistently with ascent or descent of the age and phyletic scales may be looked upon as an expression of a definite reactive tendency.*

If this criterion be accepted, a tremendous amount of detailed investigation will be required to establish conclusively the existence of even a few reactive tendencies as biological entities.

With the above in mind as a qualification of what follows, we may proceed to an interpretation of results by first presenting a summary of the values for reaction contained in the experiment:

2. The writer assumes that functional studies of the sense organs belong to physiology rather than to psychology.

(1) All of the subjects brought to the formal experiment a more or less definite awareness of the four exit doors as possible means of escape from the apparatus, hence the demand for adjustment was essentially contained in the mere necessity of clawing, scratching, or pushing at one or more previously mobile objects (all of the exit doors were left unlocked during the preliminary training) until activity proved successful.

(2) Without exception, all of the subjects gave definite evidence of trying for success (escape from the apparatus) until success was attained.

(3) For every subject a considerable percentage of trials led to more or less unsuccessful activity (trying locked doors).

(4) In every case the individual trial was terminated by a definitely directed activity (trying the unlocked door).

(5) The relation of every present trial to its immediate predecessor was such as to exact a penalty of non-success for trying the unlocked door of the immediately preceding trial.

(6) During a given trial, a second or third, etc., effort to open a particular door was invariably unsuccessful: a door which would not yield to a single, definitely directed attack during a given trial could not possibly be opened by the subject during that trial.

(7) The various doors were discriminable, one from another.

Under the conditions just enumerated, the various types of reaction that we have isolated are capable of the following psychological interpretations:

Type A. To conform to this type, the reaction must include a single, definite effort to open each of the three inferentially possible doors, and must not include an effort to open the inferentially impossible door. It will be remembered that the impossible door varied from trial to trial.

Now it is evident that only an awareness of the impossible door as such would enable any subject to manifest appreciably more than 50 per cent of Type A reactions out of his total number of classified reactions. If the impossible door were of indifferent value for reaction, either as impossible or as the object of the subject's latest successful activity, and if during no trial the subject were to make more than a single effort to open any one door, his record would tend to show 50 per cent of Type A reactions and 50 per cent of Type B or C reactions. Of course, a preference for the impossible door or a tendency to make more than a single continuous effort to open a particular door during a given trial would impair the subject's chance of approximating even 50 per cent of Type A reactions.

What reactive tendency, then, would lead to more than 50 per cent of Type A reactions? It is obvious that this cannot be the primitive tendency to reduce diffuse activity-impulses to a definite attack upon a single object. The situation rendered it impossible for any subject to associate a simple object with successful activity and to obtain thereby a formula for invariable success. On the other hand, the establishment of a simple negative association was not sufficient to enable any subject to avoid the impossible door. This spatially varying object-to-be-avoided could clearly obtain its true value for reaction only among the subjects who were able to elaborate a succession of previous experiences in such a manner as to associate, at each trial, the door last opened with an awareness equivalent to 'during any present trial the door last opened is apt to be impossible as a means of exit'. In other words, there would have to be an association in which one of the elements would be a complexly derived awareness of a principal deterrent to the activity involved in trying the unlocked door of the immediately preceding trial. The conscious avoidance of the impossible door as such may therefore be looked upon as due to a tendency to make rational inferences from a sequence of past experiences. For convenience of statement it will be referred to hereafter as '*the rational inference tendency*'.

Type B. This reaction involves trying all four doors, but once each, and in an irregular order.

From the normal adult human viewpoint this adjustment contains but one error, viz., the inferentially and actually useless effort to open the impossible door. In cases where there is clearly apparent a perception of the impossible door principle (i.e., where there is given a record of appreciably more than 50 per cent of Type A reactions), the manifestation of Type B reactions may be assigned either to mere inattention or to lapse of memory, or to the necessity of falling into the impossible door error a certain number of times before an awareness of the principle can be obtained. If we exclude these cases, the Type B reaction may be looked upon as an expression of a high type of searching tendency. Although it shows a lack of modification by the higher tendency to make rational inferences, it is of much significance as showing the absence of modification by the lower tendencies to which we shall ascribe reactions of the C, D and E types. Of course the inclusion of an effort to open the impossible door may be due, in a certain number of cases, to the interference of a tendency to associate the last successful activity with the impossible door, in which case the searching tendency is not the sole reactive factor.

But since we are dealing only with the reactive tendencies that precede the establishment of definite and habitual associations, we may, for convenience, refer to Type B reactions as due to 'the unmodified searching tendency'. This, of course, only when the number of Type A reactions is so small as to exclude the possibility that mere inattention or forgetfulness have interfered with an adequate expression of the rational inference tendency.

Type C. This highly interesting mode of adjustment can occur, as has been explained, only when Door 1 or Door 4 is the unlocked door for the trial. It involves merely the act of trying (1) Doors 1, 2, 3 and 4 but once each and in the order given when Door 4 is the unlocked door, or (2) doors 4, 3, 2 and 1 but once each and in the order given when door 1 is the unlocked door. The habit of starting at either the first or the last door from the left and working down the line of doors, striking each as it is passed until an unlocked door is found, deserves, in itself, a far more extensive investigation than it has thus far received. My observations of the higher infra-human mammals, of children and of mentally defective or diseased persons lead me to believe that in this mode of adjustment we have the expression of a reactive tendency which has extensive genetic relationships, and which can be more easily recognized in behavior than can any other reactive tendency of which we have knowledge. In the discussions that follow Type C reactions will be referred to as due to 'the tendency to adopt stereotyped modes of searching'.

Type D. This reaction involves the error of making more than one separate, continuous effort to open a given door during the same trial, but always with an interruption of such repetitions of activity by an interval of effort to open one or more of the other doors. Since this mode of adjustment is objectively continuous with a form of Type E reaction (sub-type c, described below), and yet clearly should not be made to include the latter, I have excluded from Type D all reactions involving more than six separate efforts to open doors during a given trial.

A characteristic example of the Type D reaction will render its interpretation more intelligible. During his fortieth trial Dog 16F2 made a vigorous effort to open Door 1, which was locked; failing in this effort, he tried to open Door 2, which also baffled him in his efforts to escape. Then he returned to Door 1 and made a second effort to open it by giving it two or three feeble scratches, after which he tried Doors 3 and 4, the latter of which yielded to his attack.

Anybody who has ever sought vainly, and with some irritation, a lost collar button, will readily appreciate the inner significance of this behavior. One looks into every likely nook and corner, then remembers that on previous occasions he has discovered lost articles in a drawer which is seldom used because of its tendency to 'stick'. The drawer is opened and is found to be quite empty; one turns away and looks elsewhere, only to return in a moment to the empty drawer and again to open it in a stupid, unthinking manner. The impulse to open the drawer seems to have subsided with the first failure, only to come surging back with most inappropriate persistence.

Type D reactions will hereafter be referred to as due to 'the searching tendency modified by recrudescent motor impulses'.

Type E. This type includes several different modes of behavior which have a common objective characteristic, viz., automatism. That is, the subject behaves in a relatively implastic, unadaptive manner. The objective characteristics of the various sub-types may be reviewed as follows:

Sub-type a. The subject makes two or more successive but definitely separate attempts to open the same door during a given trial. Thus he tries Door 3, finds it locked, turns away from it, returns to this same door and makes a second effort to open it without having tried any other door in the meantime, etc. In view of the fact that in the majority of cases such persistence in returning to the same door during a given trial could not be attributed to the recency with which it had afforded escape (as compared with the recency with which the other doors had afforded escape), we are justified in assuming, I believe, that the sub-type a reaction is an expression of the unmodified primitive tendency to repeat an activity, once it is begun, until it leads quite definitely to pain or success.

Sub-type b. During a given trial the subject tries a group of locked doors two or more times in an unvarying order. Cat 1's ninety-fifth trial well illustrates this mode of adjustment. When this animal entered the apparatus to meet, for the ninety-fifth time, a situation which merely required that she find the one unlocked door, she tried the exit doors in the following order: *2–1–4* – *2–1–4* – *2–1–4* – 2–1–3, I have italicised each of three exactly similar cycles of activity in order to bring out more clearly the characteristic features of a mode of adjustment which seemed to spring from a persistent impulse to try Doors 2, 1 and 4 again and again, in an unvarying order. Now during her experience with ninety-four previous trials she had found Door 3 unlocked twenty-three times, Door 2 twenty-four times, Door 1 twenty-four times and Door 4 twenty-three times. It seems that no elements in these experiences were sufficient to awaken an impulse to try Door 3 after she had given definite expression to the first impulses to try Doors 4, 1 and 2; and that these latter impulses continued to reassert themselves as a connected whole until a break in the fourth cycle of activities led her to try Door 3 instead of Door 4.

Sub-type c. The subject, having avoided a given exit door during a trial, continues to avoid it while the other doors are tried at least six times and these six or more efforts to open the other doors do not contain errors of either the sub-type a or sub-type b kind. The ninety-fourth trial of Dog 9F1 affords an example of this behavior. On entering the apparatus she went to door 3, raised her paw as if about to strike it, then desisted without having touched the door. Following this she tried the doors in the following order: 1–2–4–2–1–2–4–1–2–3. The effect of the initial inhibition of the impulse to strike door 3 is apparent, I believe, in the reaction-formula just given; this inhibition persisted, so that whenever the subject passed door 3 she failed to include it in her list of doors to be tried. If the order in which she tried the other doors had suggested a mere perseveration of active motor impulses, or if she had tried these doors less than six times, the writer would not have felt justified in tabulating her reaction as belonging to sub-type c.

In view of the fact that many of the reactions manifested by the infant and the animals presented the characteristics of all three Type E sub-types, it has been found more satisfactory to deal with all Type E reactions as a unit for analysis and interpretation. This is justified, I believe, by the fact that the three sub-types are alike interpretable in terms of a single general tendency, viz., perseveration of impulses. Finer analyses of behavior than are possible in the present investigation would doubtless show that we are here dealing with a group of several distinctly different primitive reactive tendencies. As a psychopathologist, the writer finds much interest in the fact that a clinical phenomenon common to the dementia praecox group of psychoses is met with at certain points in the normal ontogenetic and phylogenetic scales; wherever a tendency to 'perseveration' exists, it is apt to find expression in the continuous persistence of both useless activities and useless avoidances of activities. The katatonic who continues a motor impulse to the point of catalepsy, or who utters a single word for hours without interruption, is always a patient in whose behavior we expect also to find inordinate persistence of inhibitions. My investigation of normal behavior has disclosed the same association of the one phenomenon with the other in the case of dogs, cats, a horse, and a human infant. The fifth trial of the infant affords an example of this; he tried the various doors in the following order: 3–1–3–4–1–4–3–4–4–4–3–1–4–3–2. Even more striking is the fifty-ninth reaction of Cat 5, who tried the doors in the following order: 3–4–1–3–3–1–3–4–4–1–3–1–3–4–4–1–4–3–2. In each case there are apparent both types of perseveration.

VI. Summary and Conclusions

The above interpretations of Types A, B, C, D and E reactions in terms of reactive tendencies to which they may be ascribed now enable us tentatively to assign psychological values to the genetic curves of distribution in figure 3.

(1) *The rational inference tendency* (Type A) is clearly apparent in the behavior of only the eight normal human subjects whose ages range from eight to thirty-four years, and in the behavior of defective Boy A. Morgan's (10) law of parsimony as applied to interpretations of behavior, requires us to assign the behavior of all other subjects, including that of defective Man A, to lower reactive tendencies. We have not ruled out the possibility, of course, that with sufficient experience any of the subjects would manifest a sufficient percentage of Type A reactions to indicate the presence of the rational inference tendency; nor that the subjects who manifested relatively low percentages of these reactions were wholly uninfluenced by the tendency in the question.

(2) *The unmodified searching tendency* (Type B) finds its most frequent expression in the behavior of defective Man A. Among adult animals, the monkeys rank first in this respect, the dogs second, the cats third, and the horse fourth. Of all the subjects, taken as individuals and without regard to age, the horse seems to have been least affected by the unmodified searching tendency.

The ontogenetic findings parallel the phylogenetic; among human subjects, monkeys, dogs of three different age-groups, and cats, there is apparent a tendency for a sufficient decrease in age to decrease the percentage of Type B reactions.

(3) *The tendency to adopt stereotyped modes of searching* (Type C) seems to acquire its maximum phylogenetic value for the monkeys; it is but slightly apparent in the behavior of the older normal human subjects and the other mature animals.

The ontogenetic relationships of this reactive tendency are interesting. The immature monkeys and defective Boy A are especially affected by it; but it is more apparent in the behavior of the older puppies than in that of either the mature dogs or the younger puppies. The latter circumstance is a matter of some perplexity to the writer, since, as has been said, the Type C reaction becomes an habitual mode of adjustment with mature dogs who have had sufficiently prolonged experience with the situations of the experiment.

(4) *The searching tendency modified by recrudescent motor impulses* (Type D reaction), regularly increases in frequency of manifestation as we descend the phyletic scale of mature subjects until we reach the mature dogs, at which point it attains its maximum frequency. This tendency decreases as we pass further down the scale through the cats to the horse.

Ontogenetically, it increases in frequency of manifestation with descent from older childhood to infancy; but, with one exception, the younger animals are less affected by it than are their older fellows; the younger puppies give a higher percentage of the Type D reactions than do the older puppies.

(5) *The tendency toward perseveration of active motor impulses and of inhibitions* (Type E) increases regularly in the frequency of its manifestation as both the ontogenetic and phylogenetic scales are descended. It is of interest that during the total one thousand trials of the ten older human subjects (the two defectives being included) there was but one manifestation of this tendency – the first reaction of the much embarrassed Boy 7, whilst 34·21 per cent of the infant's classified reactions may be ascribed to this tendency.

The present investigation has afforded experimental evidence that the phylogenetic and ontogenetic differences of adequacy of mammalian adjustments are to be accounted for not merely in terms of sense-physiology and of associative habit formation, but in terms of reactive tendencies as well. Evidence has also been adduced to support the view that the elaboration of experience involves an interplay of conflicting reactive tendencies, and that these are experimentally isolatable according to criteria legitimate to genetic psychology.

A final and still more general conclusion to be drawn from the above is as follows: Since the ideal development of genetic psychology demands the unravelling of long and intricately interwoven mental complexes, not only as they appear in a given species or at a given age, but throughout extensive phyletic and age series, our intensive studies of behavior are apt to become irrelevant to the broader issues in which they seek justification if we do not explore, from time to time, for the general patterns according to which the threads of fact are arranged. The satisfaction derived from the accurate and conclusive determination of the quality and dimensions of a single thread as it appears in a carefully delimited part of its course is apt to blind the genetic psychologist to the historical significance of his own attitude. Darwin (11), Spencer (12), Romanes (13), and Baldwin (14), among others, have sought to deduce from extensive ranges of facts the more general principles of mental development. Their statements concerning general principles have led to the formulation of many detailed problems, and to methods appropriate to the investigation of these problems, with the result that the observations of behavior recorded by the older writers are now shown to have been made under insufficiently controlled conditions, and that their interpretations were often at fault. The obvious need of detailed investigation as thus disclosed, everywhere finds recognition in the work of the younger students of behavior. But the equally obvious need of seeking direction anew from a general survey of comprehensive collections of facts at the expense, if need be, of some sacrifice of accuracy of detail, seems to have gained nothing more substantial than verbal recognition.

The writer begs to acknowledge his indebtedness to Professor Robert M. Yerkes, Professor Adolf Meyer, and Mr George R. Agassiz for many helpful suggestions and criticisms.

References
1. YERKES, R. M., AND DODSON, JOHN D. 1908. The Relation of Strength of Stimulus to Rapidity of Habit-Formation. *Jour. Comp. Neurol. and Psychol.*, vol. 18, No. 5, pp. 459–491.
2. YERKES, R. M. 1907. The Dancing Mouse, p. 3. *New York.*
3. HAMILTON, G. V. 1907. An Experimental Study of an Unusual Type of Reaction in a Dog. *Jour. Comp. Neurol. and Psychol.*, vol. 17, No. 4, pp. 329–341.
4. BERRY, C. S. 1908. An Experimental Study of Imitation in Cats. *Jour. Comp. Neurol. and Psychol.*, vol. 18, No. 1, pp. 1–25.
5. THORNDIKE, E. L. 1898. Animal Intelligence. *Psychol. Review, Monograph Series*, vol. 2, No. 4.
6. FREUD, SIGMUND. 1900. Die Traumdeutung. *Vienna.* 1907. Zur Psychopathologie des Alltagslebens. *Berlin.*
7. JUNG, C. G. 1907. Ueber die Psychologie der Dementia Praecox. *Halle, a. S.*
8. BLEULER, E. 1906. Affectivität, Suggestibilität, Paranoia. *Halle a. S.*
9. MEYER, ADOLF. 1908. The Problems of Mental Reaction-Types, Mental Causes and Diseases. *Psychol. Bulletin*, vol. 5, No. 8, pp. 245–261.

10. MORGAN, C. L. 1904. An Introduction to Comparative Psychology, p. 53. *New York*.
11. DARWIN, C. R. 1872. Expression of the Emotions in Men and Animals.
12. SPENCER, HERBERT. 1855. Principles of Psychology.
13. ROMANES, G. J. 1883. Animal Intelligence. *New York*.
14. BALDWIN, J. M. 1903. Mental Development in the Child and the Race. *New York*.

20 N. R. F. Maier

Reasoning and Learning

Excerpt from N. R. F. Maier, 'Reasoning and learning', *Psychol. Rev.*, vol. 38 (1931), pp. 332–42.

Our definitions of learning, insight and reasoning are so vague and elastic that they convey little which is of scientific value. The conventional laws of association[1] are, however, specific and can be subjected to experimentation. Because the definitions of intelligent behavior are usually vague, it is not surprising that explanations of behavior which have recourse to the mechanical principles of the laws of association have been preferred.

At the present time many students of behavior are agreed that the laws of association are quite inadequate for explaining certain types of behavior, but definite experimental definitions of alternatives are still lacking. Insight has not been defined so as to be experimentally useful. The same behavior data may indicate evidence of insight to one experimenter and the absence of it to another.

The purpose of the present paper is to (1) define learning, insight, and reasoning in experimental terms; (2) harmonize the experimental data obtained from studies on both rats and man; and (3) suggest a mechanism which accounts for the spontaneous appearance of new behavior integrations.

I

In 1929 I published a study (7) in which an attempt was made to demonstrate that certain types of rat behavior could not be explained by the traditional laws of association. The experiments in principle consisted of giving the rat two isolated (non-contiguous) experiences and seeing whether the essentials of each of these could be combined in such a manner as to reach the goal. It was concluded that (1) rats could combine the essentials of two isolated experiences in such a manner as to reach the goal;

1. The laws of association are here understood to be the association or combination of two things which have been experienced in contiguity (spacial or temporal); the strength of the associative bond being a function of the recency and frequency of the experience, and perhaps also of the intensity and primacy of the experience. Physiologically these combinations are explained by a lowering of the resistance at the synapse, because of use.

(2) such combinations were not reducible to the laws of association; and (3) such patterns of behavior characterized reasoning.

Dashiell (2) recognizes the interpretation of results given (*i.e.*, that the rat combined the essentials of two isolated experiences) to be an explanation of the facts, but presents what he believes to be alternative and simpler explanations. He writes (p. 54) 'while such an interpretation is certainly relevant and covers the facts, the present writer is not altogether convinced that simpler explanations are not possible'. Simpler interpretations are then given.

As it is granted that 'the combination of two isolated experiences' does account for the facts, it remains for us to show that the alternative explanations are inadequate. In general the tests used for demonstrating the ability of rats to combine two isolated experiences may be described as follows. A rat was allowed to become familiar with a certain territory (*e.g.*, a room). The gaining of such familiarity was called Experience 1. Then, with food placed on a table, the rat was made to run an elevated pathway to the food.[2] This run was called Experience 2. In the test the animal was placed at a point within the territory with which it had become familiar in Experience 1. From this point the animal would have to go to the elevated pathway to obtain food.

After the experimental conditions had been varied in many different ways and chance solutions had been excluded, it was concluded that the rats reached the goal by combining the essentials of Experience 1 with Experience 2.

Dashiell suggests (p. 54) that the rat's response to the starting point of the pathway may have been a direct response to a detail in the environment. Experimental checks, however, showed that the starting point of the pathway offered neither visual nor olfactory cues, and consequently was not in the animal's perceptual environment. Rats failed when either Experience 1 (knowledge of the territory) or Experience 2 (learning pathway to food) was omitted, but succeeded when the test run was made in total darkness. If the response were determined by a detail in the rat's environment the results should have been reversed. But if we say that the rat solved the problem by combining parts of two isolated experiences, the results obtained are to be expected. The rat could not combine two experiences when only one of them had been given.

A second alternative, according to Dashiell, is that the starting

2. This pathway was placed within the explored territory, but was no present during the exploration period.

point of the pathway was an enhanced stimulus. To say that it was enhanced seems to be saying no more than that it was favored by the rat. That is, of course, the fact. The question is, how was it enhanced? In order to explain this we must postulate that two isolated experiences came together. Consequently this alternative seems not to be a substitute explanation, but rather an alternative way of describing the rat's behavior. In my monograph (p. 92) I pointed out that the starting point of the pathway may have become a more intensified experience, but that this in no way excluded the interpretation of two isolated experiences being combined.

In a situation in which the location of the food was known to the rat, but in which the indirect route to the food was unfamiliar (Experience 2 omitted), rats when running around the pathway failed to take the turns which lead in the direction of the food in preference to those which lead away from the food.[3] Dashiell considers the results of this experiment to be a disproof of intelligent behavior on the part of the rat. Yet if the pathway is unfamiliar to the rat, and only the position of the food is known, how was the animal to behave intelligently? The integration of a known and an unknown is an unknown.

However, on the basis of Dashiell's interpretation of his own results the rats should have solved the problem. He found that (1) rats when running a maze tend to enter culs-de-sac which lie on the same side of the maze as the food compartment; and (2) no particular route to food will be learned when there are a number of routes of equal length, nevertheless errorless runs will be made. The rats learn to go in the right general direction, rather than depend on local cues from point to point. He concludes that the rat has a directional sense which aids it in its runs through the maze. This being the case my rats should have preferred the pathways which led in the direction of the food in the above experiment.

Dashiell says that the experiments on delayed reaction, in which gross bodily postures were used by the rat, suggested the concept of organic postures to him. The present writer has found (8) that under certain experimental conditions rats can delay their responses for 24 hours without the aid of gross motor attitudes.

3. In this experiment (Experiment 9, p. 67) the rat was placed on a table next to food which was inaccessible because of a wire cage. A simple pathway, which was unfamiliar to the rat, led around to the food. This pathway contained 2 or 3 junctions at which points the animal could either turn away from or in the direction of the food.

The conclusion reached from this study is that bodily postures are necessitated by the method of experimentation, rather than by conditions inherent in the nature of the task. If this is the case, a general orientation sense becomes much more difficult to explain.

The evidence for behavior patterns made up of two or more isolated experiences thus seems to be worthy of further consideration. There is also a very considerable amount of evidence for behavior patterns made up of contiguous experiences. It can hardly be questioned that when two things are experienced together in space or time they *may* become associated.[4] That they are combined because of their contiguity is fundamental to our theories of learning.

In a recent study (11) I postulated two possible types of behavior integrations; the one, made up of isolated experiences and called ability R; the other, made up of contiguous experiences and called ability L.

Tests were then devised to measure these possible types of behavior patterns. Test R measured ability R, and tests $R - L$ and $R + L$ measured ability R opposed by L and ability R in conjunction with L, respectively. Thus a habit was sometimes such as to favor an incorrect response, and sometimes such as to favor a correct response. Ability R always involved the combining of two isolated experiences.

Normal rats and rats with injuries to the cortex on the frontal half of the brain were then put through the tests.

The results showed that abilities R and L both were realities. Further, ability R was markedly affected by the brain lesion, and the extent of the effect was related to the extent of the injury. Ability L, however, was affected but little if at all by lesions involving as much as 40 per cent of the exposed surface of the brain.

Thus we have further evidence to show that there are two qualitatively different types of behavior patterns. The one made up of contiguous experiences is in harmony with the usual concepts of learning. It implies that previous repetitions of the relationships involved in the behavior pattern are necessary. It therefore seems that integrations of this sort characterize learned behavior.

Behavior integrations which are made up of two or more isolated experiences are qualitatively different, and must be

4. Lewin (4) found that the conditions of experimentation determined whether or not two successive nonsense syllables would be associated.

indicated by a different term. They arise without previous repetitions (except the repetition of the isolated experiences) and consequently are new. They are not the product of trial and error.

The term reasoning implies that something new has been brought about, and that in some way, past experiences have been manipulated. It therefore seems that behavior patterns made up of two isolated experiences characterize what is meant by behavior which is the product of reasoning.

On the basis of such experimental definitions of learning and reasoning, learned behavior depends for its integration upon the order in which past experiences occurred; whereas behavior resulting from reasoning depends for its integration upon the goal or end.

In learned behavior the goal furnishes the drive which sets off a pattern of response previously laid down. In reasoning (as it is defined in this paper) past experiences are reorganized. That the combination of the essentials of two isolated experiences makes it possible for an animal to reach a goal implies a reorganization in terms of the goal. This ability thus makes reorganization of any experience possible. If two isolated experiences can be organized in terms of the goal, it then follows that two contiguous experiences may be reorganized. Consequently maze learning (although the experiences are contiguous) may be influenced by ability R as well as by ability L. With both abilities present any behavior pattern may be the product of an interaction of abilities R and L.

Problem solving by insight is regarded by the exponents of Gestalt theory as qualitatively different from problem solving on the basis of trial and error. In the light of the above definitions of learning and reasoning, insight may be defined as the experience an organism has when two or more isolated experiences come together. Thus insight is the sudden experiencing of new relations.

II

With these experimental definitions in mind we may turn to some studies on human reasoning. In my study on 'direction' (9) the solution of a problem was broken into three parts. These parts were given as separate experiences to individual subjects who had been previously divided into groups. One group was told that the three parts when properly combined formed the solution to the problem; another group had the three experiences presented to it, but was not told that the parts had anything to do with the problem. A control group was not presented with the three experiences before being asked to solve the problem.

The results showed that these three groups did not differ in their attempts to solve the problem. Only 1 out of 52 subjects solved the problem.

Thus it seems that mere experience or even the selection of the pertinent experiences was not enough for solving the problem. The integration of the parts in terms of the goal was still lacking.

In order to aid in the integration of the separate experiences an additional group was caused to see the problem in a certain way, *i.e.*, a certain point of view, or a start in a certain 'direction' was given in addition to the three parts. As a result 8 out of 22 subjects solved the problem immediately.

It was concluded that when a person attempts to solve a problem, he sees the difficulty to be of a certain sort. Past experiences are then organized in such a manner as to tend to overcome this difficulty.[5] Behavior or lines of thought which are directed at the overcoming of a certain difficulty may be characterized as the 'direction' in which a person is thinking. When the difficulty one attempts to overcome is wrong (leads to no solution), all consequent organization is in vain. The experiments showed that 'directions' were so decided and dominating that they caused helpful suggestions to be so applied as to fit in with the organizations of experiences which they were determining. Consequently many suggestions were useless and even misleading. Only when the direction in thinking was an attempt to overcome the correct difficulty were suggestions successfully used. Thus 'direction' determines which experiences will be facilitated and which will be blocked or inhibited.

In a further study (10) it was found that a suggestion might be successfully used even when the subject was unaware of having received it or even of having used it. This study indicated that the solution-integration came suddenly, and masked any cue which set it off. The solution of a problem is thus the sudden organization of a number of detached and isolated experiences.

The subjects' reports, however, were in harmony with a

5. For example, if two scientists were trying to stamp out a disease, one might see the difficulty to be that of making man immune to a germ; the other might consider the difficulty to be that of the prevention of the germ's spreading. Because these men see different difficulties they would make altogether different kinds of attempts to solve the same problem. The first would experiment with serums, the second would study the development and habits of the germ. Past experiences that would prove most valuable to the one man would be of no use to the other.

mental trial and error explanation of reasoning. Because the cue which brought about the solution was not experienced, whereas the previous unsuccessful attempts were experienced, the unsuccessful attempts were reported. The solution appearing as a complete experience was thus regarded by the subject to be just another attempt at solving the problem. It is therefore easy to understand why trial and error theories of reasoning should have arisen.

Because the solution involved the sudden integration of parts of different experiences, new relations suddenly appeared, and brought with them a sudden change in the meaning of the elements involved. Thus we see why the Gestalt school insists that reasoning carries with it a sudden change in meanings.

III

We are now confronted with the problem of finding a fundamental principle which will explain how the end, which involves the overcoming of a certain difficulty, may organize the essentials of certain isolated experiences.

Elsewhere (9, p. 139) I suggested that the 'direction' which is set up when a person is trying to solve a problem seemed to be a field of strain. Such a field of strain must determine the organization of experiences, and must inhibit certain past experiences and facilitate others.

The results of unpublished studies on association by Shepard (12) and by Shepard and Fogelsonger (13) clearly show the inadequacy of a drainage theory for explaining certain cases of reproductive inhibition. Shepard's concept of a 'pattern of stress' seems to be a necessary assumption for an explanation of their results.

The results from a study by Lewin and Zeigarnik (5) give further justification for the use of a 'field of strain' concept. They studied the effect that the non-completion of a task had on memory. A series of twenty different tasks (puzzle pictures, modeling, bead stringing, etc.) were presented to a large number of subjects. Some of these tasks were allowed to go to completion (*i.e.*, the subject was permitted to finish the task); some were interrupted and left uncompleted; while the remaining tasks were interrupted, but completed later in the experiment. The results show that tasks which were completed either with or without interruption were recalled only half as well as tasks which were left uncompleted. Thus the non-completion of a task rather than the interruption determines the ease with which the task is recalled.

Subjects who performed the experiment in a fatigued condition and recalled the tasks in a refreshed state did not show a difference in their ability to recall completed and non-completed tasks, but subjects who performed the experiment in a refreshed state and recalled the tasks in a fatigued condition did show the difference. Emotional excitement after the completion of the experiment removed the difference in subject's ability to recall completed and non-completed tasks. Children were more affected by the non-completion of a task than were adults. Finally, the difference between the ease of the recall of completed and non-completed tasks was greater for tasks which had a definite point of termination (*e.g.*, modeling a dog) than for tasks which had no definite point of termination (*e.g.*, putting beads on a string).

The authors conclude that a task which has a definite goal (termination point) sets up an energy system which is relieved when the task is completed. An interruption blocks this release so that the energy remains and affects recall. In a fatigued condition the energy necessary for such a system is not available, whereas an emotional experience destroys the system. Children (and certain adults), because they enter into the experiment in a natural way, are more affected by a blocking of the energy system than adults who think they are being tested and thus are influenced by other factors. Finally, tasks with no definite end cannot set up a well-organized energy system, and thus are not markedly affected by non-completion.

These conclusions are based on the results of a well-controlled experiment, and are further substantiated by a study by Lewin and Ovsiankina (6). The results of this study showed that the non-completion of a task established a decided tendency to complete the uncompleted tasks on the first available opportunity.

In the light of modern physiology a field of strain can hardly be regarded as an empty concept. The physiological gradient of Child (1) is a field of strain. Physiological gradients are present whenever there is a source of stimulation or a difference in growth rate. This physiological field is a fundamental concept in general physiology and is used to explain physiological organization. In psychology, organization also requires an explanation, and for the present at least, a similar field hypothesis seems necessary.

The following examples illustrate the use of the field concept for the interpretation of behavior.

In a hungry rat there is present (1) a hunger drive, and (2) the sensory experience of food *in a certain surrounding*. These two factors set up a field of strain which causes the animal's activity to be such as to tend toward the attainment of the food, and a consequent disruption of the field. The field of strain will thus determine the animal's activity, whereas the complexity of the animal's nervous system will determine the types of behavior of which the animal is capable.

In reasoning the field of strain is set up by (1) the desire to solve the problem (reach the end), and (2) the knowledge of the end, the attainment of which offers certain difficulties. The solution of the problem would be the organization of parts of different past experiences in such a manner as to overcome a certain difficulty.[6] If the difficulty is seen to be one thing, the behavior is of one character; if it is seen to be something else the behavior is of another character. There are thus different types of behavior which depend on the difficulty an individual is attempting to overcome. In other words the types of behavior depend on certain 'directions'. Whether or not a problem is solved depends on (1) whether the 'direction' or field of strain is adequate; *i.e.*, whether the individual is trying to overcome a practical difficulty; and (2) whether a certain combination of parts of past experiences will result when the field of strain is adequate.

The localization of the organization of such types of behavior will be a matter of localizing fields within which such organizations arise. There can be no point for point localization in the older sense of the term, because the neural pathways are not specific; they depend on a field within which nervous impulses may take any number of possible courses. This concept of field localization is stressed by Herrick (3) who has found it necessary to take this position after a consideration of results obtained in recent studies related to anatomy and behavior.

Thus the concept of reasoning presented in this paper is in no way out of harmony with modern physiology and neurology. Our older psychological concepts are, however, based upon a neurology that neurologists no longer accept as adequate. [. . . .]

6. We are here discussing only solutions which are new. If a situation calls up the solution of a past problem which is found to be satisfactory, then such a solution is not new at the time and is therefore not a case of reasoning. Most situations do arouse organizations which have been built up in the past. Sometimes such attempted applications solve problems, but very often they prevent a solution because of their tendency to persist. Past organizations when functioning in a problematic situation produce what we have called 'habitual directions'. (See 9, pp. 137–141.)

Summary

After an examination of the results of studies on rats and man it is found that reasoning and learning have definite characteristics which make them qualitatively different. Association by contiguity is inadequate for explaining reasoning both in rats and man. To explain the spontaneous combination of isolated experiences the concept of a field of strain has been postulated. The evidence for and the consequences of this concept are discussed in detail. It is found that the concept of a field of strain is in harmony with the results obtained from recent studies in physiology and neurology.

References
1. CHILD, C. M., Physiological foundations of behavior, Univ. Chicago Press, 1924.
2. DASHIELL, J. F., Direction orientation in maze running by the white rat, *Comp. Psychol. Monog.*, 1930, 7.
3. HERRICK, C. J., Localization of function in the nervous system, *Proc. Nat. Acad. Sci.*, 1930, 16, 643–650.
4. LEWIN, K., Die psychische Tätigkeit bei der Hemmung von Willensvorgängen u. das Grunggesetz der Assoziation, *Zsch. f. Psychol.*, 1916, 77, 212–247.
5. LEWIN, K. u. ZEIGARNIK, B., Über das Behalten von erledigten u. unerledigten Handlungen, *Psychol Forsch.*, 1927, 9, 1–85.
6. LEWIN, K. u. OVSIANKINA, M., Die Wiederaufnahme unterbrochener Handlungen, *Psychol. Forsch.*, 1928, 11, 302–379.
7. MAIER, N. R. F., Reasoning in white rats, *Comp. Psychol. Monog.*, 1929, 6.
8. ——, Delayed reaction and memory in rats, *J. Genet. Psychol.*, 1929, 34, 538–550.
9. ——, Reasoning in humans, I On direction, *J. Comp. Psychol.*, 1930, 10, 115–143.
10. ——, Reasoning in humans, II The solution of a problem and its appearance in consciousness, *J. Comp. Psychol.*, 1931, 12, 181–194.
11. ——, The effect of cortical destruction on reasoning and learning in rats, *J. Comp. Neur.* 1932, 54, 45–75.
12. SHEPARD, J. F., Unpublished Studies.
13. SHEPARD, J. F. and FOGELSONGER, H. M., Studies in association and inhibition. *Psychol. Rev.*, 1913, 20, 290–311.

21 J. Cole

A Study of Discrimination Reversal Learning in Monkeys

J. Cole, 'A study of discrimination reversal learning in monkeys',
J. comp. physiol. Psychol., vol. 44 (1951), pp. 467–72.

While training monkeys and observing their behavior before and after brain lesions, we were confronted with the problems of animal learning. As much of our work involved teaching the monkeys various discriminations and discrimination reversals, the conflict between the rival theories of learning soon became apparent, and especially the divergence of opinion between those who accept in one form or another Krechevsky's (9, 10) 'hypotheses' theory, and those who prefer Spence's (14) 'continuity' theory.

In view of this disagreement, further study of the subject seemed justified. We decided to approach the problem along the lines of a discrimination reversal test, because, unlike simple discrimination learning, reversal discrimination learning yields a curve beginning in most cases with from 95 per cent to 100 per cent negative responses. This seemed desirable in order that we might be able to arrange our data to show the relative proportion of correct to incorrect choices throughout a greater range. For our purpose this was important, for it is this variation in the relative proportion of plus and minus responses throughout the whole series of choices that gives the clearest indication as to whether learning is by hypotheses or is a gradual, cumulative process as the continuity theory asserts.

Method

Subjects

Five monkeys were used in the experiment, three male *Macaca nemestrina*, Priam, Solon, and Hector, one male *Erythrocebus patas*, Jason, and one female *Macaca mulatta*, Calypso. All five were about half-grown and had had some preliminary training in discrimination tests before the experiment.

Apparatus and procedure

The apparatus used consisted of a piece of $\frac{3}{4}$-in. board, 11 by $3\frac{3}{4}$ in., painted black, in which were sunk two wells 1 in. in diameter and 7 in. apart.

Over one well was placed an equilateral triangle with 2½-in. sides, and over the other a cross-shaped object 3 in. across the widest part; both were made of three-ply wood painted white (Fig. 1). To reach the bait placed in one of the wells, the animal had to slide the stimulus object to one side. The monkey was placed in a cage to the door of which was

Figure 1 Form board with stimulus objects in position over the bait wells.

attached a box. On the floor of this the training board was placed; the sides of the box were painted black so that it was impossible for the animal to see the board, which was also screened from the animal by a black shutter during baiting.

The bait, a piece of apple, carrot, or brown bread, was placed in one or other of the wells and covered with the stimulus object to which the animal was being trained; the negative stimulus was placed over the other well. The shutter between the animal and the board was then raised so that the choice could be made.

The position of the positive stimulus was varied in the order R L R R L R R L L L (R = right, L = left) and then reversed R R R L L R L L R L; in this way five choices in each position occurred in each series of ten, and never more than three consecutive choices were given in one position.

The standard adopted for reversal learning was a complete series of ten correct choices.

Throughout both the training to discrimination and to discrimination reversal, the 'correction' method was used, that is, if the monkey made a wrong choice he was allowed to correct his error and obtain the bait. This method was used in preference to the noncorrection method favored by Spence (14), Lashley (12), Zable and Harlow (15) and to the implicit correction method of Harlow (5), because of the finding of Hull and Spence (7) that the reversal habit was learned by rats with fewer trials by correction than by noncorrection methods and their suggestion that the correct reaction, once it has occurred, is less likely to be permanent by the noncorrection method.

Also, after having made the correct choice, our monkeys were allowed, if they wished to do so, to look under the negative stimulus; in this way what Moss and Harlow (13) call the investigatory tendency was eliminated as far as possible.

All the animals were first trained to a standard of ten consecutive correct choices with the triangle positive and the cross negative. This was in all cases completed in one day. Their respective error scores were Priam 4, Solon 3, Hector 63, Jason 3, Calypso 1. Jason and Calypso were given the original learning three months before the reversal test, although with the exception of the immediate pretest practice, none was given after they had learned the original discrimination. All our subjects were given practice for four or five days before reversal learning was begun, and on each day of practice, work was continued until they made ten consecutive correct choices.

Then on the day following the last practice day, they were, without any indication that a change in procedure was taking place, presented with the cross always positive and the triangle negative.

In the cases of monkeys Priam, Solon, Jason, and Calypso, reversal learning was achieved in one day. Hector, a tamer but apparently less intelligent animal, took nearly four times as many trials as the others to reach the required standard, and these had to be given on two successive days.

Results

Figures 2 and 3 show in the form of graphs the reversal discrimination learning curves of the five subjects. In the graphs for Priam, Solon, Jason, and Calypso the percentage of correct choices in each series of ten choices is given; Hector's graph has had to be condensed so that it expresses the percentage of correct choices in each series of 40 choices.

All five graphs would seem to indicate that the learning of a discrimination reversal problem by these subjects followed a

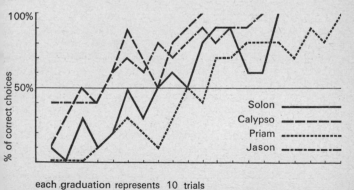

each graduation represents 10 trials

Figure 2 Curve of discrimination reversal learning by monkeys Solon, Calypso, Priam, and Jason.

consistent pattern. The difference in time between Jason and Calypso's original learning and their reversal test, and that of the other monkeys, may have affected the number of trials necessary to achieve reversal learning in these two, but does not appear to have altered the form of their curves.

At the period in reversal learning when the animals' score was around the 50 per cent correct choice level, two phenomena were

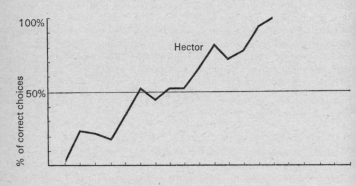

Figure 3 Curve of discrimination reversal learning by monkey Hector.

noticed. The first, observed in all the subjects, but occurring perhaps only five or six times, was a tendency for the animal's hand to waver over the board before making its choice, which might then be either correct or not.

The second phenomenon was that around the same 50 per cent correct choice level, in the cases of Calypso, Priam, Solon, and Hector, there appeared a tendency to perseverate on either the right or left position. This was shown by a sudden steep rise in the percentage of choices made of one position, which was especially marked in the case of Hector, who at this stage made 20 consecutive choices of the stimulus object on his right. None of these animals, however, when it had perseverated on, say, the left, changed to perseverate on the right, nor if it had begun on the right did it later change to the left. In these five animals with the exceptions of Hector and Solon this second phenomenon was too transitory to show clearly in the graphs.

J. COLE

Discussion

Goldstein (3, 4) has drawn attention to the importance of the ability to effect shifts of set and suggests that to do this rapidly and easily is a characteristic of the 'abstract' as opposed to the 'concrete' attitude, and might be considered to afford a measure of intelligence or at least some aspect of intelligence. It will be at once apparent from Figures 2 and 3 that our subjects were not able to effect a rapid shift of set, and this may indicate that their solution of this particular problem had not attained to the 'abstract' level.

But there is a further and equally important aspect to the apparent gradualness with which our subjects learned their discrimination reversal problem, and that is that our results would seem to be in accordance with the findings of Spence when he reports that his experiments on visual discrimination learning in chimpanzees 'support the theory that discrimination learning in animals is a cumulative process resulting from differentiated reinforcement and nonreinforcement of responses to the relevant stimulus components'.

This continuity theory opposes Krechevsky's view that systematic responses of an animal in learning such problems are self-initiated attempts at solution or hypotheses, and is itself criticized by Lashley and Harlow.

A possible cause of the rather wide divergence in the number of errors in learning a reversal discrimination by Harlow's monkeys and ours is that in the case of our animals considerable overlearning was given. With regard to the results obtained by Zable and Harlow, which support the hypotheses theory, the same considerations of overlearning and length of time between learning the original discrimination and its reversal by our monkeys may apply.

In addition, there is also the further point that, judged by these authors' description and illustration of their stimulus objects, these seem to have been both larger and less like a pattern on a ground than were ours. The importance of this is clear from Harlow's statement 'that monkeys discriminate stimulus-objects more effectively than they discriminate these self-same stimuli when presented as patterns on a ground' (6, p. 320). It is perhaps not too much to assume that Zable and Harlow's stimulus objects, being further removed from a pattern on a ground than were ours, were more easily discriminated by the animals, both in pre- and reversal training.

The effect both of the longer previous training and the overlearning given to our monkeys, combined with the more pattern-on-a-ground type of stimuli used by us, would be to make reversal learning more

301

difficult for our animals. The possible significance of this increased difficulty will be referred to again later in our discussion.

When we come to consider the two phenomena occurring in our results at about the 50 per cent correct choice level, we begin to doubt whether all is explainable by the 'continuity' theory. The hand-wavering, observed also by Jacobsen (8), occurring as it did around the 50 per cent correct level, might well mark a state of indecision; and it is noteworthy that, in the cases where perseveration on position occurred, it was always preceded by hand-wavering; that is to say, in no case were these two phenomena concurrent.

Those who favor a hypotheses theory of learning may see in these observations a period of uncertainty in the animal's mind, leading up to the formulation of the position hypothesis, which is then tried out. This view would find support in Lashley's (11) suggestion that such position habits represent attempted solutions and in Krechevsky's finding that they are most liable to occur around the 50 per cent correct choice level.

Thus, while in the main our results appear to be in agreement with the continuity theory, yet this theory is not applicable to all the phenomena observed. Moreover, what is unexplained by continuity learning may be accounted for on the basis of the hypotheses theory. This apparent contradiction in the findings of our experiment is a reflection of the divergent views of those who uphold one or other of these two theories of animal learning.

It is therefore worth considering whether the hypotheses and continuity theories are in reality contradictory or whether both are not capable of being synthesized by a more fundamental biological principle. Such a principle, which would enable us to escape the dilemma, seems to be accepted already in the field of general psychology and has recently been demonstrated to apply also in the physiology of the cerebral cortex. The principle referred to is that when an organism is confronted with a situation which it is unable to deal with successfully by the use of a recently developed ability, it reverts to a more primitive approach to its problem. In general psychology this is the basis of what the Freudians call 'regression' as observed in psychoneuroses.

In the physiology of the motor cortex, Glees and Cole (2) have shown that here, too, the same principle applies, for when a higher and more differentiated function of this area is abolished by a cortical lesion, the more primitive and holokinetic pattern of function is called into play.

If we apply this principle to our problem of reconciling the hypotheses and continuity theories of learning, we might infer that where the solution of an animal's learning problem is within the range of its more recently developed and higher capacity to form hypotheses, then we have hypothesis learning of the type recorded by Krechevsky and Harlow. But when the problem is just too difficult for the animal to form a hypothesis about it, the latent ability for what we may call the more primitive type of learning described by the continuity theory is used, and we have results like those reported by Spence working with highly complex problems.

If this is so, it would be relevant to the suggestion of Blum and Blum (1), who, when discussing our problem, 'advance the hypothesis that the contradictory experimental results are functions of different experimental designs.' These authors further suggest that when the discriminations are difficult because the distance between them in j.n.d. units is small, there is greater generalization from one stimulus to another, and in reversal learning, results are obtained in conformity with the noncontinuity theory. Whereas with easy discriminations, there is less generalization and a greater amount of differential habit strength during pretraining and the reversal results support the continuity theory.

The inference that greater generalization in pretraining means less shift of set in reversal learning and that less generalization with greater differential habit strength in pretraining means greater shift of set in reversal learning is, of course, in complete harmony with the conclusions we have drawn from our experiment.

It is also noteworthy that Harlow expressly states: 'Rhesus monkeys were trained to effect discrimination and discrimination reversals under conditions assumed to be favorable for rapid acquisition,' and again, where the conclusions of Zable and Harlow differ from ours in a similar experiment, we have shown reason for believing that the tests used by them were more easily learned than were ours.

Applying to our monkeys this previously suggested principle of regression to an earlier type of functioning when a more recently developed capacity proves inadequate, we might say that around the 50 per cent correct choice level the animals used their ability to form a 'position' hypothesis and perseverated with this for a time.

When, however, it proved inadequate, they did not achieve a 'form' hypothesis but fell back upon the more primitive type of learning described in the continuity theory. If this is so, we have an explanation both for the continuity learning type of graph they produced and for the hypothesis-like phenomenon appearing around the 50 per cent correct choice level. Moreover, an explanation has been offered for the apparent contradiction between the two types of learning.

Summary

1. Five monkeys were trained to discriminate a triangle from a cross with the triangle positive. Then, without any indication that a change in procedure had occurred, the cross was made the positive stimulus.

2. The graph of the reversal discrimination learning was in accordance with the 'continuity' theory.

3. At about the 50 per cent choice level two phenomena appeared which were explicable, not by the 'continuity', but by the 'hypotheses' theory.

303

4. An explanation of this apparent contradiction is offered and the suggestion made that the two theories are not irreconcilable.

References

1. BLUM, R. A., AND BLUM, JOSEPHINE S. Factual issues in the 'continuity' controversy. *Psychol. Rev.*, 1949, **56**, 33–50.
2. GLEES, P., AND COLE, J. Recovery of skilled motor functions after small repeated lesions of motor cortex in macaque. *J. Neurophysiol.*, 1950, **13**, 137–148.
3. GOLDSTEIN, K. *The organism.* New York: American Book Co., 1939.
4. GOLDSTEIN, K. *Human nature.* London: Oxford Univ. Press, 1940.
5. HARLOW, H. F. Studies in discrimination learning by monkeys: I. The learning of discrimination series and the reversal of discrimination series. *J. gen. Psychol.*, 1944, **30**, 3–12.
6. HARLOW, H. F. Studies in discrimination learning by monkeys: IV. Relative difficulty of discriminations between stimulus-objects and between comparable patterns with homogeneous and with heterogeneous grounds. *J. gen. Psychol.*, 1945, **32**, 317–321.
7. HULL, C. L., AND SPENCE, K. W. 'Correction' versus non-correction method of trial and error learning in rats. *J. comp. Psychol.*, 1938, **25**, 127–145.
8. JACOBSEN, C. F. A study in cerebral function in learning. The frontal lobes. *J. Comp. Neurol.*, 1931, **52**, 271–340.
9. KRECHEVSKY, I. 'Hypotheses' versus 'chance' in the presolution period in sensory discrimination learning. *Univ. Calif. Publ. Psychol.*, 1932, **6**, 27–44.
10. KRECHEVSKY, I. The genesis of 'hypotheses' in rats. *Univ. Calif. Publ. Psychol.*, 1932, **6**, 45–63.
11. LASHLEY, K. S. *Brain mechanisms and intelligence.* Chicago: Univ. of Chicago Press, 1929.
12. LASHLEY, K. S. An examination of the 'continuity theory' as applied to discriminative learning. *J. gen. Psychol.*, 1942, **26**, 241–265.
13. MOSS, EILEEN, AND HARLOW, H. F. The role of reward in discrimination learning in monkeys. *J. comp. physiol. Pyschol.*, 1947, **40**, 333–342.
14. SPENCE, K. W. Analysis of the formation of visual discrimination habits in chimpanzees. *J. comp. Psychol.*, 1937, **23**, 77–100.
15. ZABLE, MYRA, AND HARLOW, H. F. The performance of rhesus monkeys on series of object-quality and positional discriminations and discrimination reversals. *J. comp. Psychol.*, 1946, **39**, 13–23.

Analysis of a Complex Conditional Reaction in Chimpanzee

H. W. Nissen, 'Analysis of a complex conditional reaction in chimpanzee', *J. comp. physiol. Psychol.*, vol. 44 (1951), pp. 9–16.

Although much progress has been made in identifying the more 'primitive' forms of adaptive behavior, relatively little has been accomplished in reference to those more complex modes of response which are crucial for differentiation between phylogenetic levels, especially within the mammalian series. For this purpose we still have to content ourselves largely with operationally or situationally defined tests, without knowing exactly what capacities are being measured.

The concept of 'span' or 'scope' offers a promising lead in this area of analysis. Sensory thresholds and the laws of elementary perception have been extensively investigated. But intelligent behavior is often more a function of responsiveness to many elements than of extreme sensitivity to any one of them. In an earlier publication (6) I suggested 'the capacity to adjust response in accordance with two or more necessary and independent cues' as a basic dimension of adaptive behavior.

In the present experiment an attempt is made to discover whether there is a quantitative limit to this capacity in chimpanzee. The experimental design differs slightly from those previously employed (1, 2, 3, 4, 6, 8, 9, 10, 11) and is aimed at making possible an unambiguous enumeration of the independent variables to which the subject had to be 'simultaneously' responsive for solution. Finally, an attempt is made to analyze and identify more precisely the particular demands of the conditional reaction problem and the basic mechanisms which it involves.

Subject, Apparatus, and Procedure

Only one subject was used: Frank, a young adult male chimpanzee. Frank was one of the two most satisfactory and experimentally productive animals in the history of the Laboratory colony. Whether his achievements should be attributed primarily to exceptional motivation or to superior intelligence, is difficult to say. Probably it was a happy combination of both. Certainly Frank showed unusual enthusiasm for work and seemed to be motivated even more by interest in the problem as such than by the food-rewards. Until his final, acute illness, he was also one of the sturdiest and healthiest animals in the colony.[1]

The study covered a period of almost three years, but there were many interruptions of a few days or weeks and one gap of ten months. The training-testing covered 401 sessions of 25 to 100 trials each – a total of 17,740 trials.

Frank worked in his regular home cage. By reaching through the 2-inch mesh partition with his fingers, he could push directly against one of the two stimulus-plaques which were to the left and right of each other, 14 inches center to center. The plaques were cut out of quarter-inch plywood, painted, and were presented in a vertical plane parallel to the front of the cage. Pushing back the positive plaque made available a food-well containing a small piece of fruit – banana, apple, orange, or grape. The food-well under the negative plaque was empty. In case of error, the platform bearing the food-wells and plaques was withdrawn for a few seconds before it was pushed up to the cage again for Frank to make a second response (almost invariably correct). Sometimes the wrongly pushed plaque was replaced before correction, sometimes not. For baiting and placement of the stimulus-objects, the platform (which moved on skate wheels running in two U-shaped iron tracks) was pulled back some 30 inches, and an opaque screen was dropped to prevent the subject from seeing these operations.

There were 32 plaques presented in 16 pairs. The visual characteristics of these plaques, tabulated according to the five variables: size, color, form, presence or absence of margin, and presence or absence of a green peg in front of each plaque, are shown in Table 1. It will be noted that the rewarded (positive) and unrewarded (negative) members of each pair differ only in respect to size. The 16 pairs differ from each other in one to four of the other variables. Relating each pair to every other one gives 120 comparisons; in 32 of these there is a difference in only one dimension, in 48 there are two differences, in 32 there are three, and in 8 of the comparisons there are differences in respect of all four variables.

The number of variables determining response increased as training progressed and more habits were added. Habit I required only response to size. Concurrent mastery of I and II demanded responsiveness to size and color: if the two plaques were white, the larger one was rewarded, but if they were black the smaller one was correct. The addition of habits III and IV required responsiveness to size, color, and shape; 'overlooking' any one of these variables would result in chance performance (50 per cent correct) if the four plaques were presented equally often. Concurrent mastery of habits I to VIII increased the

1. Two other subjects, both young adult females, were started on this experiment but were discontinued after a few thousand trials. One of them, Alpha, mastered the first four habits but required a total of 3,496 trials to do so – as compared to 1,412 trials for Frank (see column 4, stage 2, in Table 2).

Table 1

Visual Characteristics of the Sixteen Pairs of Stimulus-objects
The figures *1* and *2* designate two 'points' on one of the stimulus-dimensions:

	1	2
Size (S)*	Large	Small
Color (C)	White	Black
Form (F)†	Square	Triangle
Margin (M)‡	Absent	Present
Peg (P)§	Absent	Present

	Dimensions									
Pair	Positive object					Negative object				
	S	C	F	M	P	S	C	F	M	P
I	1	1	1	1	1	2	1	1	1	1
II	2	2	1	1	1	1	2	1	1	1
III	2	1	2	1	1	1	1	2	1	1
IV	1	2	2	1	1	2	2	2	1	1
V	2	1	1	2	1	1	1	1	2	1
VI	1	2	1	2	1	2	2	1	2	1
VII	1	1	2	2	1	2	1	2	2	1
VIII	2	2	2	2	1	1	2	2	2	1
IX	2	1	1	1	2	1	1	1	1	2
X	1	2	1	1	2	2	2	1	1	2
XI	1	1	2	1	2	2	1	2	1	2
XII	2	2	2	1	2	1	2	2	1	2
XIII	1	1	1	2	2	2	1	1	2	2
XIV	2	2	1	2	2	1	2	1	2	2
XV	2	1	2	2	2	1	1	2	2	2
XVI	1	2	2	2	2	2	2	2	2	2

* Large square, 15 × 15 cm. Small square, 10 × 10 cm.

† Isosceles triangles; base and altitude 18 cm. for large, 12 cm. for small.

‡ The margins were pink, 1 cm. wide, along the outer edges of the plaques. All dimensions include the margin.

§ The pegs were wooden dowels, 1 cm. diameter, 3·5 cm. high, painted a light green. The two pegs were placed vertically into holes in the stimulus-carriage, centered immediately in front of each of the two stimulus-objects. The pegs projected 2·5 cm. above the lower edge of the plaque at its mid-point.

number of determining cues to four, and mastery of all 16 habits increased this number to five. Since the choice on any one trial was always between the smaller and larger of two plaques which were alike in other respects, we may speak of size as the intra-trial variable, and of color, shape, presence or absence of margin, and presence or absence of the pegs, as the conditional cues or inter-trial variables. It may be noted, incidentally, that the conditional cues were never presented to the subject for simultaneous comparison; that is, on any one trial *both* plaques were either white or black, squares or triangles, with or without margins, and with or without pegs.

In general, the training sequence was as follows: As soon as one or two habits had been learned, training was started on the next. Usually progress in learning the new habit was accompanied by deterioration in performance on the earlier habits – since what was correct in the new context was wrong in a slightly different, previous context. Before training on an additional habit or pair of habits was begun, errorless performance on the already established habits, presented in random order, was required. So, for instance, Frank responded without error in several sessions of randomly mixed trials on I, II, III, IV, V, and VI before training on habit VII was begun. In the addition of the last eight habits (IX–XVI) this procedural requirement was much less rigidly enforced. The temporal sequence and grouping of habits is shown in Table 2.

Results

The training and performance records are summarized in Tables 2 and 3. Frank's ultimate attainment – concurrent mastery of 16 inter-related habits, each demanding simultaneous responsiveness to five distinct cues – was reached in stage 13, after some fifteen thousand training and retraining trials. The records of the final 15 sessions (953 trials) are summarized at the bottom of Table 3. The two lowest critical ratios[2] of the 16 scores on these final trials are 3·4 (habit XI) and 4·0 (habit IX), indicating performance significantly above chance on all habits concurrently. The scores for the 15 individual sessions – in each of which each of the 16 habits appeared about equally often, in a thoroughly randomized order – varied between 69 per cent and 93 per cent.

It is unlikely that this performance represents the maximum attainment possible for chimpanzee. Column 6 of Table 2 shows that the number of trials increases rapidly with each added cue, but this is in part a function of the increasing number of habits which must be mastered in order to demonstrate responsiveness to the additional cue. The number of habits is doubled each time a cue is added. The number of trials *per habit* increases at a much slower rate (column 5, Table 2). Perhaps more habits, involving responsiveness to further cues, could be added indefinitely, limited only by the life span and maintained motivation of subject and experimenter.

The mastery of each new habit was usually accompanied by a

2. C.R. $=$ difference between percentage score and 50 per cent, divided by $50/\sqrt{N}$.

decrease in accuracy of response on one or more of the previously established habits. Sometimes scores on the latter went down to 20 per cent or less. The reason for this, of course, lies in the relatedness of the habits, each being in a sense antagonistic to one or more of the others. Thus, the smaller of two white squares, rewarded in habit V, is unrewarded in habit I when the pink margin is absent. Thus, more retraining was required for the earlier habits, this being reflected in the decreasing number of trials, reading from left to right, in Table 3. The over-all scores for the later habits also are lower, because during a relatively large proportion of these trials Frank was responding with less than 50 per cent accuracy.

In column 9 of Table 2 are shown the number of trials on the *new* habits only. In stage 4, for instance, a total of 1,614 trials were given (column 3), but of these only 303 were on the new habit, V; the remaining trials were devoted to 'maintenance' or retraining of habits I, II, III, and IV. Approximately 37 per cent (5,984) of the total number of trials (15,796) were used in learning new habits, the other 63 per cent being devoted to relearning habits previously perfected but disrupted by the subsequent acquisition of interfering habits. The particular figures given here are of course partly the function of a certain, somewhat arbitrary, training procedure. Presumably, the number of trials devoted to retraining could have been somewhat reduced by a less 'conservative' procedure.

The small number of trials, 111, required in stage 1 for mastery of habits I and II, deserves comment. About seven years before the present experiment was started, Frank had learned a set of four discrimination habits which included response to a large white square versus a small white square and to a small black versus a large black square. Concurrent mastery of these two habits had then required 274 trials; subsequently he was given much overtraining on these discriminations, but had had no practice on them for six years preceding the work here reported. This earlier work was done with the pull-in technique in a very different experimental setting (6). The possibility that there was some retention of this earlier learning, however, cannot be excluded.

Discussion

In searching for the method or mechanism by which Frank attained solution of the problem, one may consider what appear to be the extreme possibilities.

Table 2

Progressive Stages of Training in Mastery of Sixteen Habits
Requiring Simultaneous Responsiveness to Five Cues

	(2) Training and Retraining on Habits*																
(1) Stage	I	II	III	IV	V	VI	VII	VIII	IX	X	XI	XII	XIII	XIV	XV	XVI	(3) Trials
1	x	x															111
2	x	x	x	x													1301
3	x	x	x	x	x												433
4	x	x	x	x	x	x											1614
5	x	x	x	x	x	x	x										638
6	x	x	x	x	x	x	x	x									1672
7	x	x	x	x	x	x	x	x									1147
8	0	0	0	0	0	0	0	0	0	0	0	0	0	0	0	0	2309
9	x	x	x	x	x	x	x	x									1441
10	x	x	x	x	x	x	x	x									797
11	0	0	0	0	0	0	0	0				0	0				1443
12	0	0	0	0	0	0	0	0		0	0	0	0			0	843
13	x	x	x	x	x	x	x	x	x	x	x	x	x	x	x	x	3991

* The x's and 0's indicate habits on which training was given during each stage. Rows consisting of x's indicate that by the end of that stage Frank had concurrent mastery of all the marked habits. Rows of 0's indicate that, at any one time, Frank was still making errors on some of the old or new habits.

† S = size; C = color; F = form; M = margin; P = peg.

‡ The trials of stages 7 and 10 represent retraining after tests (reported elsewhere [7]) with novel object-combinations had been given. Since this

Table 3

Summary of the Data on Each of the Sixteen Habits

	Habit				
	I	II	III	IV	V
Total number of trials	1855	1857	1944	2102	1707
Percentage of total trials correct	95	93	92	88	86
Net trials (total minus retraining trials of stages 7 and 10)	1624	1625	1715	1876	1468
Percentage of net trials correct	94	93	93	87	84
Number of trials last 15 sessions	54	55	51	59	69
Percentage of correct trials last 15 sessions	89	87	100	83	78

(4) Cumulative trials	(5) Ave trials per habit	(6) Ave trials per cue Max. N = 4	(7) Ave trials per conditional cue N = 4	(8) Essential cues†	(9) Trials on Newly Added Habits only		
					Total	Ave. per added habit	Total per added cue (N = 5)
	55	55	111	S,C	111	55	55
1412	353	118	706	S,C,F	757	378	757
1845	369				109	109	
3459	576				303	303	
4097	586				195	195	
5769	721	1442	1923	S,C,F,M	450	450	1057
‡							
8078	§				Included in stage xiii		
9519							
‡							
10962					Included in stage xiii		
11805					Included in stage xiii		
15796	987	3159	3949	S,C,F,M,P	3969	496	3969

retraining would have been otherwise unnecessary, the trials of stages 7 and 10 are not included in the cumulative totals.

§ None of the last eight habits was thoroughly mastered and integrated with the preceding ones before training on a new habit was started. The 'average number of trials per habit' and 'per cue' therefore cannot be computed exactly until stage xiii when all 16 habits were completely established.

											Total
VI	VII	VIII	IX	X	XI	XII	XIII	XIV	XV	XVI	
1459	1373	1474	482	506	538	684	566	352	421	420	17,740
90	86	85	62	81	63	66	72	42	44	63	84
1213	1107	1199			(Same as above)						15,796
89	85	84			(Same as above)						82
63	52	56	59	65	70	58	58	55	64	65	953
76	98	82	76	83	71	91	78	82	78	77	83

1. On the one hand, it might be that each of the 32 plaques (or each of the 16 pairs of stimulus-objects) provided a discrete, unique pattern of stimulation, and that the appropriate response to each one of these was learned more or less independently. The data, however, show considerable interference among the several habits, indicating that, during the learning process at least, there was generalization from one plaque or pair of plaques to another. At the beginning, certainly, the various pairs were not distinct, independent stimulus-configurations for our subject. In order for each object or pair of objects to become discrete – to elicit a unique perception – Frank had to learn to disregard the similarities among them and to emphasize the differences. The similarities or identities consist in one or several of the variables, such as 'white' and 'square'. Sixteen of the 32 plaques were white, but only eight of these were rewarded. Eight of them were white and square, but of these only four were correct. The differences, crucial for response, consist of unique *combinations* of visual characteristics. In the final stage of the problem, nothing less than the particular combination or pattern of five variables represented by a given stimulus-object or plaque would serve to differentiate that plaque from the other 31 (see Table 1). From this viewpoint, the problem as a whole consists of a set of discriminations characterized by (*a*) much interference and generalization, this being produced by a high ratio of similarities to differences, and (*b*) the fact that the crucial differences are of combinations or patterns, rather than of single stimulus-aspects.[3]

The first of these characteristics has been emphasized recently by Lashley (5) and by Settlage, Zable, and Harlow (10) in discussing the deficits in conditional reaction and delayed reaction performances following cortical extirpations. Lashley points to 'confusion of situations which have much in common but require different reactions' as a source of difficulty in both conditional reactions and delayed response. Settlage, Zable, and Harlow postulate a phenomenon of 'perserverative interference' which, they say, 'will be encountered when successful adaptation requires that a pre-established reaction set be suppressed or modified'. The decisive role of similarity in content, widely recognized in the phenomena of associative interference, proactive inhibition and negative transfer, obviously applies also to 'perserverative interference'. To a lesser degree, such interference characterizes even a simple discrimination: the discriminanda always have some elements of similarity or identity which may lead to confusion and – in terms of recorded behavior – to indiscriminate response. In respect to overcoming the tendency to generalize – that is, the necessity of shifting primary responsiveness to differences, rather than to similarities – therefore, the conditional reaction differs from the simple discrimination only in degree; no new or 'higher' capacity is implied.

3. When the discriminanda of a discrimination problem differ in many aspects, the pattern-difference is not a *necessary* cue, and most of the component aspects are not identical.

2. At or near the other extreme stands the conceivable solution by an adult human subject; a probably verbalized formula such as: 'Of two white squares without margin or peg, the larger one is correct (habit I). Any pair differing from this one in an *even* number of respects – e.g., in color and shape (habit IV) or in color, shape, margin, and peg (habit XVI) – likewise demands response to the larger object, whereas any pair differing from this in an *odd* number of respects – e.g., in color (habit II) or in color, shape, and margin (habit VIII) – calls for response to the smaller object.' We cannot disprove the possibility of Frank's using an analogous formulation (in retention, if not in the learning process), but it seems unlikely.

Somewhere between the afore-mentioned extremes lies the possibility of the subject's generalizing the meaning or significance of a certain contextual change. For instance, having learned that a pink margin reverses the values of 'large' and of 'small' in respect to white and black squares (habits V and VI in relation to I and II), Frank might have 'applied' this principle to white and black triangles (habits VII and VIII). The data (Table 2) do not give evidence for this possibility. As a matter of fact, habit VIII required more trials (column 9) for mastery than did habits V, VI, or VII. The facts that (*a*) the number of trials per added cue increases and (*b*) the average number of trials per new habit is higher for the last eight habits (496 trials) than for the first eight (240 trials), also argue against the probability of the subject's having 'caught on' to the principle of reversal. It still remains possible, however, that Frank did become responsive to such a principle but that its expression in overt behavior was obscured by prepotent interference effects on a 'lower level'.

Summary

A young adult chimpanzee achieved concurrent mastery of 16 two-choice discrimination habits. The discriminanda employed were interrelated in such a way that correct choice on any one habit demanded simultaneous responsiveness to five distinct cues.

There is no suggestion in the data or in the general behavior of the subject that the performance here reported represents the ultimate capacity of chimpanzee in this type of problem. The later habits required more trials for mastery than did the earlier ones, but this increase is proportionately less than the increase in number of interfering habits. Analysis of the data, however, does not indicate that the subject made use of the general principle that a given change of context reversed all previously learned positive-negative values of the stimuli.

The characteristics, or special requirements of the conditional reaction problem, were identified as follows: (1) A high degree of similarity – i.e., an identity of many constituent stimulus-aspects – among the plaques and pairs of plaques, maximizes habit interference. The initial tendency to generalize from one habit to others has to be replaced by responsiveness to relatively obscure differences. It is pointed out that in this respect the conditional reaction problem only multiplies or emphasizes a requirement inherent even in simple discrimination. (2) The differences, which are crucial for correct response, are differences of stimulus-combinations or patternings rather than of one or several independent stimulus variables. From this viewpoint, the conditional reaction problem represents a set of pattern discriminations whose complexity increases with the number of distinct cues involved.

References

1. BENIUC, M. Bedeutungswechsel der Dinge in der Umwelt des Kampffisches *Betta splendens* Regan. *Z. vergl. Physiol.*, 1933, **18**, 437–458.
2. GALT, W. E. The capacity of the rhesus and cebus monkey and the gibbon to acquire differential response to complex visual stimuli. *Genet. Psychol. Monogr.*, 1939, **21**, 387–457.
3. HARLOW, H. F. Responses by rhesus monkeys to stimuli having multiple-sign values. In McNemar, Q., and Merrill, M. A. (Eds.), *Studies in personality*. New York: McGraw-Hill, 1942, 105–123.
4. LASHLEY, K. S. Conditional reactions in the rat. *J. Psychol.*, 1938, **6**, 311–324.
5. LASHLEY, K. S. The mechanism of vision: XVIII. Effects of destroying the visual 'associative areas' of the monkey. *Genet. Psychol. Monogr.*, 1948, **37**, 107–166.
6. NISSEN, H. W. Ambivalent cues in discriminative behavior of chimpanzees. *J. Psychol.*, 1942, **14**, 3–33.
7. NISSEN, H. W. Responsiveness to inter- and intra-trial variables in the conditional discrimination problem. (Unpublished.)
8. NISSEN, H. W., BLUM, JOSEPHINE S., AND BLUM, R. A. Conditional matching behavior in chimpanzee; implications for the comparative study of intelligence. *J. comp. physiol. Psychol.*, 1949, **42**, 339–356.
9. NOER, MARY C., AND HARLOW, H. F. Discrimination of ambivalent cue stimuli by macaque monkeys. *J. gen. Psychol.*, 1946, **34**, 165–177.
10. SETTLAGE, P., ZABLE, MYRA, AND HARLOW, H. F. Problem solution by monkeys following bilateral removal of the prefrontal areas: VI. Performance on tests requiring contradictory reactions to similar and to identical stimuli. *J. exp. Psychol.*, 1948, **38**, 50–65.
11. SPAET, T., AND HARLOW, H. F. Solution by rhesus monkeys of multiple-sign problems utilizing the oddity technique. *J. comp. Psychol.*, 1943, **35**, 119–132.

Part Seven MATCHING

In contrast to simple discrimination learning, which requires the animal to respond to that stimulus which leads to consistent reward rather than to another which is seldom rewarded, the matching problem demands that the animal select that stimulus which is like a model, regardless of its character. Successful performance in this task, when many different problems are used, requires discrimination at the first stimulus presentation and the capacity to avoid a stimulus object that does not match the model even though it may have been rewarded on a previous occasion. Obviously, the subject must sense identity and non-identity, either as a primary quality, as suggested by Nissen, or as a quality derived from simpler behavioral elements. This task was first exploited in Russia by Madame Ladygina Kohts with her famous chimpanzee Ioni.

Similar skills are demanded by variations of this task; for example, its opposite, the oddity task, in which three or more stimuli, all alike save one, are offered to the subject who must select the odd one to obtain reward. Task complexity can be increased by requiring the animal to select the odd shape when the stimuli are presented in one context and the odd colour in another context. Only primates have successfully performed tasks at this level of complexity.

23 B. Weinstein

Matching-from-Sample by Rhesus Monkeys and by Children

B. Weinstein, 'Matching-from-sample by rhesus monkeys and by children', *J. comp. Psychol.*, vol. 31 (1941), pp. 195–213.

1. Introduction

The method of matching-from-sample can be applied as an experimental technique to the study of a variety of psychological problems such as, set, shift of set, equivalence, symbolic behavior, and concept formation. This method, however, has been rarely used in comparative psychology because of the difficulty of adapting it to animals, even to the infra-human primates. This is unfortunate because animal subjects offer the advantages of behavioral simplicity, naiveté not to be found in man, and the opportunity for systematic investigations of the neurophysiological correlates of adaptive behavior.

The purpose of the present experiment was to investigate the degree of success of rhesus monkeys and of young children with limited language ability in solving choice-from-sample problems. The various choice-from-sample procedures used in this investigation were designed to test for four basic types of performance:

(1) Performance involving responses in accordance with the *principle of sameness* to a sample object and its duplicate choice object.

(2) Performance involving shift of behavioral set towards *choice stimuli whose positive and negative values are changed from trial to trial.*

(3) Performance involving *delayed responses to stimulus objects in the absence of spatial cues*, i.e., delayed responses to object-quality rather than to object-position.

(4) Performance involving *generalization of the principle of sameness* to stimulus objects experienced for the first time.

2. Pertinent Literature

The method of choice-from-sample was used in a scientific investigation, probably for the first time, by Itard (3) while training and observing 'The Wild Boy of Aveyron' who was discovered living alone in a forest in 1799. The extreme intellectual poverty of this boy, who was later named Victor, prompted Itard to characterize him as a 'man-plant'. Pinel had already declared him an incurable idiot.

Victor's instruction, in order 'to induce him to employ the simplest mental operations', was begun with training to match primary colors and simple geometrical figures. When he mastered this task, the number of choice objects was increased and made progressively more alike. This was followed by problems of matching printed letters of the alphabet with metal cutouts. Subsequently, Victor was taught to match printed words with corresponding objects even when delayed responses were involved. By gradual transitions, beginning with matching of identical stimuli, Victor finally was taught by means of the choice-from-sample technique, not only to use class nouns appropriately but adjectival and verbal concepts as well.

The method of choice-from-sample has been used in extensive studies with the chimpanzee by Kohts (4), and the monkey by Verlaine (7, 8, 9) and Tellier (6). Kohts used this method primarily to study color and form discrimination in her chimpanzee, Ioni. Kohts held up a sample object to the view of her subject, who was then required to select its duplicate from among a group of diverse choice objects. After about three years of training, Ioni succeeded in matching a large variety of colors and color combinations, an extensive assortment of plane and stereometric figures and even several letters of the alphabet. Delayed reaction tests showed that if more than fifteen seconds elapsed between presentation of the sample and presentation of the choice objects, Ioni's score fell to a chance level. Finally simple problems involving color and form abstraction were presented. After intensive additional training, Ioni solved these problems though they proved to be extremely difficult, and frequent errors were made.

In her interpretation of her subject's problem-solving behavior Kohts granted the chimpanzee a capacity for 'practical judgment' and 'hindsight' rather than 'foresight' (insight). Kohts concluded that the chimpanzee thinks in a manner fundamentally different from man.

The conclusions of Verlaine and Tellier, based on their matching-from-sample data, emphasize the role of generalization in the perceptions of monkeys. Lashley (5) has pointed out that their reports of the higher order concepts which their monkeys achieved with no special training, coupled with a gross neglect of experimental controls, render most of their results open to serious question.

Brief color matching experiments with anthropoid apes have been carried out by Furness (1), and Yerkes (11). Both investigators reported positive results.

3. Subjects, Apparatus and Procedure

(A) Subjects

Two rhesus monkeys, Corry and Mike, approximately four years old, and two children, Sadel and Janet, ages 37 months and 34 months respectively, were the subjects in this experiment. The monkeys had been previously subjected to an intensive taming procedure. They had been trained to approach the experimenter when called, and were transferred between home and experimental cages on the experimenter's arm. The close rapport between the animals and the experimenter is considered to be an important factor in securing the results of this study. For more than a year previous to the present investigation the monkeys were used in various experiments including a study of *minimum separable* visual acuity (10).

The I.Q.s of the children computed from scores on Stanford-Binet tests (1937 revision) were 133 for Sadel and 97 for Janet.

(B) Apparatus

The monkeys were tested in an experimental cage adapted from the one described by Harlow and Bromer (2). Stimulus objects were presented to the animals on a sliding tray 8″ by 24″. The tray was separated into a sample-object-area and a choice-objects-area by a narrow strip of wood 5″ from the left end of the tray. Two trays were used in the course of the experiment. The first tray was equipped with three food wells, one in the sample-object-area, and two in the choice-objects-area, 10″ apart from center to center. The second tray had one food well in the sample-object-area, and four wells, 5″ apart from center to center, in the choice-objects-area. This latter tray is shown, along with the apparatus used with the monkeys, in figure 1.

In the preparation of the various problems a sample object was placed over the well in the sample-object-area, and either two or four choice objects were placed over the wells in the choice-objects-area. One of the choice objects was always a replica of the sample object.

The requirements of this experiment necessitated the use of a large variety of objects as stimuli. Therefore recourse was made to household and laboratory articles such as vegetable cans,

Figure 1 Matching-from-sample test apparatus with subject (Corry) completing a choice response.

cooky cutters, oilcans, metal hinges, electric sockets, corks, and various trade cartons and boxes. These were obtained in pairs and selected on the basis of diversity of color, form, size, and brightness. Geometric forms, a circle, a star, a triangle, and a square, cut out of one-quarter inch plywood were also used. These forms were used in four colors, red, blue, yellow and green. In these same colors, geometrical paper figures centered on white cards three inches square were employed in Problems 6 and 7.

In Problem 7 a sliding panel, to which there were attached three identical wooden boxes, one in the sample-object-area, and two in the choice-objects-area, was used. These boxes which had hinged lids served as the food containers instead of the food wells in the trays. The stimulus objects were attached to the lids of the boxes. The response in this problem involved the raising of a lid instead of the displacing of a stimulus object in order to obtain the food-reward.

The children were tested with an apparatus similar to that used with the monkeys, save for the fact that a simple screen device, illustrated in figure 2, was substituted for the experimental cage. Also removable metal cups were fitted into the food wells which were washed after each session.

NS = narrow section of screen
WS = wide section of screen
SOA = sample—object—area
COA = choice—object—area
T = sliding tray

Figure 2

(C) Preliminary tutoring procedure

A special training procedure was used in the early trials of Problem 1 in order to tutor the monkeys in the matching-from-sample problem. The tray with a sample object and two choice objects was presented to the subject, just out of his reach. In order to orient the subject to the tray, a piece of banana, his preferred food, was held above it. As soon as the subject looked on, the banana was placed into one of the food wells in the choice-objects-area and covered with the positive choice object, which was the duplicate of the sample of the current trial. Simultaneously the negative choice object was placed over the other food well which was empty. Next the subject was orientated towards the sample-object-area with another piece of banana which was placed into the food well in this area and covered with the sample. The tray was then immediately pushed forward and the subject was allowed to displace the sample and secure the food under it and then shift over to the right to displace the corresponding choice object under which banana had been placed a few seconds before.

After the subject had formed the habit of commencing each trial by attending to and displacing the sample, a piece of non-preferred food, apple, instead of banana, was placed beneath it. The preferred food, banana, was now obtained by the subject only after correct displacement of a choice object. This arrangement maintained high motivation until a choice had been made and reduced the interval between displacement of the sample and the selection of a choice object to a minimum – about one second.

Table 1

Number of Training Trials and Correct Choices in Twenty-five Criterial Trials

Subjects	Training trials	Correct choices in 25 criterial trials
Corry	1199	24
Mike	1584	24
Sadel	903 (596) (307)*	25
Janet	1028 (742) (286)*	24

* See discussion of procedure with children in Section (C).

After the subject made a score of 23 correct responses out of 25 consecutive trials, the banana reward and the choice objects were placed into position behind the opaque screen. The tray was then pushed forward and a piece of apple was placed beneath the sample in view of the subject. At this stage the experimenter gave the subject help when he showed hesitation in making a choice by slightly moving the correct choice object, but not exposing the reward under it. Using the above criterion again, a change was made to the general procedure, which will be described in section (D).

The above tutoring procedure was not used with the children

in the early trials of Problem 1, because it was thought that they would quickly solve the problem without it. Instead they were merely shown in a few trials that food (a grain of Rice Krispy, non-preferred food; a small square of chocolate, preferred food) was obtainable by displacing the stimulus objects. Each trial was then begun by first raising the narrow section of the screen and then, as the child displaced the sample, raising the wide section of the screen, thus exposing the choice objects, After 596 trials with Sadel and 742 trials with Janet using this procedure, both children were still responding with chance scores. Therefore the experimenter resorted to the tutoring procedure. After this the children quickly solved the problem, as is shown in table 1.

(D) Regular procedure

In this procedure an opaque screen separated the subject from the experimenter while the food and the stimulus objects were being placed into position. The screen was then raised and the tray pushed toward the subject who now regularly orientated towards the sample at the beginning of each trial. For about five seconds the tray was held just out of reach of the subject who would make oscillatory head and trunk movements between sample and choice objects, suggesting an act of comparison. The tray was then pushed completely forward, i.e., in the position shown in figure 1. The subject first displaced the sample and next either a positive or a negative choice object. A choice, either correct or incorrect, terminated a trial.

Instead of the initial 'comparisons', the children would often look back at the sample, which they had just displaced, while in the act of making a choice. Such intra-trial 'comparisons' were rarely seen in the monkeys. In the latter part of the experiment the practice of putting food under the sample was discontinued with the animal subjects.

A negative incentive (punishment) of a rapidly dropping screen was given to the animals after a wrong choice during the early training. Later this was changed to a sharp 'No'. With the children a milder negative incentive was used. This was the remark, 'You didn't find it.' Also the tray was retracted after an error, and the lost reward was shown to the subject by lifting the positive choice object. The subject was never permitted to obtain the reward after an error, although food was given between trials when frustration appeared to be high. That the different negative incentives for monkeys and children had comparable effects is suggested by the similar doubtful and hesitant behavior before choices, and the vocal and bodily expressions of frustration after wrong choices which were manifested by all the subjects.

The monkeys throughout were much more highly motivated and were willing to work a greater number of trials per test period than the children. For the latter, verbal attention-getting devices were used, such as: 'Now let's play,' 'Are you ready?', and, 'Now find it,' the latter referring to the chocolate reward. No verbal tutoring was ever given to the children. After each session they were given an extra reward, usually a penny toy from the five and ten cent store.

For the sake of social facilitation, while one monkey was being tested, the other monkey was kept in an adjacent cage. The children had to be tested alone, since it was found that the alternate child had a distracting effect on the one being tested.

In all the problems the subjects were presented with a predetermined trial series in which the positive choice object and its position were varied in an irregular sequence. The same positive choice object, and the same positive position were never presented more than three times in succession. It should be noted that the same choice object and the same position frequently changed from positive to negative in successive trials.

(E) Matching-from-sample delayed reaction procedure

In the matching-from-sample delayed reaction procedure the sample alone was presented first, and the subject was given an opportunity to handle and fixate it for several seconds. The sample was then taken out of view, and after delays of 5, 10, and 15 seconds the choice objects were presented. These separate presentations were effected by means of the two-sectioned opaque screen attached to the front of the experimental cage and a high partition attached to the tray, which separated the sample-object-area from the choice-objects-area. The two-sectioned screen is illustrated in the children's apparatus in figure 2. With the narrow section of the screen raised and the wide section down, only the sample area was in view of the subject; and with the wide section up and the narrow section down, only the choice area was exposed.

(F) Control procedures for secondary cues

It has already been mentioned that an opaque screen served to separate the experimenter from the subject while the food reward and the stimulus objects were placed into position. The experimenter was visible to the subject, however, at the time when the choice was made. Several tests were run for possible secondary cues. In a control series with the monkeys, the experimenter was totally concealed from the subject throughout the entire proceedings of each trial by means of a set of opaque screens built across the experimental room, and an opaque window shade hung in front of the experimenter. The tray, with four choice objects and one sample object, was pushed forward by means of a rod. The experimenter could not see the subject in the act of responding. After the experimenter heard the subject displace a choice object, the shade was raised and the choice (correct or incorrect) noted. In another series all the subjects were tested by a second person with the present experimenter out of the room. There were no significant changes in scores in these control tests.[1]

4. Results

Problem 1: Matching-from-sample with two choice objects

Problem 1 was designed to test the performance of the subjects when successful responses could be made only in accordance with the *principle of sameness* and also to test their ability to shift behavioral set toward choice stimuli whose positive and negative values change from trial to trial.

The same two choice objects were used throughout Problem 1. The criterion of 23 correct choices in 25 consecutive trials was set, a score well beyond three standard deviations in a purely chance score in 25 trials. The number of training trials required by each subject to attain this criterion, and the number of correct responses in the last 25 trials – criterial trials – is presented in table 1.

Problem 2: Matching-from-sample with delayed reaction

Problem 2 was designed to test the subjects in non-spatial delayed reaction using the matching-from-sample technique.

1. An additional control for secondary cues has since been run in a matching-from-sample delayed reaction experiment. With the narrow section (NS) and the wide section (WS) of the screen both down the sliding tray is pushed into position. The sample object alone is placed on the board, the NS raised and the subject permitted to fixate and handle the sample. The NS is then lowered, the sample object removed and five choice objects placed into position. After the appropriate delay interval – 60 seconds maximum – the WS is raised and the subject is permitted to make a choice. The experimenter is hidden by a one-way visual screen from the subject throughout this entire procedure.

Table 2

Number of Training Trials and Correct Choices in last Twenty-five Trials with Delay Intervals of 5–10–15 seconds

| Subjects | Training trials | Correct responses in last 25 trials | | |
		5 seconds delay	10 seconds delay	15 seconds delay
Corry	1956	22	19	18†
Mike	2198	21	22	19
Sadel	309	20	20	20
Janet	150	18		

† With further training Corry has since shown the ability to match-from-sample after 30–60 seconds of delay with five choice objects.

In this problem delays of 5, 10, and 15 seconds were introduced between the presentation of the sample object and the exposure of the choice objects. The stimulus objects of Problem 1 were retained. It will be noted in table 2 that none of the subjects attained the 92 per cent criterion which was used in Problem 1. All the subjects either reached or approached an 80 per cent score in the last 25 trials with each delay interval. This score is three standard deviations beyond chance according to the formula for standard deviation of percentages. This problem was discontinued at this point because of the strained behavior of all the subjects. Janet refused to cooperate after more than five seconds delay.

Matching-from-sample in this problem involved delayed responses to object-quality in the absence of spatial cues. The 15 seconds delayed reaction obtained here compares favorably with the limit of non-spatial delayed responses reported by Yerkes and Nissen (12) for chimpanzee. Kohts (4) reported considerable difficulty in obtaining delayed matching-from-sample responses from her chimpanzee.

Problem 3: Generalization to new stimulus objects

In this problem the transfer of matching-from-sample behavior to a new set of stimulus objects was tested. In table 3 is presented the number of trials required to attain a 92 per cent criterion with a new pair of choice objects, and the number of correct responses in the last 25 trials – the criterial trials.

Table 3

Number of Training Trials and Correct Choices
in last Twenty-five Trials with a New Pair of
Choice Objects

Subjects	Training trials	Correct choices in last 25 trials
Corry	137	23
Mike	169	23
Sadel	25	24
Janet	49	23

These data show that the subject, Sadel, met the criterion in the *first 25 trials* with the new stimulus objects. The other subjects required varying amounts of additional training before their performance reached the criterial score.

Problem 4: Generalization to a series of new stimulus objects

Problem 4 was a test for generalization of the *principle of sameness* to a series of new stimulus objects. The subjects were first trained with 24 different choice objects which were rotated in pairs, so that in each series of 24 trials every object was a positive stimulus once and a negative stimulus once. After a score of 22 correct choices in 24 consecutive trials was made, an entirely new set of 24 choice objects were introduced, and rotated in pairs as above. The trials with these new objects are spoken of as critical trials, since the score made with these objects serves as a critical measure of the subject's performance when responding to a new and unfamiliar series of stimulus objects. The results are presented in table 4.

The data in table 4 show that all the subjects generalize the sameness principle involved in matching-from-sample immediately upon presentation of a totally new series of stimulus objects. The children required less training than the monkeys before the generalization could be effected.

Problem 5: Generalization to new configurations of four choice objects

In the four choice-object configuration of Problem 5 the number of choice objects was increased, and the distances between the choice objects was decreased. Thus the additional difficulty of

327

Table 4

Number of Training Trials and Correct Choices in Twenty-four Critical Trials with a Series of Twenty-four New Objects

Subjects	Training trials	Correct choices in 24 critical trials
Corry	74	22
Mike	174	22
Sadel	24	23
Janet	36	22

differentiating a complex perceptual field was involved in this test.

The initial training of this problem was carried out using four familiar choice objects. In the latter part of the training, groups of four choice objects were rotated from among twenty different objects, some of which were new. After the subjects had attained a 92 per cent criterion with these training objects, a series of 24 critical trials was run using 24 entirely new choice objects. Each choice object was a positive stimulus once and a negative stimulus three times. The results obtained in this problem are presented in table 5.

Problem 6: Transfer to planeometric stimuli

All the previous problems had employed only stereometric objects. In the present problem transfer of matching-from-sample behavior to two-dimensional stimuli was tested. Paper

Table 5

Number of Training Trials and Number of Correct Responses in Twenty-four Critical Trials, with Four Choice Object Configurations

Subjects	Training trials	Correct choices in 24 critical trials
Corry	349	23
Mike	989	22
Sadel	69	23
Janet	142	22

geometrical figures selected from four forms and four colors were used in pairs as choice objects. This test was discontinued with Mike after 45 trials because both his score and his mode of responding, as compared to those of Corry, indicated that his responses were purely random. The data of this test are presented in table 6.

Table 6

Number of Training Trials and Correct Choices in last Twenty-five Trials with Varied Pairs of Plane Geometrical Choice Figures

Subjects	Training trials	Correct choices in last 25 trials
Corry	175	20
Mike	45	11
Sadel	25	24
Janet	79	23

Problem 7: Transfer to a changed stimulus situation

In problem 7 the stimulus objects were black boxes whose lids were marked with the same series of stimulus figures which were used in Problem 6. Here the subjects were required to change their motor responses from pushing objects to raising lids, in order to obtain the food reward. The data of this problem are presented in table 7.

During the last four tests the children were questioned concerning the reason for their choices. The only response that could be elicited from Janet was ''cause'. Sadel's answers were pretexts such as, 'because you put it there', 'because I looked', 'because I want the candy'. Subsequently further tests were tried with Sadel in which she matched objects of the same class but differing in color, shape, and size, such as a circular red sugar bowl top, with an oblong blue top of a butter dish. It was at this time that she responded to questioning with the formulation 'because it is the same'.

Problem 8: Inhibition of response with sample object absent or sample object differing from all choice objects

This test was run with the animal subjects to determine whether or not they would attempt choices when the sameness-principle

Table 7

Number of Training Trials and Correct Choices in last Twenty-five Trials with Pairs of Boxes Marked with Geometric Figures as Choice Objects

Subjects	Training trials	Correct choices in last 25 trials
Corry	75	11
Mike		
Sadel	25	24
Janet	25	22

was inoperative. In a trial series with four choice objects, there were interspersed among the regular trials test trials in which none of the choice objects duplicated the object presented in the sample area, or in which the choice objects were presented without any object in the sample area. It might be said that if the sample actually served as the only cue for correct choices during the regular trials, then the subjects should refrain from responding altogether during the test trials. Actually such clean-cut behavior did not occur immediately. Responses were made during the early test trials to one of the choice objects, usually the one nearest the subject, or the one which was positive in the previous regular trial. However, marked doubtful and hesitant behavior in the control trials was manifest from the start. Whereas the reaction times during the ordinary trials were one to two seconds, the reaction times of inappropriate responses during the test trials ranged from five to thirty seconds. After one week of training in this control problem, both animal subjects refrained from responding for 60 seconds to the 92 per cent criterion in 25 successive test trials.

Problem 9: Responses to matching-from-sample situations with control of total areas of correct and incorrect choice objects

Another series was run to test the possibility that the subjects were responding only to maximum stimulating area and not to the principle of sameness. In all the regular settings the area of the sample object plus the area of its duplicate choice object exceeded the area of any one negative choice object. Therefore it is conceivable that the subjects were responding to cues of maximal area, instead of the cue of sameness of the sample and the correct choice object. In this series four choice objects were used, with the three negative choice objects identical. Thus the maximal area of stimulus objects was now negative. All the subjects solved this control test immediately, to a 92 per cent criterion in 25 consecutive trials. Hesitant or doubtful behavior never appeared. The results of this test indicate that responses were not made to maximal area of stimulus objects.

5. Discussion

In consequence of training during this experiment, the subjects evinced an ability for a *facile exchange of approach and avoidance responses to the same choice in successive trials*. Appropriate shifts of positive and negative set were made in response to sample objects which served as signs.

This ease of shifting set in a series of stimulus situations indicates a more flexible and complex type of behavior than is involved in problems of discrimination or of equivalent stimuli. As already pointed out by Yerkes and Nissen (12), in discriminational behavior of animals, the nature and direction of the overt response are established only after many trials, and then become so fixed that they can be exchanged or reversed only with further extensive training. A strong tendency of stereotypy towards a series of identical or equivalent stimuli is characteristic of such behavior. In contrast the subjects of this experiment, as is shown in Problems 4 and 5, made appropriate positive and negative responses to a wide range of stimuli upon initial presentation, and were able to reverse these responses without any specific training.

The final explicit verbal formulation of the relationship of sameness by Sadel strongly suggests that in the human subjects at least, an implicit cue in the nature of a symbol or concept had been effective even when they were unable to respond verbally to questions concerning the reasons for their correct choices. Determination of the psychological mechanisms involved in the successful responses of the animal subjects must await further experimentation and analysis.

Sufficient evidence has been adduced to indicate that the generalization of matching in young children has its analogue in choice-from-sample behavior in monkeys. The development of the generalization in the monkeys was relatively slow and was easily disturbed by variations in the problem situation. In contrast, the generalization formed by the children underwent a comparatively rapid evolution and remained stable in the face of substantial changes in the experimental condition. This was true even when the children lacked a verbal formulation of the principle involved.

The results of this experiment show that the method of choice-from-sample is well suited for comparative studies of intelligent behavior in infra-human primates and in young children with a minimal language ability. It is a test-method which is amenable to extensive variation and to scaling over a broad range of difficulty and therefore can be used to test many behavioral capacities of such subjects. Matching-from-sample should prove useful in the investigation of the neurophysiological correlates of higher mental processes.

6. Summary and Conclusions

1. Two rhesus monkeys and two young children with limited language ability were trained to match a sample object, which served as a sign for its duplicate in a diverse group of choice objects.

2. The various choice from sample problems in this experiment required, (a) responses in accordance with the principle of sameness, (b) a facile exchange of approach and avoidance behavior to the same choice object in successive trials, (c) non-spatial delayed responses, and, (d) generalization of matching from sample behavior towards stimulus objects experienced for the first time.

3. The performances of the animal and human subjects in the problems of this experiment were comparable. The differences appeared in the more rapid mastery of the problems by the children, in their ability to generalize more broadly, and in the ability of one child to verbalize the principle involved.

4. It is suggested that some implicit cue in the nature of a symbol or a concept was effective in the children even when they were unable to give a verbal formulation of the principle. Determination of the mechanism involved in the successful responses of the animal subjects must await further experimentation and analysis.

5. The results of this experiment show that the method of matching-from-sample is well suited for comparative studies of adaptive behavior in rhesus monkeys and in young children with limited language ability.

References

(1) FURNESS, W. H.: Observations on the mentality of chimpanzees and orangutans. Proc. Amer. Phil. Soc., 1916, **55**:281–290.

(2) HARLOW, H. F., AND BROMER, J. A.: A test-apparatus for monkeys. Psychol. Rec., 1938, **2**:434–436.

(3) ITARD, JEAN MARC GASPARD: The Wild Boy of Aveyron. New York, Century, 1932, pp. 24–104.

(4) KOHTS, N.: Untersuchungen über die Erkenntnisfähigkeiten des Schimpansen. Moscow: Zoopsychologischen Laboratorium des Museum Darwinianum, 1923, pp. 453. (In Russian. Illus. Accompanied by German translation of summary, pp. 454–498.)

(5) LASHLEY, K. S.: Studies of simian intelligence from the University of Liège. Psychol. Bull., 1940, **37**:237–248.

(6) TELLIER, M.: Le choix d'après chez le macaque. Bull. Soc. Roy. Sci. de Liège, 1933, **2**:41–45.

(7) VERLAINE, L.: De la connaissance chez le macaque. La substance. Bull. Soc. Roy, Sci. de Liège, 1935, **4**:239–242.

(8) VERLAINE, L.: La vision des formes chez le macaque. Syncrétisme, analyse et synthèse. Mém. Acad. de Belgique Cl. des Sci., 1935, **14**:1–85.

(9) VERLAINE, L.: Histoire naturelle de la connaissance chez le singe inférieur. III. L'abstrait. Actualités Sci., 1936, no. 360. pp. 1–58.

(10) WEINSTEIN, B., AND GRETHER, W. F.: A comparison of visual acuity in the rhesus monkey and man. J. Comp. Psychol., 1940, **30**:187–195.

(11) YERKES, A. W.: Experiments with an infant chimpanzee. J. Genet. Psychol., 1935, **46**:171–181.

(12) YERKES, R. M., AND NISSEN, H. W.: Pre-linguistic sign behavior in chimpanzee. Science, 1939, **89**:585–587.

24 H. W. Nissen, J. S. Blum and R. A. Blum

Analysis of Matching Behavior in Chimpanzee

H. W. Nissen, J. S. Blum and R. H. Blum, 'Analysis of matching behavior in chimpanzee', *J. comp. physiol. Psychol.*, vol. 4 (1948), pp. 62–74.

The matching and oddity techniques offer a convenient means for surveying the discriminative capacities of higher animals (4, 6, 7, 9, 10, 11, 12, 17, 20). These techniques also lend themselves readily to studies of delayed response (1, 14, 15, 17), 'categorizing' and 'symbolic' behavior (18), and 'conditional response' (2, 3, 16, 19).

The present paper describes an experiment in which seven chimpanzees were trained to respond to that one of two very different objects which matched a third object, the sample. After mastery of this habit, the animals were tested with a variety of entirely new objects to determine the extent to which the visual matching response had been generalized. Results of the generalization tests indicate that the similarity or difference of the choice object in respect to the sample determined the discriminative response. Three possible mechanisms through which similarity-difference may be effective are proposed.

Basic Training in Matching

Subjects, apparatus, and procedure

Subjects of the experiment were four adult and three young chimpanzees whose names, sex, and ages are listed in table 1. Tom, Helene, Jojo, Scarf, and Banka were born at the Yerkes Laboratories; Mimi was acquired in 1931, Shorty in 1942. Tom and Helene (twins) and Mimi previously had served in many laboratory experiments, including various discrimination problems. Tom had specific training in matching-from-sample in two earlier studies (1, 14), the more recent of these being done four years before the present experiment. Shorty had received a great deal of training as stage and screen performer, but had been a subject in only one laboratory study. Jojo, Scarf, and Banka are nursery-raised animals; they had been handled extensively for physical measurements but had limited experience in formal experiments. During the present study each of the subjects had its own living cage and the training was done by wheeling the apparatus up to the wire mesh wall of the cage; no direct handling of the animals, therefore, was necessary.

The apparatus used is one designed for general utility in discrimination experiments. Its over-all dimensions are: width 36″, depth 24″, height 56″. The stimulus-carrier contained three food-wells, 7½″ apart, each of which was covered by a stimulus-object. Baiting of the proper food-wells and placement of the objects was done behind an opaque screen. For response, the screen was raised and the carrier was rolled forwards on horizontal tracks to the wall of the cage. By reaching with its fingers through the two-inch mesh, the animal could push back the stimulus-object, uncovering the baited or empty food-well. As soon as a response had been completed, the platform was withdrawn, the screen was lowered, and the setting for the next trial was arranged. The time elapsing between trials varied somewhat with the work-tempo of the subject, averaging about 45 seconds.

For all subjects except Banka, the stimulus-objects used in the training period were two cups and two boxes. The cups were white enamel with a red rim, 4½″ in diameter, 2½″ high, placed

Table 1

Training Scores for Each of Seven Subjects on Matching-from-sample Problem with Cups and Boxes

			To reach criterion of 10 successive correct responses			To reach criterion of 25 successive correct responses			Total Experience	
Subject	Sex	Age	Sessions	Trials	Errors	Sessions	Trials	Errors	Trials	Errors
		Years								
Mimi	F	23	10	426	128				451	131
Shorty	M	14	9	396	135				1079	288
Helene	F	13	6	201	51				220	53
Tom	M	13	5	177	25	5	192	25	218	26
Jojo	F	6	17	547	217	22	644	238	644	238
Scarf	M	5	10	265	88	16	509	126	530	128
Banka	F	5	11	277	77	13	361	96	373	98
Means			10	327	103	14	427	121	502	137

over the food-wells upside-down. The boxes were unpainted wooden microscope-slide containers, $6\frac{3}{4}''$ long, presented with the ends, $3\frac{1}{2}''$ wide, $2\frac{3}{8}''$ high, facing the subject. (For Banka the cups had a high play-value; being a small animal, she was able to reach through the wire mesh of the cage almost to her elbows and thus to manipulate the cups, even to the point of bringing them up to the ceiling of her cage. For her training, therefore, the cups were replaced by empty, cylindrically shaped, tobacco cans, $5\frac{1}{4}''$ in diameter, $5\frac{1}{2}''$ high, predominantly blue in color.)

Three of the four stimulus-objects were used on every trial, two cups and one box or two boxes and one cup. The middle object was the sample, and in the food-well under it there was always a small piece of food (banana, orange, apple or other fruit, according to availability and preference of the individual animal). On one side was a box, on the other side a cup, these being the 'choice-objects'. Under that choice-object which was like the sample in the center, a larger piece of the same or of a more preferred food was placed. The food-well under the other choice-object was empty. There were, thus, four possible settings (the correct choice-object is italicized):

Cup	Cup	Box
Box	Cup	*Cup*
Box	Box	Cup
Cup	Box	*Box*

Usually response was first to the middle (sample) object, then to one of the choice-objects, but sometimes one of the latter was responded to first. In either case, the first response to one of the choice-objects determined whether or not that trial was recorded as 'correct' or as an 'error'. In the case of an error the board was withdrawn *at once*, the objects were replaced in the same positions, the food-well under the sample was re-baited if necessary, and then the animal was allowed to respond again to this same setting. If the subject again displaced the non-matching object the same setting was repeatedly presented until the matching object was chosen. Such 'correction presentations' were *not* counted as separate trials. If the subject's first response on any presentation was to the correct choice-object, it was given opportunity, if it would, to respond also to the sample. If the first response was to the non-matching object, however, no time was given to permit subsequent displacement of the middle object.

The following sequence of steps in the procedure was followed in general for all subjects; variations in the details were introduced in accordance with progress made by each individual:

Step 1: Using two cups and one box, the two possible settings (box-cup-cup and cup-cup-box) were presented in randomized sequence until a criterion of 10 or 12 successive correct trials was attained. Then the two settings of the other combination (cup-box-box and box-box-cup) were similarly presented until the same criterion was reached:

Step 2: The two combinations were alternated after attainment of criteria which were made progressively shorter (8, 5, 4, 3, 2, successive correct trials) as fast as the performance of the particular subject warranted:

Step 3: The two combinations were presented in random sequence (with the two settings of each combination also in irregular order) until a criterion of 10 (Helene, Mimi) or 25 (Tom, Jojo, Scarf, Banka) successive correct responses was reached. The attempt was made to train Shorty to a criterion of 25 successive correct trials; although he several times made 23 or 24 successive correct responses, he did not attain the criterion of 25 and the attempt was abandoned after about 1000 trials had been given.

The number of trials given in one session varied according to the motivation of the animal, averaging about 35. One session was given per day, usually on six days per week. Various controls introduced during the criterion trials, indicated that the animals were not responding to any experimentally unintended cues.

Result

Table 1 shows the total trial and error scores for each subject in the matching-from-sample training with boxes and cups. The figures given include the criterion trials described under *Step 3* of the Procedure. The last two columns, 'Total Experience', include also further trials with cups and boxes given *after* these criteria had been met and after the tests for generalization of the matching response (see below) had been started.

Variability among the animals in amount of training necessary to establish the habit is high. The lower extreme (Tom) doubtless is explainable, at least in part, by this individual's previous experience with the matching problem. The animals with the least amount of experience in formal two-choice problems (Jojo and Shorty) gave the poorest scores. On the other hand, Scarf and Banka, whose 'sophistication' in experiments of this kind was considerably less than that of Mimi, made the better scores.

A strict comparison of the learning rates of these seven animals with those of chimpanzees and monkeys used in other experiments on matching is not possible because of differences in apparatus, procedure, and criteria of mastery. Finch (1) reports that his two chimpanzee subjects required 'several hundred trials' to learn when two sets of dissimilar objects were used. Riesen and Nissen (14), using surfaces (rather than objects) differing in color, report learning in 640 trials by one subject, failure to learn after 520 and 460 trials, respectively, by two other subjects. Weinstein (17, 18) states that 1199, 1584, and 950 trials plus a certain amount of 'tutoring' were required by three rhesus monkeys in reaching a criterion of 24 correct in 25 successive trials. Harlow (2) reports that four rhesus monkeys learned the matching-from-sample problem in 500, 600, 1150, and 900 trials, respectively. The data in general suggest (a) that learning to match is easier when objects differing in several aspects are used than when the choice is between surfaces differing only in chroma (and brightness), and (b) that chimpanzees may be faster than rhesus monkeys in mastering the problem.

Generalization of the Matching Response

Immediately following completion of the basic training described above, tests of transfer or generalization of the matching response were given to each of the seven subjects. The same apparatus was employed, but eleven new pairs of stimulus-objects were introduced:

(1) Aluminum cups, 4″ in diameter, $2\frac{3}{8}$″ high, placed upside down over the food-wells.

(2) Empty Pablum boxes, cylindrical, 5″ in diameter, $7\frac{7}{8}$″ high.

(3) Unpainted wooden blocks, $3\frac{1}{8} \times \frac{3}{4} \times 4\frac{1}{4}$″, to which were fastened black rubber stoppers, $1\frac{1}{2}$″ in diameter, 1″ high.

(4) Cardboard microscope slide boxes, $3\frac{1}{8} \times 1\frac{1}{8} \times 3\frac{5}{8}$″, brown, gray, and blue.

(5) Cardboard microscope slide boxes, $3\frac{1}{8} \times 1\frac{1}{8} \times 3\frac{5}{8}$″, uniform blue.

(6) Cardboard microscope slide boxes, $3\frac{1}{8} \times 1\frac{1}{8} \times 3\frac{5}{8}$″, red and white.

(7) Cardboard microscope slide boxes, $3\frac{1}{4} \times 2\frac{1}{8} \times 4\frac{1}{8}$″, mottled brown.

(8) Tobacco cans, metal, cylindrical, $5\frac{1}{4}$″ in diameter, $5\frac{3}{8}$″ high, blue, red and white, with aluminum top.

(9) Vertical plywood squares, $4\frac{3}{8} \times 4\frac{3}{8}$″, light green.

(10) Vertical plywood squares, $4\frac{3}{8} \times 4\frac{3}{8}$″, bright red.

(11) Vertical plywood squares, $4\frac{3}{8} \times 4\frac{3}{8}$″, light tan (unpainted).

Numbers 9, 10, and 11 were mounted on horizontal wooden blocks, $4\frac{3}{8} \times 4\frac{3}{8}$″.

Together with the two original objects (enamel cups and wooden boxes) used in the basic training, this made possible 78 combinations of objects, 77 of which were new to our subjects. (For Banka, whose basic training had been with the tobacco cans instead of with the enameled cups, the latter became one of the 11 pairs of new stimulus-objects.)

During the first few days of testing, 24 of these novel combinations were presented in groups of from 4 to 12 successive trials each. The same 24 pairings were used with each subject. Each object of a given combination, and also the left and right positions, were equally often correct and incorrect.

Following 117 to 129 trials per subject under the above conditions, the remaining 53 novel combinations were presented in a thoroughly randomized sequence. Each combination was presented twice (but with such presentations separated by at least 15 trials using other combinations) – once with one member of that pair being correct and once with the other member correct. Left and right positions of the matching object were balanced.

As in the basic training, correction was permitted following an error (after the objects had been replaced over the food-wells), but such correction was not recorded as a separate trial; that is, if the first response to a given presentation was wrong, that trial was considered an error.

Each session of generalization tests was begun, and sometimes ended, with some trials using the original training objects, cups and boxes. The number of such trials given varied from subject to subject; they are included in the figures of the last two columns ('Total Experience') of table 1.

Results

Results of the generalization tests are summarized in table 2. The significantly high percentage of correct trials shows that these subjects had not merely learned specific responses to each of the four unique patterns of stimulation provided in the basic training.

Their responses evidently were determined by the similarity (visual identity) of one of the choice-objects to the sample.

Analysis of errors made in the final series of 106 randomized tests does not indicate that any particular object-combinations were more difficult than others for the group as a whole. Seven of Scarf's 8 errors were responses to the left side. Errors of the other subjects seem to be unsystematic.

Accuracy of the four adult subjects was higher than that of the three immature animals in the final 106 transfer trials, the

Table 2

Scores on Tests of Transfer or Generalization of the Matching
Response to Seventy-seven Novel Object-combinations

| Subject | 24 novel combinations presented in groupings of 4 to 12 trials each | | | | | 53 novel combinations, two trials each, randomized | | |
	Total trials	Total errors	Percentage correct	Comb's. with error	Comb's. without error	Total trials	Total errors	Percentage* correct
Mimi	129	22	83	10	14	106	5	95
Shorty	120	24	80	15	9	106	12	89
Helene	117	23	80	12	12	106	3	97
Tom	120	7	94	5	19	106	3	97
Jojo	128	28	78	20	4	106	19	82
Scarf	120	22	82	10	14	106	6	94
Banka	120	30	75	19	5	106	23	78

* All these percentages are reliably above chance at an extremely high
level of confidence.

difference between the means of the two groups being significant
at the 6 per cent level of confidence. Whether this discrepancy
reflects an age factor or is, instead, a function of differing amount
of over-training with the original stimulus-objects (see table 1) is
uncertain.

During the last 54 of the final 106 test trials (in the case of Mimi
and Helene during the last 32 trials only), baiting of the middle
food-well, under the sample, was omitted; instead, the correct
object was baited both with the regular (larger) piece of fruit and
with the smaller piece which previously had been used for the
sample. Response to (displacement of) the sample-object was
permitted as before. The relative frequency of errors during these
trials in which the sample was not baited remained virtually
unchanged as compared to the preceding part of the 106 trial test
series, increasing slightly in two cases, decreasing in four.

Inasmuch as the temporal order of responsiveness to (displacement of) the sample and choice-objects is pertinent to the
theoretical considerations of the following section, this feature of
the performances should be indicated. During the basic training
and during the first part of the generalization tests three of the
seven animals (Shorty, Tom, Banka) usually responded first to
the sample and then to one of the choice-objects. Two subjects

(Jojo, Scarf) usually reversed this order, displacing one of the choice-objects before responding to the sample. The initial responses of the last two subjects (Mimi and Helene) were about equally often to the sample and to a choice-object. During the last of the generalization tests, soon after baiting of the sample had been discontinued, all subjects except Mimi and Helene omitted displacement of the sample.

Using the symbols *1* to indicate the left-hand choice-object, *2* the middle or sample-object, *3* the right-hand choice-object, and *SBD* to indicate the point at which sample object baiting was discontinued, this behavior may be summarized in greater detail as follows:

(1) Mimi and Helene usually responded to *2* first if the subsequent choice-response was *3*; otherwise the first response was to *1*, followed by *2* (which was permitted only if *1* was 'correct'). That is, the two sequences used were: *2–3* and *1–2*. This was unchanged after *SBD*, except that Mimi tended to drop out response to *2* after the initial *1*. (Helene's displacement of *2* was often partial – a perfunctory gesture; she obviously no longer 'expected' to find food in *2*.)

(2) Shorty usually responded to *2* first, then *1* or *3*. In the few instances in which *1* or *3* was displaced first, he subsequently responded to *2*. After *SBD* there was rapid elimination of response to *2*.

(3) Tom invariably responded to *2*, usually before response to *1* or *3*. After *SBD*, he rapidly eliminated all responses to *2*.

(4) Jojo and Scarf usually responded to *2* but generally *after* initial response to *1* or *3*. There was prompt discontinuance of response to *2* after *SBD*.

(5) Banka. During the early part of basic training she usually followed the sequences *2–3* and *2–1*. Several days before *SBD* she 'spontaneously' dropped out response to *2* on most of the trials. After *SBD* response to *2* was very rare, preceding *1* or *3* when it did occur.

Discussion

Similarity and difference of stimulus-objects

It will simplify our subsequent task of analysis if we first clarify the concepts of 'similarity' and 'difference' as used in this paper. The objective difference between two visually presented objects is completely described when we specify (*a*) the number of identified aspects or characteristics (e.g. size, brightness, form) in which they differ and (*b*) the amount of discrepancy in each differentiating aspect expressed in appropriate physical or psychophysical units. In the present study we are concerned only with a rough approximation to (*a*) and can disregard altogether the refined measurements required by (*b*). The correct choice-object used was similar to the sample in *all* respects other than position, whereas the incorrect object differed from the sample in an unspecified but large number of visual characteristics. The discrepancies along those differentiating continua or stimulus-dimensions which permit measurement were, it may safely be assumed, supraliminal in amount, and their precise magnitudes have no significance for our purposes. In the following discussion, therefore, 'similarity' indicates likeness or identity of two objects in respect to all visual characteristics, and 'difference' signifies supraliminal differences in a number of visual stimulus-dimensions or aspects (e.g. linear dimensions, area, form, hue, brightness, patterning).

Function of similarity in the matching problem

It was pointed out above that a possible basis for mastery of the matching problem when, as in the original training, only two sets of stimulus-objects are used, is the learning of a definite response ('to the left box' or 'to the right box') to each of the four unique configurations formed by varying combinations and positions of three objects. The success of all subjects in the generalization tests, however, proves that something more than this had been learned; the similarity or difference of the choice-objects in reference to the sample evidently played a determining role, since this is the only factor common to the correct object in all the novel combinations presented. Theoretically there appear to be at least three general ways in which the similarity or difference between sample and choice-object may be effective in the matching problem, and these we now consider in turn.[1]

(1) According to the first of these interpretations, each trial of matching-from-sample is thought of as a conditioning situation or a learning-retention problem (the rôle of retention, however, being of minimal importance). Food under the sample reinforces response to the visual characteristics of the sample; those characteristics are repeated in the matching choice-object and are absent in the other choice-object. Correct response indicates that conditioning or learning has occurred in one trial. This interpretation involves the assumption that in the training a habit was established of responding first, in each trial, to the sample-object; in this initial response the cue is associated with an approach response, and this association determines the subsequent response to one of the choice-objects.

The fact that accuracy in the generalization tests was maintained after baiting of the sample and (in most cases) displace-

1. See also the discussions in (3, 6, 8, 11, 15, 16, 18, 20).

ment of the sample-object had been eliminated, presents no serious difficulty for this interpretation. Using the terminology of conditioning, it may be assumed that the middle position (i.e. of the sample-object) had acquired secondary reinforcing effectiveness and that the subjects continued to make their initial responses to the sample, these responses now being implicit rather than overt. However, the fact that two subjects (Jojo, Scarf) usually responded to a choice-object before displacing the sample, even in the *initial training*, two other subjects (Mimi, Helene) doing this in about half the trials, is more difficult to harmonize with the present interpretation. Here it must be assumed that the habit of making an initial *implicit* response was formed about as readily and effectively by these animals as was the habit of an initial overt response by the other subjects.

It may be pointed out that this analysis is analogous to one which has been suggested for the delayed response problem (13). In delayed response the subject must learn the correct one of two cues (e.g. red *vs*. green) for the given trial and must respond to that cue after an interval of time; in matching, the subject must also learn the correct cue (which varies from trial to trial) in one experience and respond to that cue (immediately) as it appears in another place.

The present interpretation does not in itself explain why the initial box-cup training required several hundred trials, whereas the highly accurate performances in the generalization tests with 77 new object-combinations necessitated no further training. It may be assumed that the necessary habit of responding first, in each trial, to the visual characteristics of the middle (sample) object was acquired gradually in the training period. It seems reasonable to suppose, also, that the degree of trial-to-trial interference was less in the generalization tests, where different object-combinations appeared in successive trials, than in the basic training, where the very object which had been positive on one trial was negative on the next. Finally, and this applies equally to the following two interpretations, the effectiveness of incorrect 'hypotheses' or of irrelevant cues in the situation, such as position and particular colors, sizes and forms, had to be reduced or eliminated before the appropriate association or cue could fully determine the discriminative response.

Summarizing the essentials of this interpretation, we may say that responsiveness to the visual characteristics of the sample-object is strengthened (given positive valence) by the rewarding or reinforcement (at times secondary reinforcement) of the sample, and that this one-trial learning manifests itself in response to that choice-object having the same visual characteristics as the sample. We shall designate this interpretation as the 'learning mechanism'.

(2) The foregoing interpretation of the rôle of similarity-difference involves indirection, in the sense that each choice response is mediated by a learning process specific to that trial. The second interpretation suggested here envisages a more immediate, psychologically 'simpler', process. It assumes that the similarity or visual identity of the sample and the positive choice-object, as well as the difference between these two and the other (negative) object, are given immediately in perception. No 'judgment' is required; the only learning involved occurs in the initial training and consists in the discovery either (*a*) that the homogeneous rather than the heterogeneous portion of the effective visual field is correct, or (*b*) that in an asymmetrically divided field (of vision) the larger one is correct, i.e. contains the reward or rewards.

Two slightly differing forms of this interpretation are diagrammatically represented in figures 1 and 2. The significant visual field is composed of areas *A* and *B* which, in figure 1, overlap in respect to the middle section containing the sample. Area A is homogeneous, area B is heterogeneous; the result of training is consistent response to the homogeneous area. In figure 2 the significant field is divided into two discrete parts, each containing

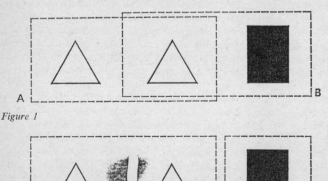

Figure 1

Figure 2

homogeneous visual characteristics; the division is based on differences of visual characteristics in the two areas. The subject learns to respond to the larger area, A.

The question of whether a chimpanzee can or does perceive the matching situation as represented in figures 1 or 2, 'assimilating' like characteristics and differentiating unlike ones, has no definite answer at present, but we know of no conclusive or presumptive evidence against the possibility. The problem of how an animal learns to respond to that part of the visual field which is homogeneous, or to that which is larger or contains a greater representation of one stimulus as compared to another, is essentially the same as that involved in other visual discrimination habits.

The fact that in some generalization tests the total linear and surface dimensions of the two similar objects were less than those of the single negative object (e.g., two slide boxes, #6, and one tobacco can, #8), may be reconciled with the second form (figure 2) of the present interpretation on at least two counts: (a) The 'total significant visual field' is composed not only of the objects themselves, but also of the area around and above the three stimulus-objects. Each of the sub-total fields, which we designate in this interpretation as the discriminanda, includes its object or objects plus the surrounding area. We may assume that the two objects which are alike, together with their surroundings, form a field which comprises two-thirds of the total significant field, regardless of the size of the objects themselves. (b) Cues such as form are independent of size; in the example given above (objects #6 and #8), 'rectangularity' of the upper surface appears twice, 'circularity' once. Relative frequency or repetitiveness of a stimulus may be psychologically comparable to, or as effective a cue as, relative area.

The basic assumption in both forms of this second interpretation, distinguishing it from the first, is that an *immediate* perception of likeness and/or of difference (between two objects) is possible and is the basis of solution. The actual cue to which the subject responds is something like 'homogeneity' or 'the larger homogeneous area', but the significance of this cue – whether it is accompanied by reward or absence of reward – is learned early in the training, and nothing more need be learned from trial to trial. The critical factor in each trial is the immediate perception of likeness or homogeneity within the situation. We shall, accordingly, refer to this interpretation as the 'perception mechanism'.

The 'perception mechanism' as here outlined, bears a marked resemblance to Klüver's 'strata function' (6) and to the concept of 'non-equilibrated' stimulus situations suggested by Nissen and McCulloch (11, pp. 166–167) in referring to the oddity problem. The single odd stimulus-object is described as a figure appearing on the ground of the multiple, identical negative objects; response is to the 'figure'. This interpretation could be applied to the three-object matching problem by introducing the simple modification of having the figure (non-matching object) associated with avoidance rather than with approach.

(3) The third interpretation assumes that the subject can respond differentially to similarity and difference as such,[2] regardless of the particular visual characteristics of the objects presented. That is, similarity and difference are cues, in the sense that other relationships such as 'smaller', 'brighter' or 'middle box' may be cues. Response to such a relationship obviously implies a rather high degree of abstraction: the subject must disregard the many variations in visual characteristics between pairs of stimulus-objects, confining his 'attention' or responsiveness to the identity vs. difference between the members of each pair.

From a purely logical viewpoint, responsiveness to similarity (or difference) must be preceded by responsiveness to the visual characteristics (such as color) of the two objects. In the first interpretation proposed above (No. 1) it is the primary sensory datum (e.g., 'red') derived from the sample-object which becomes associated with approach. In the present interpretation, on the other hand, a comparison of the primary data derived from two objects results in a 'higher order' response, and it is this secondary central response of 'similarity' which becomes associated with approach.

Responsiveness to any abstract relationship, whether it be 'similarity', 'heaviest' or 'middle', implies the convergence of diverse sensory data on a common center. Such a center, having been associated with approach or avoidance, will then be activated by a class of sensory events, resulting in the phenomena known as transposition or generalization. This is not the place to discuss theories regarding possible neural bases for such convergence. It does not seem, however, that the structures required

2. Hilgard and Marquis (5, page 200) point out that 'Response *to* similarity in the stimuli is based on the conception that stimuli are physically similar.' In the present context this conception is probably unobjectionable, since our 'similar' objects may be considered identical in every respect excepting spatial location.

346

for 'similarity-difference' will involve any more difficulty than those necessary to explain response to other abstract relationships.[3]

The present interpretation, which may be termed the 'abstract generalization mechanism', is like No. 2 above and differs from No. 1, in assuming that the basic association between a given cue and approach (or avoidance) is established once, early in training, and is then effective in all subsequent trials or instances of the matching situation. Formation of a new association between a specific cue and overt response on each trial is not necessary as it is in the 'learning mechanism'.

Mechanisms operative in primate subjects

The data available give no basis for deciding that one rather than another of the basic types of mechanism outlined above was operative in our chimpanzee subjects. It seems to us entirely possible that all three mechanisms contributed to the performances, in different subjects, in the same subject at different times, or simultaneously in the same subject.

The experimental situation used by Harlow and his collaborators with monkeys (e.g., 2), in which the sample was at one side of the two choice-objects rather than between them, would seem to make No. 2, the 'perception mechanism' in the form suggested above, somewhat implausible. The interpretation of a learned negative response to the odd or non-matching object – i.e. to the 'figure' on the 'ground' of the two identical objects – however, would apply fairly well to both experimental situations. Further work, in which the applicability of one and another of the proposed 'mechanisms' is eliminated or minimized, is obviously needed.

3. It may be noted that in our generalization tests the positive and negative objects always differed in respect to color-brightness or at least in color-brightness patterning. It is possible, therefore, that the matching response was based on similarity-difference of color-brightness only, and did not extend to similarity-difference in other visual aspects. This possibility is disproven for Tom, at least, who in subsequent matching trials (to be reported elsewhere) responded without error when the objects differed only in form. Our generalization tests included some combinations (objects 4, 5, 6 and 9, 10, 11) in which there were no form or size differences; the number of failures with these combinations were actually fewer, proportionately, than with combinations which involved multiple visual differences.

Summary

Seven young and adult chimpanzees were trained to respond to that one of two distinctive choice-objects which was a replica of the third or sample-object. The choice-objects consisted of an inverted cup and a small wooden box; the sample was a similar cup or box. This habit was mastered in from 177 to 547 trials.

Subsequently these subjects responded with a highly significant degree of accuracy to the matching member in 77 new object-combinations. The results indicate that something other than the four specific over-all patterns of stimulation, which might have been learned in the original cup-box training, was responsible for the discriminative response. The one feature which characterized the 'correct' object in all the new combinations consistently, was its similarity (identity) to the sample.

Theoretical analysis indicates that there are at least three general ways in which the similarity or difference between sample and choice-object may be effective in producing generalized matching.

(1) The 'learning mechanism' assumes that the sample-object provides primary or secondary reinforcement of specific visual characteristics on each trial, and that this learning is the basis for response to the choice-object having the same characteristics. Each trial requires an independent learning or association of this kind.

(2) The 'perception mechanism' assumes an immediate perception of likeness (homogeneity) or of difference (heterogeneity) between two objects. The subject learns (a) an approach response to the larger homogeneous area (formed by the sample and matching choice) *versus* the smaller homogeneous area (consisting of the non-matching choice-object), or learns (b) to approach the homogeneous area (sample plus matching object) *versus* the heterogeneous area (sample plus non-matching object). Once this association has been formed, no further learning (i.e. on each trial) is necessary.

(3) The 'abstract generalization mechanism' assumes that the abstract relationships of likeness and of difference may function as cues. The sensory data resulting from 'looking at' or comparing two objects converge on one neural center if the two objects are alike, on a different center if the objects differ, quite irrespective of the particular visual characteristics of any pair of objects. Once the center for likeness or similarity has been

associated with approach, that for difference with avoidance, no further learning is required.

The available data give no clear indication that one rather than another of these mechanisms was operative in the generalization tests given to the chimpanzee subjects. It seems possible that all of them were effective, separately or in combination.

References

1. FINCH, GLEN: Delayed matching-from-sample and non-spatial delayed response in chimpanzees. *J. comp. Psychol.*, 1942, **34**, 315–319.
2. HARLOW, H. F.: Response by rhesus monkeys to stimuli having multiple sign-values. In McNemar, Q. and Merrill, M. A., Editors, *Studies in Personality*. McGraw-Hill Book Co., 1942, 105–123.
3. ——: Solution by rhesus monkeys of a problem involving the Weigl principle using the matching-from-sample method. *J. comp. Psychol.*, 1943, **35**, 217–227.
4. ——: Generalization by rhesus monkeys of a problem involving the Weigl principle using the matching-from-sample method. (Unpublished manuscript.)
5. HILGARD, E. R., AND MARQUIS, D. G.: *Conditioning and learning.* New York: Appleton-Century, 1940. Pp. xi+429.
6. KLÜVER, H.: *Behavior mechanisms in monkeys.* Chicago: University of Chicago Press, 1933. Pp. xvii+387.
7. KOHTS, N.: Recherches sur l'intelligencé du chimpanzé par la méthode de 'choix d'après modèle'. *J. Psychol. norm. path.*, 1928, **25**, 255–275.
8. LASHLEY, K. S.: The mechanism of vision. XV. Preliminary studies of the rat's capacity for detail vision. *J. gen. Psychol.*, 1938, **18**, 123–193.
9. MCCULLOCH, T. L., AND NISSEN, H. W.: Equated and non-equated stimulus situations in discrimination learning by chimpanzees. II. Comparison with limited response. *J. comp. Psychol.*, 1937, **23**, 365–376.
10. NISSEN, H. W.: Primate Psychology. In: *Encyclopedia of Psychology.* (P. L. Harriman, Editor), 1946, N. Y. Philosophical Library, pp. 546–570
11. NISSEN, H. W., AND MCCULLOCH, T. L.: Equated and non-equated stimulus situations in discrimination learning by chimpanzees. I. Comparison with unlimited response. *J. comp. Psychol.*, 1937, **23**, 165–189.
12. ——: Equated and non-equated stimulus situations in discrimination learning by chimpanzees. III. Prepotency of response to oddity through training. *J. comp. Psychol.*, 1937, **23**, 377–381.
13. NISSEN, H. W., RIESEN, A. H., AND NOWLIS, V.: Delayed response and discrimination learning by chimpanzees. *J. comp. Psychol.*, 1938, **26**, 361–386.
14. RIESEN, A. H., AND NISSEN, H. W.: Non-spatial delayed response by the matching technique. *J. comp. Psychol.*, 1942, **34**, 307–313.
15. SIMPSON, M. M., AND HARLOW, H. F.: Solution by rhesus monkeys of a non-spatial delayed response to the color or form attribute of a single stimulus (Weigl principle delayed reaction). *J. comp. Psychol.*, 1944, **37**, 211–220.

16. SPAET, T., AND HARLOW, H. F.: Solution by rhesus monkeys of multiple sign problems utilizing the oddity technique. *J. comp. Psychol.*, 1943, **35**, 119–132.

17. WEINSTEIN, B.: Matching-from-sample by rhesus monkeys and by children. *J. comp. Psychol.*, 1941, **31**, 195–213.

18. ——: The evolution of intelligent behavior in rhesus monkeys. *Genetic Psychol. Monog.*, 1945, **31**, 3–48.

19. YOUNG, M. L., AND HARLOW, H. F.: Solution by rhesus monkeys of a problem involving the Weigl principle using the oddity method. *J. comp. Psychol.*, 1943, **35**, 205–217.

20. ——: Generalization by rhesus monkeys of a problem involving the Weigl principle using the oddity method. *J. comp. Psychol.*, 1943, **36**, 201–216.

Part Eight OBSERVATIONAL LEARNING AND IMITATION

Of all the aspects of intelligent behaviour which can be exhibited by an animal, few are more striking than the ability to learn from the experience of others. Most problems which have been presented to animals permit direct participation in the discovery of the significant relationships, however much they may obscure the stimuli, allow for multiple erroneous solutions or complicate the correct response. Observational learning, on the other hand, is passive in nature, i.e. the significant relationships are discovered by another animal, the 'demonstrator'. There is thus no immediate reward or punishment for the observer as a result of the demonstrator's response. No wonder then that Thorndike's early experiments failed to reveal this ability in his test subjects. Yet more recent findings, obtained with efficient experimental techniques, show beyond doubt that this ability, both in attaining reward and avoiding punishment, exists in some species of primates.

The possible significance of this ability for the preservation of life in the natural habitat cannot be overestimated. Firstly, it can contribute to the maintenance of established modes of behaviour, thus fostering intragroup harmony and communication. Secondly, it can provide safe channels of expression for the curiosity and exploratory impulses of the young, by directing their attempts chiefly towards those things which have been tried by others with impunity.

But however important we think they may be in the natural state, observational learning and imitation of specific acts are, in most instances, yet to be demonstrated. If such information becomes available, our understanding of intra-group cohesion will, in all probability be substantially altered.

25 C. Lloyd Morgan

Habit and Instinct

Excerpt from C. Lloyd Morgan, *Habit and instinct*, Edward Arnold, 1896, chap. 8, pp. 166–83.

Imitation

That imitation, or what we are accustomed to regard as such, is an important factor in animal life, especially among gregarious animals, is scarcely open to question. But the biological and psychological conditions are not easy to understand. Some forms of imitation are often spoken of as instinctive; but some are voluntary, and under the guidance of intelligence. It is to the latter that the term 'imitation', in its usual acceptation, would seem to be properly applicable. And the exact nature of the connection between this conscious and voluntary imitation and the involuntary instinctive process to which we apply the same term, requires careful consideration. Let us first look at some of the facts which illustrate imitation of the latter and apparently instinctive type.

If one of a group of chicks learns by casual experience to drink from a tin of water, others will run up and peck at the water, and will themselves drink.[1] A hen teaches her little ones to pick up grain or other food by pecking on the ground and dropping suitable materials before them, the chicks seeming to imitate her actions. One may make chicks and young pheasants peck by simulating the action of a hen with a pencil-point or pair of fine forceps. According to Mr Peal's statement the Assamese find that young jungle pheasants will perish if their pecking responses are not thus stimulated; and Prof. Claypole tells me that this is also the case with ostriches hatched in an incubator. A little pheasant and guinea-fowl followed two ducklings, one wild, the other tame, and seemed to wait upon their bills, to peck where they pecked, and to be guided by their actions. It is certainly much easier to bring up young birds if older birds are setting an example of eating and drinking; and instinctive actions, such as scratching the ground, are performed earlier if imitation be not excluded. I

1. Dr Mills records a similar observation on puppies (*Trans. Roy. Soc. Canada*, sect. iv. (1894), p. 43).

have observed that if a group of chicks have learnt to avoid cinnabar caterpillars, and if then one or two from another group are introduced and begin to pick up the caterpillars, the others will sometimes again seize them, though they would otherwise have taken no notice of them. One of the chicks, coming upon a dead bee, gave the danger or alarm note; another at some little distance at once made the same sound. A number of similar cases might be given. But what impresses the observer, as he watches the early development of a brood of young birds, is the presence of an imitative tendency which is exemplified in many little ways not easy to describe in detail.

What generalization, then, can be drawn from this somewhat indefinite group of facts? What is their relation to instinctive procedure in general? Instinctive procedure, we must remember, is congenital behaviour of a more or less definite kind, involving the inherited coordination of motor activities due to outgoing nerve-currents, and initiated by an external stimulus under organic conditions of internal origin. Now, it would seem that where the external stimulus is afforded by the behaviour of another organism, and the responsive behaviour it initiates is similar to that which affords the stimulus, such responsive behaviour may be described as imitative. A chick sounds the danger note; this is the stimulus under which another chick sounds a similar note, and we say that the one imitates the other. Such an action may be described as imitative in its effects, but not imitative in its purpose. It is objectively, but not subjectively imitative. Only from the observer's standpoint does such instinctive behaviour differ from other modes of instinctive procedure. It is for him that the instinctive response falls under the head of imitation. We seem justified in asserting that, from the biological point of view, any stimulus or group of stimuli may give rise to a congenital response of any kind. In the case of an imitative action, the stimulus is afforded by the performance by another[2] of an action similar in character to that which constitutes the response. From the observer's point of view, this is noteworthy, and, from the point

2. This seems to be part of the accepted implications of the word 'imitation.' Prof. Mark Baldwin uses the term with an extended signification, so as to include, under the head of imitation, repetition of an action by the same individual. From the observer's point of view, it is, of course, open to us to call the repeated act one that is imitative of the previous act of which it is a repetition; but if we do so we must abandon the accepted usage, according to which 'imitation' is applied to the repetition by one individual of the behaviour of another individual. There appears to be no sufficient reason for such a complete change of accepted usage.

of view of biological interpretation, important. But from the performer's point of view, if one may so say, it is in line with all other cases of instinctive activity. A stimulus, visual, auditory, or other, is followed automatically by a coordinated response, and there is no similarity between either the stimulus or the states of consciousness accompanying it, on the one hand, and the response, or its conscious concomitants, on the other hand.[3] Such, it would seem, is the nature of instinctive imitation, or that congenitally automatic behaviour which, from the observer's standpoint, is imitative.

Passing reference may here be made to those instinctive actions for which mimicry is now a recognized biological term. Certain distasteful butterflies, for example, are mimicked by others, which are believed to have escaped destruction because of their mimetic resemblance to the others. There is no intentional imitation. The mimicry is of purely objective significance. And not only in form, but also in their instinctive behaviour, are many of these insects, and perhaps some birds, mimetic of others. Such behaviour is, from the purely objective point of view, imitative. But since there does not seem to be any good ground for supposing that the mimetic behaviour is called forth by the stimulus of such behaviour in the models, it does not fall under the head of the instinctive imitation we are considering. By using the term 'mimetic' in its biological signification,[4] we may mark off these cases of mimicry in behaviour from true examples of instinctive imitation – that is to say, instinctive behaviour called forth by similar behaviour in others.

Now, as we have already seen, instinctive procedure forms part – and a not unimportant part – of the raw material on which intelligence exercises its influence, fashioning and moulding it, and guiding the activities concerned to finer issues in individual adaptation. The first performance of an instinctive activity, whether imitative or not, affords the data to consciousness for the perfect-

3. Prof. Mark Baldwin has suggested that imitation should be defined as a response which tends to reproduce its own stimulus – a 'circular activity', as he describes it. But the instinctive imitations of young animals do not necessarily tend to reproduce their own stimuli. A chick, seeing its companions run away or crouch, will do so itself; and this we should describe as an imitative action, but (save for the observer) there is here no reproduction of the initiating stimulus (see *Mental Development of the Child and the Race, passim*).

4. Mr C. A. Witchell, for example, in treating of the song of birds, uses the term 'mimicry' as equivalent to 'imitation', which is confusing to the biologist, for whom 'mimicry' as a technical term has acquired a restricted signification.

ing or the modification of the activity and the formation of instinct habits – that is to say, acquired modifications of congenital responses. Given, therefore, a congenital and instinctive imitation, intelligence may utilize it as the basis of an imitative action of the conscious type. To such conscious or intentional imitation we may now turn.

When a child consciously and of set purpose tries to imitate another child or an older person, his action is in all cases founded on a certain amount of preliminary experience. Let us suppose that he is imitating the action of another in tracing with a pencil a simple curve. This is impossible unless he has already acquired some data in the light of which control over his arm and finger movements may be exercised. His object is to apply this control in such a way as to reproduce the movements of the other so as to obtain the same results. He must have some data to work with. Either instinctive imitation has afforded such data, or acquired experience of the use of his limbs and fingers has taught him that, to do this thing which another is doing, and so reach similar results, he must guide his movements in certain definite ways. Given such preliminary data, further progress would seem to be a matter of trial and error, the repressing of such movements as lead to failure, the emphasizing and repeating of such movements as lead to success. Failure is accompanied by more or less painful dissatisfaction; success, by more or less pleasurable satisfaction. Thus, step by step, further control is gained until the imitative action is sufficiently perfect.

It would be convenient to distinguish between two allied, but at the same time somewhat different, processes; and for our present purpose, though the distinction of terms cannot, perhaps, be conveniently maintained, we will describe the reproduction of another's action as imitation, and the reproduction of the objective results of the action, copying. In the case of the curve, the child first imitates the action – holds the pencil and moves the fingers in certain definite ways. But as soon as a passable result is reached, it is on this, and not on the movements, that he fixes his attention. His object is no longer to imitate the action so much as to reproduce the copy. Copying, though often based upon imitation, as we are using the words, may thus be distinguished therefrom. And just as instinctive imitation is in line with, and similar in character to, all other instinctive activity, so is copying in line with, and similar in character to, all other intelligent acquisition. Certain actions are performed, and according as their results afford satisfaction or dissatisfaction, they are enforced or suppressed. At the same time, just as instinctive imitation is marked off from other modes of instinctive activity by the fact that it gives rise *in the observer* to a visual or other impression similar to that which initiated the response, so too is copying to be distinguished from other modes of intelligent activity by the fact that (both from the observer's and the performer's point of view) its results reproduce the stimulus[5] which initiated the appropriate activity. And it is on these results that, in copying, the attention is chiefly fixed.

A further example will bring this out more clearly. In the reproduction by the normal child of the sounds its companions utter, there is far more of copying than of intentional imitation, as we have used these words. The child probably inherits a congenital power of articulation, which may fairly be termed instinctive, since articulation involves a relatively definite coordination which is absent in the case of merely inarticulate sounds. His own articulations afford auditory stimuli which, by association, become linked with the effects in consciousness of those motor processes by which they are produced. He obtains certain results from his own activities, and hears also the results of the activities of others. Thus the data are afforded for copying these results, and the child gradually learns to reproduce articulate sounds, and incidentally and unconsciously to imitate certain motor activities. I say 'incidentally and unconsciously', because the action of the vocal cords is hidden from his sight, and the learning to produce certain sounds cannot, in the normal child, be in any important degree the result of imitating the lip-movements of others. And it is instructive to note that the acquired articulation of deaf mutes *is* mainly a matter of imitation, and not of copying, since the sounds produced are inaudible to the producer, and thus afford no data for copying. The normal child, in learning to articulate like its companions, thus copies certain sounds, and unconsciously imitates certain actions – though, from the observer's point of view, the actions are, no doubt, imitative.

As has before been said, the distinction in the use of the terms 'imitation' and 'copying' – often used interchangeably – could not, perhaps, be conveniently maintained. The distinction is here used as a temporary one to emphasize the difference between reproducing an action or movement, and reproducing a given

5. This reproduction of stimulus is made a cardinal feature in Prof. Mark Baldwin's treatment of imitation in his *Mental Development in the Child and the Race*.

result of such activity. Sometimes the attention is chiefly fixed on the one, sometimes on the other. Both are commonly called imitation; when, for example, we say that a child imitates the tones of another's voice. Both are commonly called copying; as when we say that monkeys copy their masters. The context, as a rule, sufficiently indicates which process predominates – whether the attention of the imitator is chiefly fixed on the curve to be reproduced, or on the movements necessary to reproduce it; on a sound to be made, or the actions necessary to make it.

We have already seen that intelligent procedure is the result of certain processes in the cerebral cortex or elsewhere, which have pleasurable or unpleasant concomitants in consciousness. The actions which bring pleasure are repeated and strengthened; those which are unpleasant are checked or inhibited. What, then, are the special and peculiar conditions of intelligent imitation? Wherein lies the distinguishing feature of the incentives in consciousness to the voluntary copying, either of movements or their results? A child hears certain articulate sounds produced by his companions, and hears also certain articulate sounds which he himself utters. What is the incentive to imitation? The only answer to this question which seems admissible is that the resemblance of the sounds he utters to the sounds he hears *is itself a source of pleasurable satisfaction*; and that, within certain limits, the closer the resemblance the greater the satisfaction. The tendency to imitate is based upon an innate and constitutional bias to get pleasure out of such resemblances; to gain satisfaction by reproducing what others are producing. If there be no such innate proclivity, it is difficult to see whence the incentive to imitation can be derived. At a later stage in the process of development, emulation is, no doubt, an important factor, and there arises a desire not only to imitate but to improve upon the copy.

And here it may be well to remind the reader of the distinction which has already been drawn between what is instinctive and what is innate. Both have their foundations in heredity. But we have restricted the term instinctive to the congenitally responsive behaviour evoked by an external stimulus under given internal conditions. We have treated the instinctive activity from the frankly objective and biological point of view, and have regarded the instinctive response as prior to experience. That which is innate, on the other hand, is the inherited tendency to deal with these data in certain ways. Acquisition is impossible if there be not an innate power of association, and if there be not innate susceptibilities to pleasure and pain. The instinctive response as

C. LLOYD MORGAN

such is independent of association, and independent of the pleasurable or unpleasant effects of that response. That which is instinctive is the basis of definite congenital and organic responses; that which is innate is the basis of acquisition, rendered more or less definite in experience, and leading up to habit. Instinctive imitation is thus an organic response independent of experience; intelligent imitation is due to conscious guidance, the result of experience, and based upon the innate satisfaction which accompanies the act of reproductive imitation.

Let us now pass on to consider the place of intelligent imitation – what we may perhaps fairly term imitation proper – in the animal kingdom. Its very ubiquity makes it difficult to exemplify in a way that shall be adequately convincing. The abnormal arrests our attention more readily than the normal, and hence the cases of imitation usually cited are generally of this class. In the song of birds, for example, imitation is probably a most important factor, but it is chiefly the imitation of another species that arrests our attention. Thus the mocking-bird's feats of imitation are as familiar as an oft-told tale. Mr L. M. Loomis told Mr F. M. Chapman of one in South Carolina which during ten minutes' singing imitated the notes of no less than thirty-two different species of birds found in the same locality. Mr Chapman adds that this was a phenomenal performance, and one he had never heard approached, for, in his experience, many mocking-birds have no notes but their own, and good mockers are exceptional.[6] It would be interesting to gain further information of the conditions under which good mockers are developed. Is the sequence of imitative strains always similar in the same individual? Or does he recombine them in new order? There would seem to be here a field for careful experiment and observation.

Our common English jay has the reputation of being a consummate imitator, sometimes of strange sounds. Montagu says that the low song of one individual was interspersed with sounds imitative of the bleating of a lamb, the mewing of a cat, the note of the kite or buzzard, the hooting of an owl, and the neighing of a horse! Bewick describes how a jay imitated the sound of a saw so well as to cause much surprise, the day being Sunday. And a correspondent in the *Magazine of Natural History* – he may have been of Irish extraction! – says that one imitated the goldfinch's song 'most inimitably' (!), and also the neighing of a horse.[7]

6. *Birds of Eastern North America*, p. 378.
7. These cases are taken from Yarrell, *British Birds*, 2nd edit. vol. ii. p. 122.

One more example among wild birds must suffice. Mr Warde Fowler, in his 'Summer Studies of Birds and Books',[8] gives a quotation from the diary in which he noted the performance in Switzerland of a marsh warbler. 'I am now writing,' he says, 'in a cool spot between the allotments and the Aar, and listening to the marsh-warbler, whose song is as wonderful as ever. Sometimes a grating outburst like that of a sedge-warbler; sometimes a long-drawn sweet note like a nightingale's. Then I have within the last few minutes certainly heard the chaffinch imitated, and even the nuthatch's metallic note. But a low pleasing soliloquy also goes on at intervals. Ah! there is the great tit; now the white wagtail, and I am beginning to get bewildered. This bird creeps about a good deal in the bushes, but now and then appears on a topmost shoot, and sits there singing with his bill wide open, and a red-yellow "gape" showing very plainly. Now and then he flies into a tree over my head. Ah! there is the call of the redstart, and surely this is the skylark's song; and there is the chaffinch again, if ever I heard a chaffinch.'[9] [. . . .]

It is clear that further evidence based on observation under test conditions is needed. But if we may not yet unreservedly accept the view that the song of birds is wholly a matter of imitation, with little or no congenital tendency to sing true to type, yet it is an established fact that imitation is an important factor.

If the question be now asked, – Of what service can it be to the individual or the race to possess such an innate tendency to imitate song, and, as Mr Witchell contends, to incorporate alien strains? – the answer does not appear to be altogether adequate or complete. According to Mr Wallace, song is primarily for purposes of recognition. According to Darwin it is a means to sexual selection. Since most song-birds pair, we may perhaps surmise that the slight variety reached through the incorporation of alien strains is a means of recognition not only specific, but also individual, in its character. The hen bird, on this view, not only recognizes her mate as one of her own species, but as her own special mate. And if we admit sexual selection we may perhaps suppose that such modifications of song evoke in different degrees the emotional state that accompanies the act of pairing. For those who believe that the hen birds select those who most strongly stir the sexual emotion, we have here the diverse modifications of song which may thus have differential effects. Such may

8. Pages 80, 81.
9. Mr C. A. Witchell has given a great deal of evidence on the subject of imitation among wild birds in chap ix. of his *Evolution of Bird Song*, p. 159.

be the advantages of imitation in the particular field of bird-song. But should not the question be made broader and more general? Should we not ask, What is the organic value of the imitative tendency as evinced in many ways in the life of birds or other creatures? I cannot but think that in a number of cases it would make all the difference between survival and destruction. Mr Tegetmeier states[10] 'that if pigeons are reared exclusively with small grain, as wheat or barley, they will starve before eating beans. But when they are thus starving, if a bean-eating pigeon is put among them, they follow its example, and thereafter adopt the habit. So fowls sometimes refuse to eat maize, but on seeing others eat it, they do the same, and become excessively fond of it.' Is it not clear that such imitation as Mr Tegetmeier here describes might be a means of saving those who acted on it from starvation and death? Young water-fowl that, seeing their parents dive, did the same, would stand a far better chance of survival than those who stayed at the surface. One can well understand how natural selection would foster the imitative tendency, and working on congenital variations might eventually render the imitative behaviour a truly instinctive activity.

It has certainly in many cases produced a predisposition to imitate the actions of their own kind rather than those of another species. When chicks and ducklings are brought up together, they keep to some extent separate, and there is little imitation on the part of either of the habits of the other species. Spalding noted that chicks showed no signs of imitating the peculiar habits of young turkeys in the matter of catching flies. It would seem, indeed, that imitation serves to initiate or to emphasize those activities to the performance of which there is already a congenital bias. Thus a blackbird which had been in captivity for two years in a large aviary, and had never been mated or troubled with family cares, seeing some recently introduced young thrushes fed by their parents through the bars, began himself to feed them in a similar manner.[11] Here an activity to which there is a congenital bias was called into play through the suggestive touch of imitation.

If, then, the young have a tendency to imitate the actions of their parents; if, too, among the members of gregarious species, there is much imitation; – it is clear that we have here a conservative factor in animal life of no slight importance. Just as imitation is of great value in bringing the human child to the level of the

10. Quoted in Mr A. R. Wallace's *Darwinism*, p. 75.
11. *Nature*, vol. xlviii. p. 369. Letter signed 'E. Boscher.'

adults who form the family and social environment, so too does the less fully conscious imitation of the lower animals serve to bring the young bird or other creature into line with the members of its own species.

I have several times observed that, in broods of chicks brought up under experimental conditions by themselves, and without opportunities of imitating older birds, there are one or two more active, vigorous, intelligent, and mischievous birds. They are the leaders of the brood; the others are their imitators. The presence raises the general level of intelligent activity. Remove them, and the others show a less active, less inquisitive, less adventurous life, if one may so put it. They seem to lack initiative. From which one may infer that imitation affords to some extent a means of levelling up the less intelligent to the standard of the more intelligent; and of supplying a stimulus to the development of habits which would otherwise be lacking. [. . . .]

26   E. L. Thorndike

Animal Intelligence; an Experimental Study of the Associative Processes in Animals

Excerpt from E. L. Thorndike, 'Animal intelligence; an experimental study of the associative processes in animals', *Psychol. Rev. Monogr. Suppl.*, vol. 2 (1898), pp. 47–52.

[. . . .]
Imitation

To the question, 'Do animals imitate?' science has uniformly answered, 'Yes.' But so long as the question is left in this general form, no correct answer to it is possible. It will be seen, from the results of numerous experiments soon to be described, that imitation of a certain sort is not possible for animals, and before entering upon that description it will be helpful to differentiate this matter of imitation into several varieties or aspects. The presence of some sorts of imitation does not imply that of other sorts.

There are, to begin with, the well-known phenomena presented by the imitative birds. The power is extended widely, ranging from the parrot who knows a hundred or more articulate sounds to the sparrow whom a patient shoemaker taught to get through a tune. Now, if a bird really gets a sound in his mind from hearing it and sets out forthwith to imitate it, as mocking-birds are said at times to do, it is a mystery and deserves closest study. If a bird, out of a lot of random noises that it makes, chooses those for repetition which are like sounds that he has heard, it is again a mystery *why*, though not as in the previous case a mystery *how*, he does it. The important fact for our purpose is that, though the imitation of sounds is so habitual, there does not appear to be any marked general imitative tendency in these birds. There is no proof that parrots do muscular acts from having seen other parrots do them. But this should be studied. At any rate, until we know what sort of sounds birds imitate, what circumstances or emotional attitudes these are connected with, how they learn them and, above all, whether there is in birds which repeat sounds any tendency to imitate in other lines, we cannot, it seems to me, connect these phenomena with anything found in the mammals or use them to advantage in a discussion of animal imitation as the forerunner of human. In what follows they will be left out of

363

account, will be regarded as a specialization removed from the general course of mental development, just as the feathers or right aortic arch of birds are particular specializations of no consequence for the physical development of mammals. For us, henceforth, imitation will mean imitation minus the phenomena of imitative birds.

There are also certain pseudo-imitative or semi-imitative phenomena which ought to be considered by themselves. For example, the rapid loss of the fear of railroad trains or telegraph wires among birds, the rapid acquisition of arboreal habits among Australian rodents, the use of proper feeding grounds, etc., may be held to be due to imitation. The young animal stays with or follows its mother from a specific instinct to keep near that particular object, to wit, its mother. It may thus learn to stay near trains, or scrabble up trees, or feed at certain places and on certain plants. Actions due to following pure and simple may thus simulate imitation. Other groups of acts which now seem truly imitative may be indirect fruits of some one instinct. This must be kept in mind when one estimates the supposed imitation of parents by young. Further, it is certain that in the case of the chick, where early animal life has been carefully observed, instinct and individual experience between them rob imitation of practically all its supposed influence. Chicks get along without a mother very well. Yet no mother takes more care of her children than the hen. Care in other cases, then, need not mean instruction through imitation.

These considerations may prevent an unreserved acceptance of the common view that young animals get a great number of their useful habits from imitation, but I do not expect or desire them to lead to its summary rejection. I should not now myself reject it, though I think it quite possible that more investigation and experiment may finally reduce all the phenomena of so-called imitation of parents by young to the level of indirect results of instinctive acts.

Another special department of imitation may be at least vaguely marked off: namely, apparent imitation of certain limited sorts of acts which are somewhat frequent in the animal's life. An example will do better than further definition.

Some sheep were being driven on board ship one at a time. In the course of their progress they had to jump over a hurdle. On this being removed before all had passed it, the next sheep was seen to jump as if to get over a hurdle, and so on for five or six, apparently sure evidence that they imitated the action, each of the one in front. Now, it is again possible that among gregarious animals there may be elaborate connections in the nervous system which allow the sight of certain particular acts in another animal to arouse the innervation leading to those acts, but that these connections are *limited*. The reactions on this view are specific responses to definite signals, comparable to any other instinctive or associational reaction. The sheep jumps when he sees the other sheep jump, not because of a general ability to do what he sees done, but because he is furnished with the instinct to jump at such a sight, or because his experience of following the flock over boulders and brooks and walls has got him into the habit of jumping at the spot where he sees one ahead of him jump; and so he jumps even though no obstacle be in his way. If due to instinct the only peculiarity of such a reaction would be that the sense-impression calling forth the act would be the same act as done by another. If due to experience there would be an exact correspondence to the frequent acts called forth *originally* by several elements in a sense-impression, one of which is essential, and done *afterwards* when only the *non-essentials* are present. These two possibilities have not been sufficiently realized, yet they may contain the truth. On the other hand, these limited acts may be the primitive, sporadic beginnings of the general imitative faculty which we find in man. To this general faculty we may now turn, having cleared away some of the more doubtful phenomena which have shared its name.

It should be kept in mind that an imitative act may be performed quite unthinkingly, as when a man in the mob shouts what the others shout or claps when the others clap; may be done from an inference that since A by doing X makes pleasure for himself, I by doing X may get pleasure for myself; may, lastly, be done from what may be called a transferred association. This process is the one of interest in connection with our general topic, and most of my experiments on imitation were directed to the investigation of it. Its nature is simple. One sees the following sequence: 'A turning a faucet, A getting a drink.' If one can free this association from its narrow confinement to A, so as to get from it the association, 'impulse to turn faucet, *me* getting a drink', one will surely, if thirsty, turn the faucet, though he had never done so before. If one can from an act witnessed learn to do the act, he in some way makes use of the sequence seen, transfers the process to himself; in the common human sense of the word, he *imitates*. This kind of imitation is surely common in human life. It may be apparent in ontogeny before any power of

365

inference is shown. After that power does appear, it still retains a wide scope, and teaches us a majority, perhaps, of the ordinary accomplishments of our practical life.

Now, as the writers of books about animal intelligence have not differentiated this meaning from the other possible ones, it is impossible to say surely that they have uniformly credited it to animals, and it is profitless to catalogue here their vague statements. Many opposers of the 'reason' theory have presupposed such a process and used it to replace reason as the cause of some intelligent performances. The upholders of the reason theory have customarily recognized such a process and claimed to have discounted it in their explanations of the various anecdotes. So we found Mr Romanes discussing the possibility that such an imitative process, without reason, could account for the facts. In his chapter on Imitation in *Habit and Instinct*, Principal C. Lloyd Morgan, the sanest writer on comparative psychology, seems to accept imitation of this sort as a fact, though he could, if attacked, explain most of his illustrations by the simple forms. The fact is, as was said before, that no one has analyzed or systematized the phenomena, and so one cannot find clear, decisive statements to quote.

At any rate, whether previous authorities have agreed that such a process is present or not, it is worth while to tackle the question; and the formation of associations by imitation, if it occurs, is an important division of the formation of associations in general. The experiments and their results may now be described.

Imitation in Chicks

No. 64 learned to get out of a certain pen (16 × 10 inches) by crawling under the wire screening at a certain spot. There was also a chance to get out by walking up an inclined plane and then jumping down. No. 66 was put in with 64. After 9 minutes, 20 seconds, 66 went out by the inclined plane, although 64 had in the mean time crawled out under the screen 9 times. (As soon as he got out and ate a little he was put back.) It was impossible to judge how many of these times 66 really saw 64 do this. He was looking in that direction 5 of the times. So also, in three more trials, 66 used the inclined plane, though 64 crawled under each time. 67 was then tried. In 4 minutes, 10 seconds, he crawled under, 64 having done so twice. Being then put in *alone*, he, without the chance to imitate, still crawled under. So probably he went under *when with 64* not by imitation but by accident, just as 64 had learned the thing himself.

The accompanying figure (1) shows the apparatus used in the next experiment. A represents the top of a box (5 × 4 inches), 13 inches above the level of the floor, C. On the floor C were the chicks and food. B is the top of a box 10 inches high. Around the edges of A except the one next to B a wire screen was placed, and 65 was repeatedly put upon A until he learned to go quickly back to C *via* B. Then the screen was bent outward at X so that a chick could barely squeeze through and down (A to C). Eleven chicks were then one at a time placed on A with 65. In every case

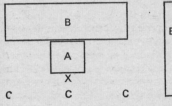

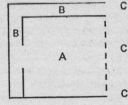

Figure 1   Figure 2

but one they went A–C. In the case of the chick (75) who went A–B–C, there could have been no imitation, for he went down *before* 65 did. One other went through the hole before 65 went to B. The remaining nine all had a chance to imitate 65 and to save the uncomfortable struggle to get through the hole, 65 going A–B–C 8 times before 68 went A–C, 2 times when with 66 and 76, once in the case of each of the others.

In still another experiment the apparatus was (as shown in figure 2) a pen 14 inches square, 10 inches high, with a wire screen in front and a hole 3½ inches square in the back. This hole opened into a passage-way (B) leading around to C, where were the other chicks and food. Chicks who had failed, when put in alone, to find the way out, were put in with other chicks who had learned the way, to see if by seeing them go out they would learn the way. Chick 70 was given 4 trials alone, being left in the box 76 minutes all told. He was then given 9 trials (165 minutes) with another chick who went out *via* B 36 times. 70 failed to follow him on any occasion. The trials were all given in the course of two days. Chick 73 failed in 1 trial (12 minutes) to get out of himself, and was then given 4 trials (94 minutes) with another chick who went out *via* B 33 times. In this experiment, as in all others reported, sure evidence that the animals wanted to get out, was afforded by their persistent peckings and jumpings at the screen or bars that stood between them and C. Chick 72, after 8 unsuccessful trials alone (41 minutes), was given 8 trials with a chance to imitate. After the other chick had gone out 44 times, 72 *did go out*. He did not follow the other but went 20 seconds later. It depends upon one's general opinion whether one shall attribute this one case out of three to accident or imitation.

I also took two chicks, one of whom learned to escape from A (in figure 1) by going to B and jumping down the side to the *right* of A, the other of whom learned to jump down the side to the *left*, and placed them together upon A. Each took his own course uninfluenced by the other in 10 trials.

Chicks were also tried in several pens where there was only one possible way of escape to see if they would learn it *more quickly* when another chick did the thing several times before their eyes. The method was to give some chicks their first trial with an imitation possibility and their second without, while others were given their first trial without and their second with. If the ratio of the average time of the first trial to the average time of the second is smaller in the first class than it is in the second class, we may find evidence of this sort of influence by imitation. Though imitation may not be able to make an animal *do* what he would otherwise *not do*, it may make him do *quicker* a thing he would have done sooner or later any way. As a fact the ratio is *much larger*. This is due to the fact that a chick, when in a pen with another chick, is not afflicted by the discomfort of loneliness, and so does not try so hard to get out. So the other chick, who is continually being put in with him to teach him the way out, really prolongs his stay in. This factor destroys the value of these quantitative experiments, and I do not insist upon them as evidence against imitation, though they certainly offer none for it. I do not give descriptions of the apparatus used in these experiments or a detailed enumeration of the results, because in this discussion we are not dealing primarily with imitation as a slight general factor in forming experience, but as a definite associational process in the mind. The utter absence of imitation in this limited sense is apparently demonstrated by the results of the following experiments.

V was a box $16 \times 12 \times 8\frac{1}{2}''$, with the front made of wire screening and at the left end a little door held by a bolt but in such a way that a sharp peck at the top of the door would force it open.

W was a box of similar size, with a door in the same place fixed so that it was opened by raising a bolt. To this bolt was tied a string which went up over the top of the edge of the box and back across the box, as in D. By jumping up and coming down with the head over this thread, the bolt would be pulled up. The thread was $8\frac{1}{2}$ inches above the floor.

X was a box of similar size, with door, bolt and string likewise. But here the string continued round a pulley at the back down to a platform in the corner of the box. By stepping on the platform the door was opened.

Y was a box $12 \times 8 \times 8\frac{1}{2}''$, with a door in the middle of the front, which I myself opened when a chick pecked at a tack which hung against the front of the box $1\frac{1}{2}$ inches above the top of the door. [. . . .]

27 C. L. Darby and A. J. Riopelle

Observational Learning in the Rhesus Monkey

C. L. Darby and A. J. Riopelle, 'Observational learning in the rhesus monkey', *J. comp. physiol. Psychol.*, vol. 52 (1959), pp. 94–8.

Numerous attempts have been made to demonstrate that species of animals other than man are capable of learning by observation or imitation. An especially important study for our present purposes is that by Crawford and Spence (1939), who, using two opposing cages with a stimulus tray between them, trained a chimpanzee to observe another depress one of three stimulus objects. After several trials by the demonstrator, the observer was given a test trial to determine if the observer would depress the same object. Both demonstration and test trials continued alternately until the observer either learned the problem or evidenced inability to learn. Results were ambiguous, with only one of eight chimpanzees learning a 'pure' imitation problem. The ambiguity of the results suggested that although the general procedure was correct, the stimulus-display conditions were not conducive to rapid discrimination learning.

Data collected since have defined the conditions necessary for rapid discrimination learning by primates (Harlow, 1944; Jarvik, 1953; Jenkins, 1943; McClearn & Harlow, 1954), and it was thought that by utilizing the results of these recent researches, unambiguous data might be collected on observational learning. Because of these considerations, we were motivated to try a demonstration of observational learning under more efficient conditions and to learn what we could about factors contributing to successful performance.

Two studies were conducted. In the first, described in detail elsewhere, Darby (1956) placed two monkeys that could solve object-quality discrimination problems in a single trial (i.e., had formed learning sets) side by side in the Emory version (Riopelle, 1954) of the Wisconsin General Test Apparatus (Harlow, 1949). One animal, the demonstrator (*D*), was given 1, 2, or 3 trials on an object-quality discrimination problem, then another animal, the observer (*O*), was given 3 trials on the same problem. The *O*s made approximately 65% correct responses on their first trials of the 400 problems given. Although intraproblem performance improved rapidly, interproblem performance remained unchanged throughout the series of problems. Also O's performance was no better after 3 than after 1 or 2 demonstration trials. The results suggested that the display aspects of the stimulus presentation were probably still inefficient. Nevertheless, the results were encouraging, and we undertook the present investigation hoping that, with a few additional alterations in the procedures, the efficiency might be high enough to permit the use of inexperienced monkeys, thereby permitting us to trace the development of proficiency in observational learning.

Method

Subjects

Four experimentally naive adolescent and young adult rhesus monkeys (No. 58, 61, 65, 70) were used as Ss in this experiment. They were subjected to a standardized training and test-adaptation procedure in which they were accustomed to the apparatus, to E, and to the displacement of a single object from the test tray in order to obtain a morsel from a foodwell.

The animals were grouped in pairs, each pair constituting an experimental unit. The pairings were maintained throughout the experiment. On a particular problem, one member of the pair served as D and the other as O.

Apparatus

The device, illustrated schematically in Figure 1, consisted of two restraining cages and a sliding test-tray between them. This tray was retracted from the testing location during the baiting and placing of the test objects, and it was returned at the beginning of each trial.

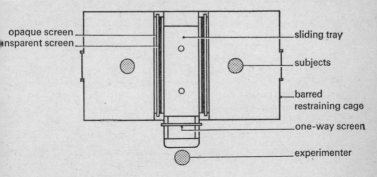

Figure 1 Schematic diagram of apparatus.

Two foodwells, 1·5 in. in diameter and 10 in. apart, were drilled in the 12- by 18-in. test board. The distance from the foodwells to the bars of the restraining cages was approximately three-fourths of the maximum reach of the animals.

The cages were completely enclosed with sheet metal with the exception of the side facing the test surface; this was barred. The opaque walls served to restrict observation to the quadrant containing the test tray. Immediately in front of the barred side of the cage was a double screen consisting of an inner, opaque screen, constructed of $\frac{1}{4}$-in. plywood, and an outer, transparent screen, made of $\frac{1}{4}$-in. transparent plastic.

The screens were so arranged that the opaque screen could be raised, leaving the transparent screen in place. This arrangement constituted the 'observing' position, for the animal could see but not touch the test objects. By raising the opaque screen further, the transparent screen was carried with it, allowing the animal access to the test board. This constituted the 'testing' position.

The problems used in testing were drawn at random from the laboratory's random assortment of over 1,000 mutually different stimulus objects.

A one-way screen, fixed at one side of the apparatus, prevented the monkeys from seeing E.

Procedure

Testing was initiated after both members of a test pair had entered the restraining cages. All screens were lowered, and the test tray was baited. Depending on whether or not the first, or demonstration, trial (D trial) was to be rewarded, food was placed in both or neither (each precisely 50% of the trials) of the foodwells and covered with the stimulus objects. The tray was then moved to the testing location. The screens were then raised to the observing position and held there for approximately 1 sec. The screen in front of D was then raised to the testing position to permit a choice. The other monkey, O, was not allowed a response on this trial.

As soon as D displaced an object, all screens were lowered and the test tray was retracted and baited for the first O trial. If the D trial had been rewarded, food was placed under the object which had been displaced and it was removed from under the other object. If the trial was not rewarded, food was placed under the object which had not been displaced. The O was then given its first trial, the task being to select the object displaced by the demonstrator on Trial D_1 if D had received reward or to select the nondisplaced object if D had received no reward. Four additional trials completed the problem. The above procedure was repeated in each subsequent problem in the experiment.

Six trials were allowed on each problem, 2 for D and 4 for O. The D was allowed a single trial, and then O was given 1, 2, or 3 trials. Then D was permitted a second opportunity to respond. On each O trial, D

was allowed to observe O's response. Following this, O was allowed as many more trials as were necessary to make 4 trials on that particular problem.

The order of presentation, the side on which reward was presented, the sequence in which the observer role was played, and the side on which the animal was placed were all randomly determined.

Between 10 and 15 problems were allowed per day for each pair of animals. Training was continued until each animal had served as O on 500 problems. Necessarily, each animal also served as D on 500 problems. Therefore, every monkey received some training on 1,000 problems.

Results

Figure 2 shows the performance of O on its first trial (O_1) and on its second trial (O_2). Also shown is the performance on D's

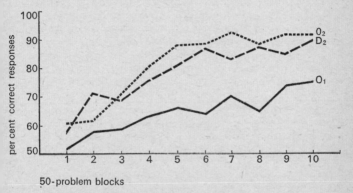

Figure 2 Development of proficiency in observational and discrimination learning. Curve O_1 denotes performance by Observer after a single demonstration trial. Other curves denote performance on second trial of Observer and Demonstrator.

second trial (D_2), that for D_1 having been fixed precisely at 50%. The most important curve is that labeled O_1; it is a measure of how much information O gained by the single demonstration trial. The curve starts at 52% and rises gradually to 75% correct. The linear trend of this curve rose significantly (·01 level), and it shows that as the experiment progressed, the Os learned increasing amounts from the single observation trial on each problem.

Curve O_2 contains the usual learning-set performance; it is superior to O_1 and rises to 90% correct. Curve D_2 shows the same thing for the demonstrator. The slight but consistent superiority of Curve O_2 over D_2 suggests that it is more efficient to have the first observation trial precede a test trial rather than succeed it. Both curves are higher than Curve O_1. This superiority of discrimination learning-set performance over observational-learning performance shrinks but does not disappear when the learning-set curves are combined and extended over 1,000 problems rather than over the 500 problems as plotted in Figure 2.

What are some of the factors determining observational proficiency? According to Spence (1937), 'stimulus enhancement', by which he means that O will respond to those aspects of the problem manipulated by D, is an important factor, especially in problem boxes. If we apply this argument to the discrimination-learning situation, we would predict that O will tend to displace the object displaced by D, regardless of whether or not D obtained reward. If so, the percentage of correct responses made on Trial O_1 when D_1 was rewarded should be higher than that for responses when D_1 was wrong (unrewarded), for in the former case O chooses the same object as was chosen by D, and in the

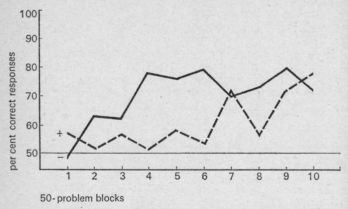

Figure 3 Observational-learning performance after a rewarded (+) and after a nonrewarded (−) demonstration trial.

latter case it chooses the other object to obtain reward. Figure 3 shows these data. In seven out of ten points on the graph, performance on O_1 after a nonrewarded D_1 surpasses that after a rewarded D_1.

The data from which Figure 3 was derived contained all the information relevant to the major purpose of the investigation. Those data were therefore subjected to analysis of variance, a summary of which appears in Table 1. In addition to the ever present individual differences, we found a significant difference among blocks of problems, reflecting the over-all improvement in performance. Also, whether or not the *D* trial was rewarded was a significant factor in determining *O*'s level of proficiency. The absence of significant interaction effects suggests that the superiority of a nonrewarded *D* trial over a rewarded *D* trial holds for most monkeys and throughout an important portion of the acquisition of proficiency in observational-learning performance.

Discussion

The results of this investigation clearly show that rhesus monkeys can acquire information about the solution of an object-quality discrimination problem simply by watching another monkey execute a single trial on the problem. Thus, we have demonstrated that they can acquire some degree of proficiency in observational learning. Doubtless, had the experiment continued, even greater proficiency would have obtained. Moreover, the method used, which involves multiple presentations of simple problems, permits repeated demonstrations of the phenomenon, and is thus useful for further systematic experimental analysis.

What is the nature of *O*'s response on its first test trial? Clearly, *O* is not 'imitating' in the 'matched-dependent' sense of Miller and Dollard (1941), for *O*'s response does not consistently match (or oppose) *D*'s response nor does it occur simultaneously with it. Also, *O* is not imitating via a mediating process of 'identification',

Table 1

Summary of Analysis of Variance

Source of Variation	df	MS	F
Animals (A)	3	50·28	4·45*
Blocks (B)	9	25·37	2·25*
Reward (R)	1	115·20	10·21**
(A) × (B)	27	5·66	
(A) × (R)	3	11·30	
(B) × (R)	9	17·95	1·59
(A) × (B) × (R)	27	11·28	
Total	79		

* $P \gtrless \cdot05$.
** $P \gtrless \cdot01$.

as has been proposed by Mowrer (1950) in the case of the 'talking' birds, for O does not reproduce D's actions and O derives no reward from D, so essential for the development of the identification. Indeed, D frequently competes with O for food.

Spence's notion of stimulus enhancement (1937) does not explain O's behavior either, also for the reason that O can correct for D's mistakes. Indeed, O's performance is better if D makes a mistake than it would be if D made a correct guess. This latter finding is not without precedent (Moss & Harlow, 1947; Riopelle, 1955) and perhaps results from a distracting effect of seeing food. Thus, when D obtains food, O's attention is distracted from the critical stimuli. The desirability of witnessing of errors by O in a problem-box situation has been emphasized by Herbert and Harsh (1944).

The present experimental arrangement satisfies all the requirements of a nonspatial delayed-response test. Although this test is admittedly of great difficulty, even for chimpanzees, when conducted under the usual procedures (Yerkes & Nissen, 1939), successful performance has been demonstrated previously for rhesus monkeys in an observational-learning situation (Harlow, 1944). Highly successful delayed imitation has been demonstrated by the Hayeses (1952) with their home-raised chimpanzee, Viki.

In the present situation, O simply uses D as a sign stimulus to denote the object O must displace to obtain food. It is interesting to note also that this response satisfies Maier's requirements for a test of reasoning.

Summary

Four monkeys were each given 500 object-quality discrimination problems to solve. Prior to their first trial on each problem they witnessed another monkey execute a single demonstration trial. In the 500 demonstration trials viewed by each observer, exactly half were 'correct', i.e., the demonstrator received reward for its selection. The observer was never rewarded on this trial. Its reward came whenever it made a response to the appropriate stimulus object. Appropriateness was defined as a response to the object selected by the demonstrator if the demonstrator had been rewarded or a response to the non-selected object if the demonstrator had received no reward.

All observers showed improvement in their ability to derive information from the observation trial; the observers' first test-trial performance rose from chance level to 75% correct and was still rising at the end of the experiment.

Performance on later trials in the same problems was even higher. It was also found that observational-learning performance was higher if the demonstrator had made a 'mistake' than it was if it had made a 'correct' response.

The similarity between the procedure of this experiment and that used to test nonspatial delayed response was emphasized.

References

CRAWFORD, M. P., & SPENCE, K. W. Observational learning of discrimination problems by chimpanzees. *J. comp. Psychol.*, 1939, **27**, 133–147.

DARBY, C. L. Observational learning in the rhesus monkey. Unpublished doctoral dissertation, Emory Univer., 1956.

HARLOW, H. F. Studies of discrimination learning by monkeys: II. Discrimination learning without primary reinforcement. *J. gen. Psychol.*, 1944, **30**, 13–21.

HARLOW, H. F. The formation of learning sets. *Psychol. Rev.*, 1949, **56**, 51–65.

HAYES, K. J., & HAYES, C. Imitation in a home-raised chimpanzee. *J. comp. physiol. Psychol.*, 1952, **45**, 450–459.

HERBERT, M. J., & HARSH, C. M. Observational learning by cats. *J. comp. Psychol.*, 1944, **37**, 81–95.

JARVIK, M. E. Discrimination of colored food and food signs by primates. *J. comp. physiol. Psychol.*, 1953, **46**, 390–392.

JENKINS, W. O. Spatial factors in chimpanzee learning. *J. comp. Psychol.*, 1943, **35**, 81–84.

McCLEARN, G. E., & HARLOW, H. F. The effect of spatial contiguity on discrimination learning by rhesus monkeys. *J. comp. physiol. Psychol.*, 1954, **47**, 391–394.

MILLER, N. E., & DOLLARD, J. *Social learning and imitation.* New Haven: Yale Univer. Press, 1941.

MOSS, E. M., & HARLOW, H. F. The role of reward in discrimination learning in monkeys. *J. comp. physiol. Psychol.*, 1947, **40**, 333–342.

MOWRER, O. H. On the psychology of 'talking birds' – A contribution to language and personality theory. In *Learning theory and personality dynamics.* New York: McGraw-Hill, 1950.

RIOPELLE, A. J. Facilities of the Emory University primate behavior laboratory. *J. Psychol.*, 1954, **38**, 331–338.

RIOPELLE, A. J. Rewards, preferences, and learning sets. *Psychol. Rep.*, 1955, **1**, 167–173.

SPENCE, K. W. Experimental studies of learning and the higher mental processes in infra-human primates. *Psychol. Bull.*, 1937, **34**, 806–850.

YERKES, R. M., & NISSEN, H. W. Pre-linguistic sign behavior in chimpanzee. *Science*, 1939, **89**, 585–587.

Imitation in a Home-raised Chimpanzee

K. J. Hayes and C. Hayes, 'Imitation in a home-raised chimpanzee',
J. comp. physiol. Psychol., vol. 45 (1952), pp. 450–59.

The popular opinion that subhuman primates possess a high
order of imitative ability is supported by a considerable amount
of *observational* data. In summarizing such evidence with regard
to chimpanzees, Yerkes and Yerkes say:

> . . . we feel entirely safe in asserting, as the consensus of opinion
> among competent students, that the chimpanzee commonly and with
> extreme facility imitates acts, in some instances for the mere satisfac-
> tion of performing them, and in other cases for the sake of a desired
> reward or objective (12, p. 347).

However, the numerous *experimental* studies of imitation reported during the past fifty years have given little support to this
view. Crawford and Spence (2) found imitation in a simple discrimination problem with only one of their seven chimpanzees.
They criticized earlier reports on monkey imitation, including the
paper of Warden and Jackson (10), as being explicable by mere
enhancement of the stimulus value of the apparatus. This and
other objections have led most comparative psychologists to reject the meager positive data available. Detailed discussions of the
literature are available elsewhere (9, 10, 12).

In the present study, we have attempted to resolve the disagreement between observation and experiment by using both techniques with the same subject.

The consensus quoted above from Yerkes and Yerkes was
based largely on the behavior of apes that differed from typical
laboratory animals in having had experience with a wide variety
of tools, materials, and situations. Often, too, they have had much
contact with people, and have been subject to close and continued
observation. This description applies particularly well to the
chimpanzee, Viki, principal subject of the present investigation.

Viki was adopted by the authors a few days after her birth at
the Yerkes Laboratories. She has lived in their home for the past
four years, and has had most of the experiences common to young
human children. This paper is concerned only with Viki's imita-

ive behavior, other aspects of the project having been reported lsewhere (4, 6).

In order to provide direct evidence on the influence of environ-nent, our experimental tests were also given to a cage-raised himpanzee, whose opportunity for varied experience had been ery limited. Human children were also tested, to provide an xperimental reference point.

We shall use the word *imitation* in the full breadth of its popular neaning, rather than attempt formal classification, definitions, nd lists of criteria. We hope that our results will justify this pproach for the present purpose, and at the same time facilitate ater detailed analysis, should it prove desirable.

imitative Play

Most of Viki's imitation occurs in play. At about 16 mo. of age he began to imitate such bits of household routine as dusting urniture and washing clothes and dishes. Her early efforts were uite crude and could perhaps be ascribed to stimulus enhance-nent. Before she was two years old, however, some of her play vas much too complex and precise to be so explained. For in-tance, she appropriated a lipstick, stood on the washbasin, ooked in the mirror, and applied the cosmetic – not at random, ut to her mouth. She then pressed her lips together and moothed the color with her finger, just as she had seen the act erformed. A similar performance occurred involving face owder.

By the time she was three years old, we were sufficiently familiar vith these incidents to predict their occurrence and be prepared o record them with a motion picture camera. In one such case, she vas allowed to watch the experimenter pound a wooden stake nto the ground with a hammer. When the experimenter stepped side, Viki attempted to duplicate this new use of a familiar tool. The experimenter then rubbed the stake with a piece of sandpaper which Viki had never used before). She promptly copied this rocedure, keeping the abrasive side of the paper against the vood. The motion picture record of this and other instances of nitation is available (5).

Delayed imitation. Many of Viki's recent imitations have occurred ome time after the original demonstration. For instance, when he saw an experimenter sharpen some pencils, she could not nitate immediately; but within a minute she got a pencil from the next room, returned with it, put it in the sharpener, and turned the crank.

Delayed imitation often results when Viki watches an activity through the screen door of her room. She once saw the windows being cleaned with a solution from a bottle with a small spray gun built into the cap. When she was admitted to the living room about 15 min. later, she went directly to the bottle and sprayed its contents on a window. On another occasion she saw photographs being flattened between the pages of a book. When she saw the pictures again, about 6 hr. later, she began to put them in a book. (She later generalized this game not only to scraps of paper but also to bulkier objects.)

A delay was introduced into one of the situations set up for motion picture recording: Viki was allowed to watch us use a screwdriver to pry off the friction-type lids of several empty paint cans. She was then taken away and brought back 1 hr. later. She set to work immediately, and after some effort succeeded in opening two cans. (She was already familiar with various other containers and had often used a screwdriver as a lever; but this combination was new to her.)

We have presented only a small sample of the large number of instances of spontaneous imitation which we have observed, additional examples having been described elsewhere (4). It must be emphasized that we are dealing here with patterns of behavior which Viki had had no opportunity to acquire by trial and error or by reward for chance performance. She has been under almost constant observation since birth, and a detailed diary record has been kept, so that her previous opportunities for experience with various objects are known.

The Imitation Set Series

From the age of 17 mo. until 34 mo., Viki was given occasional training on a series of tasks intended to establish a set for learning by imitation, in the hope of making this a more useful pedagogical tool. We wanted her to learn that imitating an action accompanied by the command 'Do this' would be rewarded, so that she would try to imitate even though the action itself had no intrinsic play value.

Procedure. Each of the 70 items of the series consisted, typically, of a simple, arbitrary, often meaningless act. The experimenter said 'Do this', and then, for instance, clapped his hands, blinked

is eyes, or patted his head. If Viki imitated within a few seconds,
he was given a bit of some favorite food; otherwise we either
repeated the demonstration or helped her to make the response –
whichever the situation seemed to require. Some of the items were
more complicated and involved use of materials, such as a pad-
lock to be opened with a key. Other items required various uses of
the same material – a whistle might be blown, tapped on the table,
or slipped over a finger.

Results. At first it was necessary to put her through the actions of
each new item many times (by manipulating her hands, etc.) before she began to perform them herself. However, as soon as she
was able to execute the first few items, she discriminated correctly
among them. Her behavior thus far could, of course, be explained
on the basis of learned responses to cues, without regard to the
similarity of cue and response.

Beginning with the twelfth, however, certain new items were
imitated immediately, without preliminary tutoring – provided
that she had previously done them in other situations. Number
12, for instance, was saying 'Mama', which she had previously
done in solicitation; and Number 13 was a 'Bronx cheer', which
she had made before only in play.

Beginning with the twentieth task, at least ten were copied immediately, even though we were quite certain that she had never
done them before under *any* circumstances. Examples are:
stretching the mouth with two forefingers (shown in figure 1),
whirling on one foot, and operating various new toys.

Many of our 70 items were difficult for her. We seldom got the
impression that her trouble was with the observational aspect, but
it often seemed to involve the execution of the act. For example,
she apparently saw clearly enough that we put a card in an en-
velope, but her attempted imitation was too clumsy to succeed.
Blinking the eyes seemed to be absent from her voluntary motor
repertory – though she finally adopted the pseudosolution of
putting a finger to her eye, which caused it to close.

She occasionally did poorly on tasks which did not appear to
present motor difficulties. Her general behavior at such times
suggested shyness or negativism. We have observed the same
thing in human children of Viki's age, who accompany their resistance with such remarks as 'No!' or 'I don't want to.'

Despite these difficulties, 55 of the tasks were finally learned,
and she could then imitate our demonstration of them with very
little confusion among the various items. Since the completion of

Figure 1 An imitation set series item, and the stick-and-tunnel problem.

the original series, we have given her many additional items informally, with similar results.

Solving Problems by Imitation

Between 28 and 34 mo. Viki was tested on six problems in which a
lure could be obtained by imitating the procedure demonstrated
by the experimenter. Four human children from 26 to 36 mo. of
age were also tested,[1] and four of the problems were given to a
caged chimpanzee, Frans, 9 mo. older than Viki.

1. We are indebted to Lyla Kleemeier for her assistance with this work.
Mrs Kleemeier determined the Merrill-Palmer MA's for the human
subjects, and aided us in testing their imitative ability.

Before the first demonstration of each problem, a 2-min. period was allowed in which the subject could attempt a solution by insight or trial and error. Two-minute test periods were also allowed after each demonstration, until a solution occurred, or until it appeared improbable that the subject would succeed.

Stick and tunnel problem. In a variation of the classical 'box and pole' apparatus, our tunnel consisted of a long, narrow, wire-mesh roof over a wooden base. The lure, which was placed in the center of the tunnel, could be seen and could be pushed out with a stick which lay nearby (figure 1).

During the predemonstration test, and after the first demonstration, Viki played with the stick, fingered the screen over the lure, and attempted to reach in the end of the tunnel with her hand. After the second demonstration these ineffective activities were repeated for the first 30 sec.; but then she picked up the stick, put it into the tunnel, and began to push the lure out. An additional trial was given without further demonstration, and this time she used the stick immediately. (Such repeat tests were also given in the following problems, with essentially the same result.)

Ball-throwing problem. The lure was suspended loosely overhead, where it could not be reached by jumping but could be knocked down by throwing a ball, which lay beneath it.

This was the only problem in which an appropriate response occurred before demonstration. Viki threw the ball at the lure five times during the initial test period. Her throws were inaccurate, however, and two demonstrations were given, which encouraged her to keep trying until she hit the lure.

Light-switch problem. The lure was suspended from a magnetic device attached to a light fixture near the center of the ceiling. It could be released by operating a toggle switch on the wall of the room. Viki solved this problem after three demonstrations. The time before solution was occupied with attempts to reach the lure by climbing and jumping, and by searching for things to throw at it.

Stick and string problem. The lure was placed in a wooden box with a transparent plastic door. The door could not be opened by direct manipulation, but only by displacing a short length of string, which was stretched between two posts beyond the box. The subjects were not allowed to approach the string, but a stick was provided, with which they could reach it (figure 2).

Figure 2 The stick-and-string problem, and the string-and-candle problem.

Viki solved this problem after a single demonstration. She devoted 35 sec. to manipulation of the door, then took the stick and pushed the string upward with it. (As is often the case her procedure differed from the experimenter's in detail: he had struck downward at the string.)

String and candle problem. Here a string extended from the side of a box to a nearby post. The door opened when this string was burned through with a lighted candle, which stood near the box (figure 2).

Viki had not solved the problem after three demonstrations.

Therefore, during the fourth trial, the experimenter encouraged her by picking up the candle and thrusting it a little way toward the string. She then solved it immediately. Her solution of this problem was apparently delayed by her great fascination with the candle flame – she spent her test periods dancing around it, jumping over it, and deliberately singeing her hair with it.

Lever-box problem. This problem was intended to test imitation of a particular sequence of performing three successive, homogeneous acts. Three small levers protruded from a board placed next to the box. When they were pulled in the sequence demonstrated by the experimenter, the door opened. (The experimenter actually released the latch by a hidden mechanism, when the correct response was made.)

Viki imitated our lever pulling immediately, but without regard to sequence. She finally learned the sequence: left, middle, right – but only after 32 trials during which the experimenter often guided her hand or pointed to each successive lever. This, of course, was not imitation. Additional sequences were taught by the same method, and she had considerable trouble with them also.

Results with human children. None of the four children solved the ball-throwing problem spontaneously, as Viki had done. Three of them imitated after one or two demonstrations. The youngest child (CA = 26 mo., MA = 28 mo.) refused to try, even after four demonstrations.

They all did the stick and tunnel problem after one or two demonstrations, and the stick and string problem after one to four demonstrations. They showed none of Viki's fascination with the candle flame, and three of them solved the string and candle problem after a single demonstration. The youngest child refused to try. They all solved the light-switch problem after the first demonstration. (They were less inclined to attempt climbing, jumping, and throwing than Viki was.)

The three older children solved the first lever-box sequence (left, middle, right) after from one to four demonstrations, and reversed this sequence after a single demonstration. The oldest child (CA = 36 mo., MA = 49 mo.) solved the third sequence (left, right, middle) after seven demonstrations. The youngest child was inattentive and did not succeed on the first sequence after ten trials which included guidance and pointing as well as demonstration.

385

Results with the caged chimpanzee. Franz threw the ball at the lure after two demonstrations. Although his throws were not quite accurate enough to be successful, we considered this imitation. He did not solve the light-switch problem after ten demonstrations. (We had previously attempted to familiarize him with a similar switch, in another room, but we do not know how effective this experience was or how well it may have transferred to the problem situation.) He made no progress on the stick and tunnel problem after 11 demonstrations, nor on the stick and string problem after 6. We later attempted to help him learn these problems by direct experience. We put the stick part way into the tunnel, for instance, or laid it across the string; we also manipulated his hands in the appropriate ways. Even this type of tuition had little effect, however, and his behavior indicated that a major difficulty was his lack of understanding of the properties of the stick-as-a-tool (1). Frans was not given the candle or lever problems.

Discussion

Much of the behavior which we have described as imitative would fail to meet Warden's criteria (10) that the response must follow the observation immediately and must be substantially identical with that of the demonstrator. These criteria would be appropriate in the context of problems so simple that their solutions might easily occur in 'random' activity. We suggest, however, that in the context of the present investigation, responses which are delayed, or altered in detail, may be taken as examples not only of imitation, but of imitation combined with additional 'higher mental processes'.

Our home-raised chimpanzee subject did not differ greatly from human children of similar age in her ability to utilize imitation in problem solving. Our cage-raised chimpanzee, however, showed little ability at such tasks, and there is evidence that lack of experience with the materials and mechanical principles involved contributed heavily to his failures. Viki's occasional difficulties in the imitation set series appeared to be due largely to inability to make the required response. Her trouble with the lever-box problem extended to learning by experience, as well as by observation, and may have been due to a general deficiency in dealing with arbitrary sequences – a possibility which is also suggested by other aspects of her behavior.

Such 'imitation failures' (which have nothing to do with imitative ability, *per se*) might have been predicted from three principles:

1. Problem-solving ability is a function of past experience.
2. A response cannot be imitated unless its components are in the subject's available repertory of voluntary acts.
3. A subject cannot learn readily by observation a problem which he cannot learn readily by more direct methods.

(The third principle does not contradict the idea that imitation is a more efficient method of learning: Imitation may 'trigger' insight which might otherwise occur spontaneously, though perhaps much later – in the stick and tunnel problem, for instance. Or imitation may substitute for direct experience which is unlikely to occur in 'random' activity – as in the light-switch problem.)

The applicability of these principles is not always obvious. Attempts have been made, for instance, to induce chimpanzees to imitate human speech sounds (8, p. 286; 11, p. 54); but later work has indicated that chimpanzees have very little ability to vocalize voluntarily (4, 6, 7).

Crawford and Spence (2) looked for imitation in discrimination problems which their chimpanzees would have learned very slowly by direct experience. More recently, Harlow (3) has trained monkeys to solve discrimination problems in a single trial. All three of his subjects were then able to learn new discriminations *observationally*, as the result of a single demonstration.

Another factor which may be involved in failure of laboratory animals to imitate concerns their assumptions regarding the situation which the experimenter has set up. Viki, like human children, has had much experience in doing the same things the people around her do. It is not unreasonable for her to assume that she can solve a problem by using the method the experimenter uses. A caged ape, on the other hand, has little such basis for assuming that the experimenter's procedure will also work for him; and he is therefore unlikely to try it.

In the experiment by Crawford and Spence (2) the subjects might well have assumed, initially, that they could do what the chimpanzee demonstrator had done; but this assumption would be contradicted by their experience on test trials, where random baiting was employed.

We have seen nothing in our experience with Viki to support the idea that chimpanzees have a greater *drive* to mimic than man has; but her performance on the imitation-set series suggests an explanation of the 'monkey see, monkey do' tradition. Occasional zoo animals may have been subjected, perhaps accidentally to a sort of informal 'imitation-set series'. The imitative tendency so established would probably not be extinguished by intermittent reinforcement, and might even be adequately reinforced by the social reward of attention.

Conclusions. The imitative ability of chimpanzee appears to be much like that of man. Whether or not a given individual can imitate a particular task depends, however, on other abilities which are determined by heredity, experience, or a combination of these.

The likelihood that an individual will attempt to utilize his imitative ability in a given situation probably depends on the set established by past experience.

Summary

The imitative ability of a three-year-old chimpanzee, who has been raised in a human environment, was found in a variety of situations to be very similar to that of three-year-old human children.

Explanations are suggested for the frequent failures of laboratory primates to imitate in experiments, and for the popular tradition of 'instinctive imitation' in primates.

References

1. BIRCH, H. G. The relation of previous experience to insightful problem-solving. *J. comp. Psychol.*, 1945, **38**, 367–383.
2. CRAWFORD, M. P., & SPENCE, K. W. Observational learning of discrimination problems by chimpanzees. *J. comp. Psychol.*, 1939, **27**, 133–147.
3. HARLOW, H. F. Studies in discrimination learning by monkeys: II. Discrimination learning without primary reinforcement. *J. gen. Psychol.*, 1944, **30**, 13–21.
4. HAYES, CATHY. *The ape in our house*, New York: Harper, 1951.
5. HAYES, K. J., & HAYES, CATHERINE. *Imitation in a home-raised chimpanzee.* (16 mm. silent film.) State College, Pa., Psychological Cinema Register, 1951.
6. HAYES, K. J., & HAYES, CATHERINE. The intellectual development of a home-raised chimpanzee. *Proc. Amer. phil. Soc.*, 1951, **95**, 105–109.
7. HAYES, K. J., & HAYES, CATHERINE. *Vocalization and speech in chimpanzees.* (16 mm. sound film.) State College, Pa., Psychological Cinema Register, 1951.
8. KELLOGG, W. N., & KELLOGG, L. A. *The ape and the child.* New York: McGraw-Hill, 1933.

9. SPENCE, K. W. Experimental studies of learning and the higher mental processes in infra-human primates. *Psychol. Bull.*, 1937, **34**, 806–850.

10. WARDEN, C. J., & JACKSON, T. A. Imitative behavior in the rhesus monkey. *J. genet. Psychol.*, 1935, **46**, 103–125.

11. YERKES, R. M., & LEARNED, BLANCHE. *Chimpanzee intelligence and its vocal expression.* Baltimore: Williams & Wilkins, 1925.

12. YERKES, R. M., & YERKES, ADA W. *The great apes.* New Haven: Yale Univer. Press, 1929.

29 K. R. L. Hall

Observational Learning in Monkeys and Apes

K. R. L. Hall, 'Observational learning in monkeys and apes', *Brit. J. Psychol.*, vol. 54 (1963), pp. 201–26.

In natural groups of mammals, there is a variety of social influences which seem to inhibit or facilitate the expression of instinctive behaviour-patterns, and indeed which contribute importantly to the form the repertoire of behaviour characteristic of the species takes. Such influences include what goes under the terms 'social facilitation' and 'imitation', as well as other terms such as 'identification' which imply a special affectional relationship.

From an analysis of the evidence about these influences on monkeys and apes, it is clear that negative experimental findings have often been due to the limitations of the experimental procedures, and that some of the positive findings are difficult to interpret or assess for validity because of deficient method. By and large, there is convincing observational evidence, chiefly from informal developmental and from field studies, that young monkeys and apes acquire certain basic feeding and avoidance habits chiefly by applying their exploratory tendencies to places and objects indicated in the behaviour of their mothers or others of the group.

Although, in terms of learning operations, it is unlikely that much more than stimulus-enhancement or place discriminations is usually involved, a 'new' motor sequence almost never being in evidence, there is no doubt that the affectional situation of the participants is crucial as to whether a 'demonstrator' is attended to, closely approached, and 'imitated', or not. The nature of the affectional variables and their influence upon learning require extensive experimental study and analysis, and a comparison with related forms of early learning, such as imprinting, can then be made.

Introduction

In the natural social groupings of animals, at least at the vertebrate level, there is a variety of 'conformity' processes going on, some of which seem to involve arousal of innate propensities or tendencies through the apparent occurrence of innately recognized social releasers, while some, perhaps at the 'highest' level – that of the anthropoid apes – seem to be ascribable to individual learning. All would appear to have in common the function of co-ordinating and 'conventionalizing' behaviour so that a social 'norm' or central tendency is achieved. Before considering in detail the evidence for such conventionalizing in monkeys and apes, it seems logical to suppose that we are dealing here with a fundamental evolutionary tendency, the result of which is to produce individuals within a population, within a total species-distribution area, in whom can be discerned, in the very nature of things, so-called species-characteristic behaviour-patterns. But, further, within the actual life experience of individuals within a group, there is a pattern of habits relating to feeding, sheltering, etc., determined largely by the ecological circumstances of the group, in which the details, at any rate of sign or external-stimulus 'meaning', are filled in by the learning of the individual through observing that which other, usually 'senior' in the literal sense of 'older', individuals of the group do in the course of their daily routine. Aberrant, or eccentric, individuals, more venturesome (i.e. exploratory) than the rest of the group, may conceivably be instrumental in starting off a new and advantageous feeding habit or habit of avoidance, and this may sometimes percolate through the rest of the group until, eventually, the 'new' habit is a part of the group norm.

Now, the generality of such normalizing tendencies in human societies has been heavily emphasized by Darwin (1874), Tarde (1904), McDougall (1908), and others. But the comparative assessment of the importance of such tendencies in non-human animals has been somewhat neglected. Axiomatically, it seems likely that the origins, in individual mammalian life experience, of the conventionalizing tendency come early in ontogeny as the infant animal learns to achieve a certain independence of its mother, having of necessity conformed to the mother's control during the period of weaning, and having, inevitably in the natural group situation, observed almost exclusively the behaviour of those closest to the mother. Then, as the young animal matures, its spontaneous and characteristic playfulness leads it to learn certain social habits in the rough-and-tumble of the play subgroup, but its physical survival habits, such as those connected with feeding and drinking and avoidance of the noxious, are probably early established in the daily process of observing the mother and her immediate associates.

All this sounds obvious, but so suspiciously obvious that one finds the real nature of the conforming process in the higher animals has by no means been elucidated experimentally or in the course of naturalistic studies of wild groups. Only in the most general terms have the complex processes involved been described, and, within the broad comparative framework, it has been usually assumed that *Homo sapiens*, then the anthropoid apes (with first and foremost the chimpanzee), then the monkeys, and so on, with also-rans in the carnivores, such as cats, benefit, in that order, by the individual acquisition of basic conformist attitudes which thus are a product of acquired 'tradition' rather than of a genetic endowment.

The evidence, however, is chiefly of the informal and even anecdotal kind of reliability and validity, and few attempts, so far, have been made to link up 'imitative learning' and its origins with, say, imprinting in birds and any corresponding tendencies in young mammals, although Scott (1958), amongst few, has been looking for the origins of social attitudes, at least in dogs, in a 'critical physiological period' of ontogeny during which the conventions of the group are established. The isolation method, however, has serious disadvantages for our purpose, because, in its usual form, it consists of depriving the young animal of exactly the characteristic social environment of mother and litter-mates for which its propensities have been evolved to fit it. Hence, the failure to find certain 'characteristic' behaviours emerging in an isolated young animal certainly does not mean that the germs of these behaviours are not in its repertoire. On the contrary, as is known nowadays from many mammalian studies, the lack of suitable *stimulation* from the mother may result in the tendency inherent in the young animal never fully emerging.

One is, of course, immediately in danger of circular argument about the complex interactions of the genetic endowment with the variety of environmental circumstances necessary for eliciting its full potential, and it is probably best simply to avoid the issue by postulating that the genetic endowment *normally* fits into a more or less constant sequence of mother-contact, mother-feeding, etc., stimulating situations, and that this sequence radiates out into the usual situation of playing with and learning about a lot of other members of the group of varying degrees of seniority and status.

It will not here be possible to attempt to relate the evidence on the monkeys and apes, such as it is, to the human species, on the one hand, or to the conventions set up by the non-primate animals, but it is hoped that the picture achieved at the end will lead to at least an elucidating critical programme and a programme for experimental research. Before beginning to review the evidence, it is necessary to deal with a few of the many terms that have been used to describe conventionalizing tendencies.

Terminology

Hediger (1950) refers to the 'contagious' effect of the sudden occurrence of an eccentric feeding behaviour in mammals. For example, one member of a herd of red deer starts to strip bark, and the behaviour spreads rapidly to other members of the herd. He quotes evidence which indicates that 'safe' habits are learned, in some herd animals, and passed on from adults to young, but no attempt has yet been made to analyse experimentally the process of transmission although a reasonable hypothesis would be that it derives from the following tendency characteristic of the young of ungulate species.

The term 'mimesis', on the other hand, apparently refers to an 'instinctive' sequel of more or less identical behaviour being aroused by observing this behaviour's occurrence in another of the species, but without the observer-animal necessarily perceiving that which *releases* the sequence in the demonstrator. Verplanck's (1957) definition of 'behaviour/mimetic' is as follows: 'An animal is placed in the environment of another animal of the same species: if the second animal then makes some species-specific response, and thereafter the first animal makes the same response under conditions where it can be demonstrated that the response of the second animal is the stimulus for that of the first and that no opportunity for discrimination and differentiation training has been given to either animal, then the behaviour is termed "mimetic"' (p. 4). It will be noted that Verplanck's apparently scrupulous definition does not say that the behaviour of the first animal is more or less exactly what the second animal then does, but presumably this is intended, for otherwise we would be dealing here, in many instances, with a form of social conditioning. Mimesis seems to be synonymous with what the older writers called 'instinctive imitation'. Thus, Washburn (1908) diagnoses the latter's occurrence '... when the sight or sound of one animal's performing a certain act operates as a direct stimulus, apparently through an inborn nervous connexion, to the performance of a similar act by another animal' (p. 238). As an example, she cites Lloyd Morgan's description of one of a group of chicks which learns by casual experience to drink from a tin of water. Other chicks will then run up and peck at the water and will themselves drink. Although, therefore, the *action* is instinctive, in the sense that it is a part of the natural repertoire of the chicks independently of their observing its occurrence in other chicks, individuals do learn *where* to peck, and *what* to peck at, sometimes by means of the gregarious tendency to do what another chick, or perhaps the adult hen, has been doing. This, we shall see, seems to be more or less exactly what is meant by 'imitative learning' in some accounts of the behaviour of monkeys and apes, for it involves nothing new or even modified on the *motor* side, but it does involve a social *focusing* on the stimulus side. Koffka (1924) likewise summarizes his views on imitation by distinguishing between cases where configurations already belonging to an individual's equipment are made to function by the performance of an act of the same kind by another individual and those where a *new* configuration is aroused as a result of the observer perceiving another action in a certain manner. The former category may itself be subdivided into instinctive and acquired.

Hence, one would suppose that this process also is more or less the same as what goes under the terms 'social facilitation', defined by Crawford (1939) as any increment of individual activity which results from the presence of another individual. But this is a very broad inclusive statement, and would cover the obvious example of the puppy that has eaten all it apparently requires returning with avidity to the food-trough as soon as another puppy begins feeding there. Is no learning involved here? One would be rash to suppose this is due to a straightforward arousal of an instinctive tendency, for the social facilitation is presumably itself determined by the early litter experience of the animal.

And what of the process known as 'empathy'? Mowrer (1960) defines empathy as an 'imitation of affect' (p. 115), and it is thus distinguishable, so he implies, from the sort of imitation of, say, an instrumental conditioned response, the use of a tool, or a discrimination learning task. Experiments supposed to exemplify this kind of emotional limitation are, for example, Church's (1959) study which demonstrated that rats experience fear, as indicated by behaviour inhibition, in the presence of other fearful rats, and that of Miller, Murphy & Mirsky (1959) who taught monkeys to operate a lever when afraid, and who showed that such behaviour can be activated by the mere sight of another monkey in a state of fear. Thompson (1958), however, attempts to raise empathy to a rather 'higher' form of behaviour in his interpretation of one of Köhler's (1925) reports of his chimpanzees, where one chimpanzee was watching another reaching for fruit hanging at a precarious distance away, and was able 'to identify itself with its fellow to such an extent that it made spontaneous reaching movements in empathy with the other animal' (p. 295). The empathizing animal must not only be keenly aware of the other individual, but must be able to act as if he were in the place of the second animal. 'Thus empathy demands from the individual the ability to dissociate himself from his immediate concrete environment and to react to an absent or hypothetical one' (p. 295). One may question whether it is necessary to infer, on the behavioural evidence, the 'awareness' or the 'dissociation' that Thompson refers to in this instance, for no thorough attempt at a constructive experimental elaboration of such performances has yet been made.

Yet another 'emotional' aspect of the conventionalizing tendency goes under the term 'identification', for it is assumed by Mowrer (1960) and others that the individual, usually a young one, will learn a great deal by watching, and perhaps copying, the actions of a person, or animal, with whom it has identified itself, i.e. sees itself as having the same role. Possibly this also emerges from the 'filial' or 'following' tendency in some young animals, but goes for much more than mere 'following' when it involves the acquisition of feeding habits, of aversions, and so on.

In a very loose sort of way, these various conceptions indicate that something socially (conventionally) important by way of early learning goes on in intimate relationship with positive emotional attitudes or 'affectional' responsiveness, such as concerns alleviation of anxiety – perhaps as in contact-comfort seeking, and in just drawing near to a dominant but protective animal such as a mother or another 'sympathetic' adult. The real distinctions between the variously named processes of instinctive imitation – mimesis, social facilitation, empathy and identification – are not clear, and one would suppose that the processes involved in imprinting and any mammalian parallels to this must be considered in relation to them. The quite difficult effort must undoubtedly be made to view the various phenomena in which a young animal gets itself usually spatially close to another, or is visually, though at a little distance, 'interested' in another animal, not as though they were self-explanatory, but as though they merited the most thorough experimental and observational attention.

We might finally, in this section, concern ourselves briefly with the kind of imitation in which the animal, or person, does apparently do something after observing, which does not fall within its habitual repertoire. Köhler (1925) and Koffka (1924) would both seem to deem this as a special case of insight learning, for the new configuration is achieved, not simply by a reorganization of parts of the problem, as in the tool-using or box-stacking situation, but by perceiving the reorganization in the performance of an experienced demonstrator. Similarly, Washburn (1908) defines inferential, or reflective, imitation as occurring '. . . where an animal, watching another one go through an action and observing the consequences, is led to perform a similar act from a desire to bring about the same result' which, as she says, does not really differ from '. . . any other case of learning by ideas' (p. 239).

In effect, we find, as is clear from the review in Miller & Dollard (1941), that imitation is so broad a term that it can be made to cover almost any kind of performance where the behaviour of an observer has apparently been influenced by the behaviour of a demonstrator. The defined result is usually a facilitation or improvement of some kind on the part of the observer, but it may be a decrement or inhibition, as in the case of fear-responses. It is clear, however, that, although the *operations* whereby the observer learns, where it does learn, thus to modify its own behaviour can be variously classed with conditioning theory of some sort, as by Humphrey (1921), Pavlov (ed. Koshtoyants, 1955), or Mowrer (1960), with recourse to latent learning and secondary reinforcement in the latter case, or with field theories of the Gestalt kind, as in Köhler (1925) and Koffka (1924), the essence of the importance of the assimilative or conventional behaviour within the group is simply overlooked in such formulations. The tendencies apparent under the various terms are far from easy of explanation, for the reason that they are so simple-looking, *and so familiar*, that they are taken more or less for granted. *Why* does the infant animal watch the mother feeding, or watch her flinch away from a dangerous object? Because it 'identifies' itself with her? What, in terms of learning, does this process of identification, or empathy, or mimesis, or social facilitation, really involve? Hebb (1960) asserts that the mental processes of self-perception are the same processes, in large part, that constitute the perception of another person, and '. . . the sight of a hand making some movement is inevitably associated closely with the corresponding somesthetic sensations, when the hand is one's own, so that the sight of another making the same movement must arouse the same central process that causes one's own movement – and tend to produce imitation' (p. 742).

Perhaps one of the simplest ways of arriving at some sort of explanation of what goes on in imitation, or what we can very generally call 'observational learning' in an attempt to avoid the conundra associated with 'imitation', will arise from studying the ways in which monkeys and apes try to deal with what goes on when they perceive themselves performing in a mirror.

The Evidence on Monkeys and Apes

Anecdotal

The general supposition amongst animal keepers and others who have informally or casually studied the monkeys and apes has always been that they readily imitate one another and that they also learn to copy the actions of human beings. There are many examples of which a few only need be cited, for they chiefly bear upon the initially important questions of method which we shall see below account for much of the discrepancy in the more formal experimental laboratory findings.

Romanes (1886) quotes his sister's description of how the Cebus monkey she looked after learnt to open a stiff-lidded trunk, undoing it with a key, mainly by *copying* the actions of the sister's mother. Similarly, Witmer (1910) supposed that his *Macaca cynomolgus* monkey learnt to open a greenhouse door, by hanging down by her hindlegs and thus reaching the latch, without preceding trial-and-error, through '... making an intelligent attempt to imitate the persons whom she had seen going in and out of this door' (p. 225). He goes on to suppose that this is a conscious, intelligent process. This interpretation is heavily criticized by Watson (1911) who describes this paper as a return to the worst type of anecdotalism with no attempt to control the experimental conditions. Shepherd's (1915) observations of a chimpanzee fall into the same category: 'As a test of imitation, I took out my watch and pressed on the stem, slowly, and opened the watch three times while Peter (the chimpanzee) watched my actions with attention and apparently with interest. Then I reached it to him; he held it and pressed on the stem correctly several times, as if to open it. However, he did not press hard enough, and the watch did not open. He thereupon attempted to open it with his finger nails. The keeper stated to me that the ape had not received any training on that act' (p. 393). Furness (1916) recorded observations on intelligent imitation in two young orang-utans and two young chimpanzees, and stated that simple actions, such as digging with a spade or trowel, scrubbing, sweeping, screwing in a screw, were learned by the female chimpanzee 'entirely by imitation' (p. 289).

Such observations lack controls, such as adequate knowledge of previous experience of the animals studied, and lend themselves readily to the preconceptions of the particular investigator as to the animal's intelligence. Nevertheless, we shall find that the fact of learning such performances as these, partly by observing humans doing them, seems clearly established, although even some of the 'rigorous' experiments are surprisingly naïve in their design and in their neglect of rather obvious factors such as the amount of improvement that could be made by the animal on such a task, without opportunity for *seeing* it performed. There are two things of some importance about these sorts of observations. One is that they are carried out on animals with whom the 'experimenter' is on very friendly terms. The other is an interesting point made by Furness (1916) who says that the use of spoons, forks, needles, etc., which seems to come so readily to at least the anthropoid apes that live in close contact with human beings, may represent '. . . but slight modifications of instinctive actions of use in the pursuit of food, or to satisfy a natural curiosity. A twig or a stick may be poked into a hole to pry out a grub . . . a drink of water out of the hollow of a leaf is like drinking from a cup. . . . Therefore, I do not think that such actions demonstrate any marked degree of intelligence' (p. 289). This surprisingly modern view is amply confirmed in recent work (as, for example, Morris-Goodall's, 1962, report on the feeding behaviour of wild chimpanzees). It is, perhaps, even more surprising to find that Mills (1899) is able to defend his naturalistic approach to animal intelligence in general, and to imitation in particular, in a way that would do credit to a present-day ethologist. He points out that the anecdotes of animal trainers and others, '. . . though their reliability must be checked' (p. 262) and though 'caution in conclusion is necessary', should not be discounted simply on the results obtained in highly restrictive and unnatural experimental situations such as those provided by Thorndike (1898). An animal cannot, he says, be expected to behave naturally or in terms of its real capacities unless it is viewed in a natural kind of environment. Further, one great fallacy in Thorndike's experiments is that '. . . he overlooks the many possible and actual inhibitions to response to a stimulus' (p. 267). And: 'Even to witness a performance of trick animals is enough to enable one to see how at one time a tendency to imitate assists and at another mars the performance' (p. 268).

Experimental

The dividing line between casual observation and true experiment is obviously an artificial one, as indeed sometimes is the division between naturalistic observations of a more comprehensive kind, such as those of Yerkes, and controlled experiment. Nevertheless, it is convenient to consider the 'experiments' in laboratory-type situations as distinct from the free situations in which the above early results were obtained. The chief methods used in studying imitation in mammals are set out by Adler (1955) as follows: (1) the single-cage method, where observer (O) and demonstrator (D) are together in the problem-situation; (2) the observation-cage method (Thorndike, 1901), where O watches D do the problem, and is then transferred to the same problem-cage after D has been removed; (3) the duplicate-cage method (Warden & Jackson, 1935), where O is in a cage, watching D's performance, and is thereafter able to work on the same problem, from its own cage, without the delay and disturbance necessitated by method (2), usually through the watching-screen being taken away so that O then has immediate access to the problem.

But variation in method is, as we shall see, not the only reason for discrepant experimental results. Other reasons are suggested by the anecdotalists, and some will be found to bear simply upon the sheer artificiality of the imitation situation which so often takes no account of the probably critical social, emotional, and general motivational factors involved.

The experimental studies can be roughly divided into those which claim to have demonstrated imitative learning in monkeys and apes, and those which are unable to demonstrate its occurrence. Typical of the latter are those of Thorndike (1901) and Watson (1914). Thorndike used the same instrumentation tasks as in his 1898 study of cats, dogs, and chicks. He carried out only *five* experiments relating to imitation with *one* Cebus monkey only as an O. As Ds, there was himself and also two Cebus monkeys. At the time of the experiments, O was 'on terms of war' with one of the two D monkeys. Using method (2), O had the chance to watch D carry out, correctly, a manipulatory problem, and then O was moved into D's cage, D having previously been removed. Hence, there was obviously delay intervening between observing and trying to perform what was observed, together with the very strong likelihood of arousing motivation inhibitory of any kind of experimental performance in the process of being moved from one cage to another. Thorndike's negative conclusion that on none of the experiments did O gain any benefit from observing D must be taken as more or less valueless: 'Nothing in my experience with these animals then favours the hypothesis that they have any general ability to learn to do things from seeing others do them. The question is still an open one, however . . .' (p. 42).

He noted also that O showed little *curiosity* about D's performance, and, in fact, this lack of interest in each other's activities struck him very forcibly in all three animals, while he goes on to note that probably imitation would most readily be observed as between parents and offspring. The limitations of these experiments are so obvious, when seen in context, as to need no further emphasis. They have all the general flaws of the anecdotal observation – such as too few cases, lack of knowledge of previous life experience, and so on – without the merit of at least observing the animal in a 'social' setting where a 'social' form of learning, such as imitation, would be likely to occur.

Watson's (1914) experiments are of the same order. He used four monkeys, selected out of nine, because of their gentleness or alertness. One of the four was a baboon which he said was so stupid that its experimental performances were not worth considering. One was a Cebus, and the other two were Rhesus. Manipulative tasks were used, and Watson himself served as D, except for the two Rhesus who were set to imitate each other. In no instance did an O show any gain from watching performances on the tasks, including correct solutions, but the whole situation was so unnatural as to preclude the likelihood of any imitation occurring. No consideration was given to the possibility that the performance of O might be *inhibited* by the setting – which included the visible presence of the experimenter even when O was supposed to watch a D monkey.

To offset these two negative studies there have been a number of experiments, beginning with those of Hobhouse (1901), which demonstrate that some form of increment of performance is apparent in the O monkey or ape as a result of observing the practised performance of a D. It is by no means always clear, however, exactly what it is that elicits this improvement, and whether it is really an improvement due to observing *that particular performance or set of performances* rather than to some factor relatively independent of the actual task, such as a sheer increase in 'interest' in the task because of the presence of another monkey doing *something*. The findings are therefore of very varying degrees of importance.

Kinnaman (1902, I and II) succeeded in getting two Rhesus monkeys to imitate one another's success on a box-opening problem, but not to benefit by observing the experimenter doing this task over and over again. Thus, the female Rhesus was said to have 'copied' the act of the male in pulling out a plug in a more or less precise replica of the way he took hold of it and the direction in which he pulled it. 'He went immediately to the box, she following some four feet away. Knowing the trick perfectly he seized the end of the plug with his teeth and removed it. I set the box again; this time the female rushed to it, seized the plug by the end as the male did, and procured the food. This she repeated immediately eight times in exactly the same way' (p. 121, I). Other than that, however, he was only able to discern 'instinctive imitation', as where the female 'took a peep in exactly the same way' when the male looked under the bottom of one of the trees in the room.

Haggerty (1909) produced positive evidence of imitative learning in a study using eleven monkeys of different species. These animals were grouped in small cages, '. . . the aim being to secure for each congenial cage-mates' (p. 347). Eight simple mechanical problems were set for the animals, with the following experimental procedure: (1) each monkey was given five preliminary trials of 15 min., on successive days, on a particular problem, at the end of which most of the animals had either succeeded or become indifferent; (2) 'imitation' tests were then begun using those monkeys 'that had failed to learn of their own accord' (p. 353), the trained D performing in the presence of O. Of the eleven 'failed' monkeys, nine were successful on the tasks after demonstration performances. The obvious difficulty about these results is that they may merely be eliciting latent learning or social facilitation in the new 'social' situation of being paired in the performance with another monkey, instead of performing alone. He does, however, pay heed to certain social factors that might be relevant in imitation experiments, such as the degree of congeniality or animosity between D and O, but is unable to show convincingly how these factors might operate in facilitating or inhibiting performance. He goes on usefully to grade at least four different levels of imitative behaviour, beginning with simple arrest of attention by looking at another monkey and ending with exact repetition in detail by O of D's performance. These results cannot be considered at all conclusive because, as Zuckerman (1932) points out, the success of the O's may be due to sheer perseverance or simply to the tendency of O to *follow* another monkey when it goes for the 'key' to the problem, i.e. 'stimulus enhancement' (Spence, 1937).

Kempf's (1916) experiments, using six Rhesus monkeys, are also inconclusive, for, using method (1), it cannot be clearly established that anything more than the *place* relevant to solution was what the O learned, by watching the successful D, to discriminate. Indeed, Kempf says as much in concluding: 'Imitation seems possible only when similar movements under similar circumstances have already been previously acquired by the organism. Imitation seems to permit of a very limited margin for new modifications of the old repertory of movements' (p. 265). Kohts (1928) likewise (quoted by Zuckerman, 1932, p. 165) states that, for example, demonstrative unlocking of a device does not teach the monkey anything, but only *stimulates* him in the performance of his task and shows him a definite spot where some kind of work is to be fulfilled.

Only with the studies of Warden & Jackson (1935) do we get a clear analysis of at least some of the essential controls and criteria to be used in imitation experiments. This is the first thorough use of method (3), duplicate cage, on monkeys, the problems used being of the usual simple mechanical kind, such as pulling a chain which hung down within easy reach of the front of a panel, thus raising a door and exposing a raisin in a hole. *O* was allowed only 60 sec. to perform the task, after *D*'s trial, *D* having been previously trained to correct performance. The *same animal* served as *D* throughout for all of 15 *O*s. This was in order to try to keep the social factor more or less constant, for: 'Although somewhat nervous in temperament, his [*D*'s, a male about 43 months old] performances were consistently definite and speedy. He was especially suitable for our purposes since he did not attempt to fight back when the other animals exhibited pugnacity from time to time' (p. 110). However, they note that it might have been better to have trained a female to serve as *D* for the females for several of the older females tended to show more interest in this male than in the problem: 'This factor probably had the effect of reducing the score of imitative behaviour in such cases below the potential level' (p. 110). Prior to the imitation tests, each animal had been caged alone 'so as to prevent the formation of social attachments that might prove troublesome' (p. 111).

For the first time, explicitly in the method, an attempt is made in this study, in at least a preliminary way, to control the social variables which are thus recognized as being significant influences upon imitation. Their results show successes by *O*s, within 60 sec. (= immediate imitation), in 46·3% of the 354 tests. This figure was raised to 72·4% when the records of six *O*s were eliminated because of serious sexual distractions.

In order to distinguish 'intelligent imitation' from other social effects on behaviour, five criteria must be met: (1) the task must be novel and sufficiently complex; (2) the response must appear immediately after O has observed the D; (3) practice must be excluded by the experimental conditions; (4) the act of O must be substantially identical with that of D; (5) a sufficient number of instances must occur, under varied conditions, to eliminate the chance factor. No experiments before this could be said to have fulfilled these conditions, but it still seems that results such as those of this study might be explained on the basis of *some* kind of previous experience, on other sorts of problem, which, combining with the extra incentive of D's *presence* and movements (and not necessarily his actual correct performance), bring out very readily a correct solution. As in other studies, the essence of the problem is simply to locate the meaningful cue, such as chain or latch, and the experimental fiddling of the active animal would do the rest. The line between 'social facilitation' and 'intelligent imitation' is certainly not entirely clear, for the persistent exploratory–manipulatory behaviour of these animals must build up an extensive repertoire, through stimulus and response generalization, some aspect of which can readily manifest itself in the so-called 'novel' situation. However, as Zuckerman (1932), quoting from Adams, points out, the mere location of the key area or object through the action of a D leads to an altered attitude on the part of O through '. . . amplification of perception, accrual of meaning or enhancement of context' (p. 170). This, in itself, is due to the continuous social conditioning of natural monkeys or apes, and is, psychologically and ethologically, just as important as any evidence of imitation of a more deliberate and 'conscious' kind.

Another study by Warden, Fjeld & Koch (1940) used the same method and procedures on six monkeys, all of which, as was the case with the 1935 animals, had taken part in previous instrumentation and problem-solution experiments, though none of the present experiments resembled in *detail* those on which they were experienced. Instant imitation (within 10 sec.) occurred on 40% of tests, and immediate imitation (within 60 sec.) on 76·4% – a very similar result to that of 1935. It is thus assumed that, in addition to the 'social facilitation' evident on all the tests, there is an extensive 'copying' of D's performance. As with the other study, however, it seems that we have the following factors at work: social facilitation, previous practice, and local enhancement.

So far, imitation has been studied in terms of performances involving some kind of manipulation, the schemes for which are undoubtedly within the genetic and habit repertoire of the animals. In addition, simple discrimination-learning tasks have also been used in the O and D setting on monkeys and chimpanzees. Crawford & Spence (1939) used a new method in which an O chimpanzee, previously trained in discrimination learning, is given a series of chances to observe another (D) chimpanzee's differential responses to a pair of stimuli, D's choices being irregularly rewarded with food. The duplicate-cage method was used, O, on a series of trials, being able to watch D (who could not watch O) press down on a plate of different shape or colour, and being then given the opportunity of itself responding to one of two stimulus-plates. Results on nine animals are said to be inconclusive and variable, and to provide little evidence of imitation over and above effects attributable to the social facilitation (through D's *activity*, as such) '. . . adding, in some way, excitatory strength to the chosen stimulus' (p. 144). Two of their incidental comments are of some interest. The first is that the 'friendly' relation between the D and O of a pair led to immediate improvement on imitation trials by O, in contrast with the same O observing another D animal. The second is that movements of the experimenter were suspected of acting as secondary cues for one of the Os imitation trials, and, when this was controlled, Os performance dropped from 75% correct to chance.

In contrast with this inconclusive result on chimpanzees, Darby & Riopelle (1959), using similar techniques and problems on four experimentally naïve Rhesus monkeys, found that Os learned increasing amounts from their single observation trial on each problem, and, further, where the D-trial was *not* rewarded, O was significantly more successful than when following rewarded D-trials. Thus they conclude: '. . . Rhesus monkeys can acquire information about the solution of an object-quality discrimination problem simply by watching another monkey execute a single trial on the problem' (p. 96). As they point out, Spence's (1937) notion of stimulus-enhancement does not fit the results, for O's performance is better if D makes a mistake than it would be if D made a correct guess, and they suggest that O is distracted by seeing D getting a food reward. The design of these experiments is, of course, such as simply to test out the degree of *following* by O of differential responses made by D. Though technically ingenious, they contribute little that is meaningful on the nature and extent of the imitative processes. This restriction also applies to Riopelle's (1960) study of four experimentally naïve female Rhesus monkeys using the same apparatus as in the 1959 study and selecting from 100 pairs of identical objects. Each monkey was used as both O and D, and the degree of following of D's position choice by *O* improved to above chance level (63% correct), whereas the *D* animals, who were learning 'by participation' showed a rather better rate of 'correct' (food-rewarded) position choices.

Little, so far, has been done to elucidate how imitation may affect the avoidance-response learning of monkeys and apes, and this area of study seems highly likely to elicit important results, for ability to learn to avoid a noxious object through observing the avoidance by another animal of the group would seem of great survival value. The 'contagion' or 'facilitation' consequent upon alarm-barks or other species indications of fear in the animals is well documented, though not well analysed. Haslerud (1938) says of chimpanzees: 'Species tradition or group experience must also be important in increasing avoidance reaction to inanimate objects (as it does to moving objects – the subject of that particular experiment). Learning through species tradition occurs particularly well in chimpanzees because there is so much social facilitation and inhibition. Let one chimpanzee see any object that scares it and elicits the fear cry, in a moment the whole colony is in flight and takes up the cry . . . species tradition may increase and reinforce a persistent caution toward objects' (p. 526).

Only one adequate experiment to test out a very limited hypothesis about imitation and avoidance-learning has yet been reported on monkeys. Presley & Riopelle (1959) trained *D*s to avoid electric shock by leaping over a barrier within the first 4 sec. following appearance of a red light, until they made twenty-eight avoidance responses in a block of thirty trials. The *O* watched the whole performance from an adjacent compartment and was then transferred to the shock compartment. Results showed that the slowest *O* learned the avoidance response in as few trials as did the fastest *D*: 'these data thus show that Rhesus monkeys learn an avoidance response more rapidly after having observed another learn it than they would have without this observational experience' (p. 253).

Experiments by Miller *et al.* (1959), using what they call 'inter-animal' conditioning techniques, produced the same sort of result, one monkey serving as the CS for avoidance behaviour on the part of a second monkey. Further, pictures of 'fearful' posters and expressions tended also to elicit more avoidance responses than non-fearful ones. Hence it is concluded that the fear affect can be communicated from monkey to monkey through observation of 'fearful' monkeys or pictures of them, but this seems, in a complicated way, to tell us little that was not already evident from natural observation.

We have seen that the social factors which might very materially influence the form and extent of imitation have scarcely been investigated. Remarks about their possible significance have occurred in a few studies, and in one, at any rate, the attempt was made to hold the social factor constant. The conventionalizing tendency is so obviously a product of the social group climate that it is surprising to find how little has been done here. One of the earliest experiments is that of Aronowitsch & Chotin (1929, quoted by Spence, 1937, p. 822): 'A single dominant male [monkey] and a group of 3 others were given opposed training. The former was trained to open a food box when light A was present and not when light B was present, while the group of 3 were trained in the reverse manner. The subjects were then all placed in the same cage and the conflict between their learned behaviour and the opposed social example observed. It was found that the average amount of imitation was 25%, and, furthermore, that the individual animal imitated the group more than he influenced them.'

There is nothing very surprising in this result but it does suggest that independent behavioural evidence of the relative dominance of an O and D pair in an imitation experiment should be obtained at least *after* the experimental trials were concluded.

Nissen & Crawford (1936), and Crawford (1937), made very valuable experimental attempts to work out, respectively, how habits of food sharing and co-operative problem solving could be trained in young chimpanzees. In neither of these studies is imitation specifically studied. In the former study, it was found that transfer of food and food-tokens from one cage to another of a pair of chimps occurred according to any one of three modes of behaviour: independent acquisition, begging, and unsolicited passing. The results provide evidence for mutuality of behaviour, and hence for the kind of conformity tendency that seems to be the crux of the imitative process. In Crawford's study, there is much more of direct relevance to our topic, for the essence of the co-operative work is the learning both to pull and to pull synchronously with the other chimp, or with the experimenter, and this is achieved largely through 'watching' the other animal: 'This "watching" behaviour . . . has been considered the distinguishing characteristic of the second stage in learning to cooperate, in which the animals first showed a response to each other' (p. 25). In neither of these studies is anything 'new', either of movement or of discrimination, achieved through observational learning, but, nevertheless, a new achievement over and above the capacity of each of the two animals individually results from the social interactions of the two.

Recent social-experimental studies on Rhesus monkeys by Mason (1960, 1961) relating to effects of social restriction on the general behaviour-repertoire, including sexual responsiveness, strongly emphasize the degree to which adolescent or adult monkeys learn conformity habits by imitation of other monkeys. Indeed, these few social experimental studies all indicate clearly that the true problems of 'imitation' in monkeys and apes have been largely neglected by experimenters who have been more concerned with a kind of 'school learning' idea of benefiting from 'demonstrations' on 'problems'. What is of fundamental importance is to know how simple, basic habits of avoidance, of mutual tolerance, of feeding, and so on, are formed in the context of the group through *observing*, and not necessarily, at the time, *copying*, the behaviour of members of that group.

Naturalistic observations

The experimental findings examined have been somewhat barren, not so much because of the attempts at standardization and control of conditions as because the most interesting factors, social and affectional, were not usually the concern of the investigators. Free investigations or observations, on the other hand, tend to produce highly suggestive results which are, as they stand, simply hypotheses which may be studied in detail so that the complex of factors probably underlying the naturalistic data may more clearly emerge.

The data under this heading include that from full-scale field studies in the wild, studies of captive animals in a semi-natural setting, and observational studies of animals living in laboratory or cage conditions or in human homes. It is here we find some information – completely lacking, so far, in the experimental work – about how the young animals may learn to imitate others or adults, while some important inferences can also be drawn about the probable function of imitation in creating the 'traditions' of various free-living groups of monkeys and apes.

Developmental studies

Most of the observations relating to imitation are incidental to the general purpose of assembling all relevant life-history data on the young animals. One of the earliest of such studies is that of

Lashley & Watson (1913) whose only observations directly bearing on our problem are as follows: 'Dolly's [the mother Rhesus] movements sometimes served to draw the baby's attention to some object, but his own reactions to it never seemed to imitate hers. At times also, his responses appeared to be determined by those of adults, as when Dolly's threatening attitude after some acts of the observer induced fright in him although he had not shown fear of the act itself. His response in such cases was, however, quite different from that of the adult and in no sense imitative' (p. 139). At this time, the infant Rhesus was only 1 month old, so that it is difficult to see how its sensorimotor co-ordinations could possibly allow of imitation in the way they are using the term. Nevertheless, these comments do point to some interesting possibilities. The first, and probably basic, fact is that the mother's movements sometimes lead to the infant attending to certain objects – probably approaching them and touching or mouthing them. The second is that fear is apparently aroused in the infant by the mother's antagonistic behaviour, but possibly this has no bearing upon a conditioned social reaction, for the infant's fear could have been directly caused by the *inattention* of the mother to the infant.

Tinklepaugh & Hartman (1930) make some observations on 11 parturitions in Rhesus monkeys some of which are suggestive of ways in which feeding habits may be acquired by the infant. Thus, the yearling son of one female '. . . participated with his mother in eating a small part of her afterbirth. Though this limited evidence would in no case justify conclusions, imitation may be offered as a possible explanation of the behaviour of the male. Frequently monkeys and apes, when they see human beings or animals of their kind partake of it, eat food which ordinarily they would not touch. The young monkey . . . during a series of observations was caged with a turtle as his sole companion. Offered raw beef or liver, he refused it, but when the turtle approached this food and began to eat, the monkey rushed up, seized the meat, and eventually chewed and swallowed it' (p. 90).

Mitchell (1922) was probably the first person to produce reliable evidence on the discrepancy between the reactions of adult and infant apes to 'noxious' objects, such as live snakes. He had hoped to test out the differences on an infant monkey or ape born and raised in a Zoo. Failing this, however, he studied a very small baby chimp not much more than weaned when it came to the Zoo. He took a very active tree-boa and placed it in a box near to the chimp, who leaned out towards it. He allowed the flicking tongue of the snake actually to touch the chimp's face. The chimp '... showed no sign of alarm and was quite ready to kiss the snake's mouth. It was clear that, in this case, no particle of dread of the serpent was present. Since then, the chimp has on several occasions been shown snakes, including a large King snake. The latter he handles quite freely, plays with it and pulls it about' (p. 348). The author says that, although this may be a case of 'instinct failure', it is more likely that fear of snakes as characteristically seen in adult chimps is '... an acquisition due to experience or the imitation of other chimps which have had individual experience' (p. 348).

Jacobsen, Jacobsen & Yoshioka (1932) report similar observations on a chimp during her first year of life, these being in marked contrast to the fear responses shown by adult chimps. After presenting the infant with a number of neutral objects, such as a bottle and an electric bulb, with which she played, a piece of soft rubber tubing was put on the floor near her. Though showing no definite fear, her response '... was notably different from that made to other objects in that she approached it cautiously, retreated, and approached again' (p. 66). A rather sluggish live puff-adder was then placed near her. At first, she gave it no special attention, but: 'After a few seconds, she approached the snake and struck it several times with the back of her hand as chimps very commonly react to small living objects such as insects or rodents. The snake, thus disturbed, responded by puffing and hissing pronouncedly. She gave no visible attention to either of these reactions, nor did she definitely avoid the snake' (p. 66). The authors stress that this marked difference between the reactions of the young chimp and those of the older animals '... emphasizes the importance of an undetermined factor, either maturational or experiential, in the development of this interesting snake–primate relationship ...' (p. 67). It must be stated, however, that none of the observations quoted made any attempt to control for the possible influence of the human observer's attitudes upon the responses of the experimental object. Probably this factor is not important, but a control of it is necessary in further work.

Nissen (1944) indicates that the characteristic nest-building behaviour of chimps in the wild is something in which early life experience plays an important part, for: 'Our nursery-raised chimps ... never construct nests, no matter how favourable the opportunity. Unlike birds, in whom nest-building is an instinct, this activity is evidently a cultural acquisition among chimps, something that the younger generation learns from its elders. Where such educational opportunities are lacking, the custom drops out' (no page reference). Yerkes (1943) gives details of this in describing how five young captive-born chimps made no attempt to build nests when roaming free on a New Hampshire farm, though one started what looked like nest construction but never completed it, while Bernstein (1962) has confirmed that all wild-born but only a few captive-born chimps build nests when a variety of materials is made available to them. Harrisson (1960) likewise suggests that all young orangs, once introduced to nest-building by others, build nests in trees or inside their cages, thus implying that this kind of performance requires at least something of imitative learning for its full form. The mere tendency to handle and pull about sticks and branches, seen in all the young animals, needs something in the example of the experienced elders for it to be directed to actual nest construction.

Harrisson (1960) is clear also that the young orangs she kept in captivity learn something of their feeding habits by observing their mothers and other orangs. Thus, one infant did not like bananas, and only took to eating them after observing another young one eating them with gusto. One orang, about 4 years old, watched intently when workmen lifted a heavy cement cover of a sewage tank in order to clean it. The following day when this orang was let out, it went straight to the sewage tank and tried to lift the lid. He had never before taken the slightest notice of the lid and this observation shows how the active exploratory tendency and curiosity of the young animal may, through example, be directed to a new object, though the object has never been associated in its experience with, say, food or other 'primary' reward.

These informal naturalistic observations on captive young monkeys and apes are very far from negligible in their implications for the importance of learning by observing. As with the field-study data to be reviewed later, it is, however, difficult to disentangle all the possible factors that may be operating. Focusing of attention is clearly the major factor, but it is also obvious that this is done almost always in the process of going near to and closely watching an animal with whom the watcher is on positively affectional terms. Thus, Yerkes (1943) says regarding the learning of feeding habits by the infant chimp: 'It greatly facilitates acceptance if the mother or other experienced individual sets an example of acceptance or avoidance, or actually offers the substance to the infant' (p. 119).

The best-known studies in which imitation is reported are those of Kellogg & Kellogg (1933) and Hayes & Hayes (1951, 1952, 1953). In the former study, the young female chimp, Gua, was brought up for 9 months with the authors' son, Donald, who was $2\frac{1}{2}$ months older than her. Their observations chiefly demonstrate the superiority of Donald's powers of imitation over those of Gua. Thus: 'Probably the most convincing proof of the child's superiority in imitation was his direct mimicry of the ape herself' (p. 141). Imitative play was a feature of the behaviour of both, and the ape often followed the child's example, as when he went to a small radio bench and hammered its seat with his hands to produce a metallic drumming sound. 'She would also open cabinets and cupboards, probably as a result of her observation of others, and during the later months she needed no encouragement to put a hairbrush to her head and make brushing movements like the child' (p. 139). Particularly in vocal imitation (of her grunts and barks) the child was obviously superior, and there seems no evidence of any reciprocal imitation of this kind on the chimp's part.

The subject of the Hayes studies was a female chimp, Viki, adopted by them a few days after her birth, and brought up in their home to all intents and purposes like an adopted human baby. Their informal observations showed (1951) that Viki could imitate in response to the command 'do this' by copying the action which they demonstrated. This technique was useful in teaching her to learn new skills and the appropriate manipulation of objects with which she had not previously done more than play. The more formal problem-solving experiments on imitation (1952), using stick-and-tunnel, ball-throwing, stick-and-string tasks, and so on, led the authors to conclude that she was clearly able to profit by their demonstrations of correct solution in a way that could not be attributed merely to trial-and-error and insight-learning. They compared her successes with the relatively poor results achieved by another cage-raised chimp on the same tasks. Further, her 'imitative play' seems to have included acts of genuine copying, while her success on a delayed imitation task was particularly impressive: 'Viki was allowed to watch us use a screwdriver to pry off the friction-type lids of several empty paint-cans. She was then taken away and brought back one hour later. She set to work immediately, and after some effort succeeded in opening two cans. (She was already familiar with various other containers and had often used a screwdriver as a lever, but this combination was new to her)' (p. 451). They emphasize that Viki had had no opportunity to acquire the necessary technique by trial-and-error, or by reward for chance performance. They also tested her (1953) on an 'imitation set series' in which she was shown, in order of testing, the following representations of humans and of Viki herself clapping hands, patting the head and protruding the tongue: (1) motion pictures, (2) projected stills, (3) photographic prints, (4) simple line-drawings. She performed fairly well in response to these, transferred readily through the various stages from movies to line-drawings, and would often work without being rewarded for correct responses, treating the tests as a game. However, although 'she seldom failed to imitate preferred actions (those which she often performs spontaneously, in play), . . . she often made errors by performing such preferred actions in response to pictures of non-preferred items' (p. 471).

The Viki observations are convincing, and give detailed support to the generalization of Yerkes & Yerkes (1929): 'We feel entirely safe in asserting, as the consensus of opinion among competent students, that the chimpanzee commonly and with extreme facility imitates acts, in some instances for the mere satisfaction of performing them, and in other cases for the sake of a desired reward or objective' (p. 347). Nevertheless, it is still too soon to be able to state explicitly on the basis of this kind of evidence or that of the formal laboratory kind, exactly what weight should be given in such performances to the several factors involved. These factors clearly include a spontaneous (imitative) play tendency, social facilitation, and processes of learning which may still turn out to differ from trial-and-error, classical conditioning, and insight, in the important fact that they are embedded in a strongly positive affectional background of social relationships.

Captivity studies of adult animals

Observations of imitation by mature monkeys and apes are probably of less significance than those which have just been reviewed. Nevertheless, as the Yerkes & Yerkes (1929) quotation says, there is strong observational support, at least on anthropoid apes in captivity, that mature animals are, under favourable conditions, able readily to learn by imitating the performances of another adult of the species or of a human demonstrator.

Most of the work has been done on orangs and chimps, but Carpenter (1937) gives some data on two mountain gorillas in the San Diego Zoo, aged about 8 years. He says: 'There seemed to be considerable imitator–imitatee relationships between the two gorillas when their moods and behaviour were properly synchronized. However, the problem is raised of what is meant by imitated behaviour. Acts which are merely imitated by the activity of another animal are not acts of imitation' (p. 191); thus, '. . . simple forms of behaviour such as playing with objects, swinging ropes or rings, are copied from one animal by another', but these acts are already a part of the action system of the second animal (the copier). However, as he points out: 'When the behaviour of one animal stimulates similar behaviour in another, there is shown an interesting and important type of social behaviour that deserves further study, be it imitation or a more simple form of activity' (p. 191). Yerkes & Yerkes (1929) report consistent failures in teaching a female gorilla to imitate on padlock-hasp and other instrumental tasks, although she did learn, apparently by following Yerkes' example, to acquire more extensive feeding habits.

Yerkes & Yerkes (1929) cite numerous examples of imitation in orangs and chimps. Captive orangs have frequently been observed to imitate each other and also the human uses of various objects, but they more readily imitate what is seen than what is heard. The orang Julius had failed, after abundant opportunity, to solve the two-box stacking problem, so Yerkes demonstrated the correct placing of the boxes beneath the suspended banana, and then climbed upon them and reached it. Julius immediately climbed on to the boxes and obtained the food. In other words, the orang did not himself solve the problem, but merely took advantage of the correct arrangement left for him. In fact, Julius failed to do the task correctly on the next three successive days, and, on the fifth and sixth days, he was again given the demonstration. Only after this third demonstration did Julius suddenly succeed in doing the task for himself.

There is nothing to indicate in these observations that Julius had learned from the demonstrations any more than he might have learned from an equal number of unaided trials. The most that might be inferred is that his interest was renewed, following his own repeated failures, and that he had learned to place the boxes for himself after seeing the correct arrangement. This might have been achieved without Yerkes himself, or anyone else, playing the part of demonstrator. Their conclusion that '. . . definitely purposive imitation plays a highly important role in the adaptive life of this ape' (p. 176) needs much further supporting evidence from controlled observation and experiment.

413

Far the most comprehensive observations from the Orange Park laboratories concern imitation in chimps (Yerkes & Yerkes, 1929; Yerkes, 1934, 1943). The chimp is deemed to be easily the readiest imitator of the three great apes: '. . . in the order gorilla, orang-utan, chimpanzee, the great apes provide evidence of increasing frequency, complexity, and serviceableness of imitative behaviour' (p. 574, Yerkes & Yerkes, 1929), and: 'the level of social development in the chimpanzee may be gauged also by its degree of suggestibility and imitativeness' (p. 51, Yerkes, 1943). The observations relied upon are, however, almost entirely informal and non-experimental. Thus: 'Literally scores of times I have seen our [chimpanzee] subjects acquire useful acts by watching apes or men. Examples . . . are most frequent in connexion with eating and drinking and the use or adaptation of objects as tools' (p. 142, Yerkes, 1943).

Yerkes & Yerkes (1929) clearly recognize the complexity of what goes under the general term 'imitation' in pointing out at least three phases of behaviour in chimps: (1) attraction to and intent observation of the behaviour of its fellow; (2) this may lead to near approach to its fellow and effort to keep near it; (3) sometimes this may lead to '. . . prompt and obvious reproduction of the act observed, the one organism being stimulated by observation of the other to do the same sort of thing or to achieve the same result' (p. 345). Such distinctions in the phases of the social behaviour involved in the usual imitation situation, whether experimentally set or informally observed, should, together with others that could be equally clearly defined, be more frequently used, for they may well illustrate more precisely what goes on than the usual simple criterion of a scorable difference in speed or accuracy of imitative versus non-imitative performance.

The nearest approach to actual experimental controls of chimp imitation is Yerkes's (1934) study of suggestibility, in which he used twenty-one subjects. The experimenter (E) first presented on 4 successive days to one chimp, the others having the opportunity to look on, pieces of filter-paper just prior to the mid-day feed. On the next 4 days, E took the piece of paper, put it in his mouth, and chewed it, while the chimp was watching. Broadly, the results showed that some chimps evinced a marked interest in the actions of the E, but that, thereafter, their attention wandered. Response to the suggestion seemed greatest in the 10-year-old animals, less in the 5- and 15-year-old ones, and varied also with the social status of the individual. None of the chimps attempted to chew or swallow the paper in the way demonstrated by E.

There is thus nothing precisely verified under controlled conditions nor fully analysed in the repertoire of imitativeness described for these animals, and, further, it follows that comparisons between the anthropoids are prematurely made in that the tasks set and the circumstances of the observations vary so much. While it would be unreasonable to doubt that these animals do gain much from observing the behaviour of their fellows, and of human beings, the extent to which the modifications are due to social facilitation, to localizing, and perhaps to accentuation of play and exploratory tendencies, as much as to the learning of additional skills, is difficult to determine. Probably, as the Hayes studies indicate, facility and readiness in this respect is cumulatively brought about in the life experience of the individual, with progressive transfer from early habits accounting for the more dramatic examples sometimes recorded in the adult animal. It is further of great importance to try to discover the circumstances of the natural social group within which the infant is brought up, for such knowledge may have a vital bearing upon the contribution of imitative learning or even tuition to the mature animals' behaviour. Thus, Bingham (1928) says: 'It is not improbable that imitation in a chimpanzee group is a potent factor in the ontogenesis of copulatory efficiency' (p. 37), and this is supported by Morris-Goodall's (personal communication) field observations, which may also do much to establish how the other essential habits, of feeding, avoidance of noxious objects, and so on, are influenced in the wild.

Köhler's (1925, 1926) observations on imitation in chimpanzees add little to those already examined. He believes that imitation, in the sense of an intelligent and insightful perception of the significance of a demonstrator's solution of a problem, is not particularly common in chimps: 'Imitation is almost as difficult for apes and as rare in them as it is in lower vertebrates. One does observe imitation of different forms or types in apes, but not so very often, and only after certain conditions are fulfilled' (p. 156, 1926). He goes on to describe the 'serious play' type of imitation in children, and gives examples of this in chimpanzees, as where one observed a man paint a pot white, leaving behind a brush and a pot of white paint. The chimp soon took the brush, put it into the pot, and painted a big stone white. 'The whole time the ape behaved completely seriously. So did others when imitating the washing of laundry or the use of a borer' (p. 157). Something more than serious play was said to be involved when a chimp that had failed repeatedly on a box-stacking problem responded immediately and successfully after Köhler had himself demonstrated the correct solution. This sort of imitation is said to involve essentially the perception of a new set of relationships which are, for the first time, demonstrated to the watching animal, and it thus facilitates the reorganization of the parts of a problem when the trial-and-error efforts of the animal had led to repeated failure. While such imitated solutions are said to be difficult for the chimp, these animals will imitate with ease if they are already familiar with and understand the action to be imitated.

On monkeys, there are scarcely any naturalistic observations of imitative behaviour, but Corner's (1955) interesting account of the training of Pig-tailed macaques to aid him in botanical collections of twigs, flowers, leaves, fungi, etc., in the Malayan forests certainly suggests that the training programme is aided by human demonstration. He further describes how a young macaque, taken from its mother's breast in the wild, gradually learned what to eat in the forest by watching an experienced monkey.

Field observations

The evidence on imitation in wild groups of monkeys and apes is limited by the fact that the observations must be made at so close a distance from the animals as to be unambiguous of interpretation. Carpenter (1934) reports that Howler mothers control and condition their infants by facilitating their 'spontaneous' activity at times, and on other occasions by restricting it. An example of facilitation is where the female '. . . pulled off a terminal twig filled with buds, and after eating part of them, gave the rest to a small infant which was associated with her. The infant nibbled at the food' (p. 74). One suspects that this example comprises little, if anything, more than the focusing of attention of the infant on what is appropriate for eating, rather than anything in the way of 'tuition'.

Hall (1962), in making very close-range observations of a wild Chacma baboon group, has frequently observed how dark-phase infants, prior to their actually eating food-plants, watch the feeding of their mothers or of other mature animals near them, and tend to direct their exploratory movements upon the same plants, chewing them or putting parts of them in their mouths. Older juveniles following, for example, feeding adult females have stopped to dig for bulbs in exactly the same place (film of the feeding behaviour of the Chacma baboon, photographed by S. Peet, and directed by the writer). The extensive range of food plants used by these animals are located and treated in many different ways by the group. Some edible bulbs can be located by only a tiny outgrowth above the surface of the ground. These have to be dug out. Others can be pulled from the soil by a tug on the leaves. Of some plants, such as the wild geranium, only the stems are sucked, the leaves being ignored, and so on. One may suppose that the group feeding-pattern, at least in the details of discriminations and manipulations, is largely acquired through the accumulations of daily observational learning. Some corroboration of this came when we released a tame baboon in the vicinity of a wild group. The tame animal came from North Transvaal, and had been in captivity, from about 6 months after its birth, for $3\frac{1}{2}$ years in the Cape. It was thus unlikely to have had the opportunity to acquire many, if any, of the feeding habits of the local Cape group. In the course of several days following its release, it came to be accepted, through a series of greetings episodes involving mutual embracing, kissing, and so on, by most of the animals in the group. As it came thus to be accepted, it spent much of the day feeding close to the others, and could sometimes be seen sitting very close to one of the others as the latter dug in the ground for bulbs. It then dug in the same place.

Chacma baboon groups vary, of necessity, quite markedly in their feeding habits in different parts of their distribution. In South-West Africa, a recently captured young male readily took and ate live scorpions. In the Cape, each of twenty different baboons of a group reacted with avoidance or hitting away when discovering live scorpions given to them experimentally under stones or in paper bags which they had learned to associate with desirable foods such as sweets (Hall, 1963). In South-West Africa, the same young baboon readily ate live legless lizards, while, in the Cape, the wild baboons reacted with fear to similar creatures. One could multiply the examples of these studies which strongly indicate that at least some of the local feeding habits and aversions are conditioned in some way, probably through observational learning, by social example.

The work of the Japanese field-studies on *Macaca fuscata* groups observed over very long periods, and often at close range (Imanishi, 1957, 1960; Frisch, 1959; Reports of the Primates Research Group, 1955), not only indicates how the spread of a new feeding habit occurs in a group, but describes how social status may itself be in part determined by the status in the group of the animal's mother. Thus, it is suggested, the attitudes of the individual *vis-à-vis* others in the group are, to some extent at least, taken over (i.e. imitated) from observing the mother's behaviour in the group and the behaviour of the group to the mother. According to Imanishi (1960): 'Children of dominant females involuntarily learn attitudes of the dominant and those of submissive females learn attitudes of the submissive. Moreover, children of dominant females in the central portion [of the group] are more intimately related to the leader than those of submissive females in the peripheral portion, as their mothers are more intimately related to the leader' (p. 3). Further: 'If other things are equal, males growing up with successful identification will co-operate with leaders more willingly, be accepted by them as well as by females more easily, and finally succeed their leaders . . .' (Imanishi, 1957, p. 53).

Such field observations upon the social matrix in which basic emotional attitudes relating to dominance and submissiveness are acquired within a wild group are of the greatest interest, for they indicate, perhaps for the first time in non-human primate studies of any kind, that the processes of imitation, in its broadest and most realistic sense of the social modification of individual behaviour, need to be studied not merely in the problem-type of skill acquisition experiment but in the simple setting of social variation.

The spread of a new feeding habit is likewise graphically described in these Japanese studies. Thus, a habit of washing sweet potatoes in a shallow stream before eating them was started by a female aged 3 years, then was transmitted to two infants of 1 and 2 years, and one of these infants transmitted the habit to its mother, then, later, altogether eleven other members of the group acquired the habit (Primates Research Group, 1955; Imanishi, 1957). Similarly, some juveniles of a group picked up the habit of eating caramels, when these were offered by visitors, and passed it on to their playmates. From the children the habit spread first to the mothers, then to the dominant males, while the last to pick up the habit were the subadult males who are furthest removed from and without contact with the members of the centre of the group (Frisch, 1959). In this group, the spread of the new habit took over 3 years. Although, as Imanishi (1957) states, infants acquire a new feeding habit very readily, the adults are usually rather slow in picking it up, but, as already stated, mothers quite often learn to eat a new food by observing their own infants, as well as the reverse.

The importance of these field observations lies in indicating a great variety of new experimental approaches to the problem of imitative learning in monkeys and apes. We are faced with un-equivocal evidence that certain fundamental social attitudes, feeding habits, and aversions, are acquired by the members of a group, and that the habit patterns or 'traditions' of groups vary to some extent from one group to another of the same species and even within the same population area. As Zuckerman (1932) says: 'Living as they do in permanent social relationships, they [monkeys and apes] are provided with numerous opportunities for modifying their behaviour through imitation' (p. 165). Field and laboratory experiment should now be devoted to testing far beyond the narrow framework of the traditional imitation study the nature of the affectional and social factors that make for, or inhibit, imitation. Care in technique, method, and criteria defini-tion, while valuable accessories, should now be imaginatively used on the realistic social learning problems of these animals.

Concluding Comments

Looking back over the evidence, the experimental approach has been mainly concerned with demonstrating, or not demonstrat-ing, that imitation learning occurs in adult monkeys and apes, keeping some factors constant, but often not the important ones. Naturalistic observations and informal studies, such as most of the early ones, usually indicate that observing the acts of a *D*, whether human or of the same species as the *O*, leads to a change in the behaviour of the *O*, which it seems is unlikely to have occurred without the action of the *D*. However, in all types of study, controls of previous experience or a sufficient knowledge of it are often lacking, and it is hard to tell whether the increment in performance was due to something specific which the *O* had seen or whether it was caused by a simple accentuation of interest or a change of 'set', i.e. a distraction away from an inadequate trial-and-error approach, which might conceivably have been achieved by any of several other kinds of diversion.

Developmental observations, scanty though they are, have been particularly suggestive, for they strongly indicate that, in the affectional context provided by the mother and others of a species group, places or objects are discriminated as significant rather than neutral by 'following' the actions of the *D* animal, but not necessarily by 'copying' the motor patterns of the *D*. Avoidance-habits and feeding-habits may well be largely determined in this way, as also may some of the attitudes of preference, aversion, dominance or submissiveness towards other members of the group.

It is perfectly reasonable to suppose that there is a highly formative period in the early years of life of the juvenile monkey and ape during which avoidance and other importantly transferable general social habits may be very readily acquired, but one may doubt whether, in these animals, there is any evidence of a critical physiological period during which alone certain fundamental attitudes are acquired through social observing. It seems likely that, because of the 'natural' affectional context in which the young of these animals, and perhaps of all mammals, develop, a tendency to learn by observing others is characteristic of all young monkeys and apes unless there is prolonged isolation from the species stimulation more or less from birth or weaning onwards. Probably this tendency is determined during the period of mother-dependence, and then, normally, carries over in the process of gradual independence when the young associate more and more with others of their own play-age group. One must also take into account the fact that the normal young primate is a highly exploratory animal, and that its explorations go far beyond a mere tinkering with all or any objects, for it tends selectively to explore what others explore, and tends also, in the same sort of way, to learn appropriate attitudes towards others in the group, including the dominant animals.

What, then, is involved in the various forms of observational learning? As Thorpe (1956) has pointed out, there is plenty of evidence for social facilitation and local enhancement in mammalian behaviour, but the evidence for 'true imitation, in the sense of copying a novel or otherwise improbable act – some act for which there is clearly no instinctive tendency' (p. 411) – is hard to discern. However, 'true', or what used to be called 'intelligent' or 'inferential', imitation is only one aspect of what might be considered a continuum of conformity processes going on in the natural life of monkey and ape. Indeed, it would seem more interesting scientifically to pay much less attention in experimental studies of these animals to the possibilities of human-like performance – involving 'awareness' of self and of another self – and much more attention to the ontogeny of simple habits of avoidance, social attitudes, and so on within the setting of the natural or experimental group. There seem likely to be several profound questions here for developmental research which are obscured by the fact of their 'ordinariness' or 'naturalness'. In considering, for instance, the cohesive forces that keep together year after year a group of wild monkeys, it is evident that far more is involved than is comprehended even in the broadest definition of sexual motivation. The dynamics of the group processes can best be studied by means of experimental manipulations in the zoo park or even in the natural situation.

It would be premature to try to discuss the comparative extent and quality of imitation in the monkeys and apes and man, for there is too little reliable experimental or naturalistic evidence. But it is reasonable to suppose that a profound analysis of the conformity processes in the non-human primates will be of significance for our understanding of the origins of basic social attitudes in the human child, at least in providing new hypotheses for investigation which might not so easily emerge from the accustomed observations of the children themselves. Indeed, it would be useful to concentrate upon the acquisition of attitudes that are *not* verbally associated and transmitted, leaving aside the obvious differences between monkeys, apes and man in the use of symbols.

Finally, there seems no point in trying to sort out the precise relationships amongst the several conformity processes evident in this review to the standard learning processes of habituation, conditioning types I and II, insight, and so on. For, in a real sense, the processes under discussion cut across these forms, any one or more of which might be involved in the behaviour sequences. And, further, we must be primarily concerned with the ontogeny of social learning, not with a cross-section of that which the adult representatives of any particular species can be made to achieve on a sample of imitation tasks. The apparent confusion of terms referred to earlier on in this paper may not be so much the outcome of semantic inefficiency as a real indication of the complexity and variety of the conformity processes. What is now needed is a sustained observational and experimental attack designed, not at first to reduce the processes to simple order, but to bring clearly into evidence the 'non-intellectual' factors that seem to be crucially important.

References

ADLER, H. E. (1955). Some factors of observational learning in cats. *J. Genet. Psychol.* **86**, 159–77.
ARONOWITSCH, G., & CHOTIN, B. (1929). Über die Nachahmung bei den Affen (*Macacus rhesus*). *Z. Morph. Ökol. Tiere*, **16**, 1–25. (Quoted by Spence, 1937, p. 822.)
BERNSTEIN, I. S. (1962). Response to nesting materials of wild-born and captive-born chimpanzees. *Animal Beh.* **10**, 1–6.
BINGHAM, H. C. (1928). Sex development in apes. *Comp. Psychol. Monogr.* **5**, 1–165.

CARPENTER, C. R. (1934). A field study of the behaviour and social relations of howling monkeys. *Comp. Psychol. Monogr.* **10**, no. 2, Serial no. 48.

CARPENTER, C. R. (1937). An observational study of two captive mountain gorillas. *Human Biol.* **9**, 175–96.

CHURCH, R. M. (1959). Emotional reactions of rats to the pain of others. *J. Comp. Physiol. Psychol.* **52**, 132–4.

CORNER, E. J. H. (1955). Botanical collecting with monkeys. *Proc. Roy. Instn,* **36**, no. 162, 1–16.

CRAWFORD, M. P. (1937). The cooperative solving of problems by young chimpanzees. *Comp. Psychol. Monogr.* **14**, no. 2.

CRAWFORD, M. P (1939). Social facilitation. *Psychol. Bull.* **36**, 407–46.

CRAWFORD, M. P., & SPENCE, K. W. (1939). Observational learning of discrimination problems by chimpanzees. *J. Comp. Psychol.* **27**, 133–47.

DARBY, C. L., & RIOPELLE, A. J. (1959). Observational learning in the rhesus monkey. *J. Comp. Physiol. Psychol.* **52**, 94–8.

DARWIN, C. (1871, 2nd ed. 1874). *The Descent of Man.* London: Murray.

FRISCH, J. E. (1959). Research on primate behaviour in Japan. *Amer. Anthrop.* **61**, 584–96.

FURNESS, W. H. (1916). Observations on the mentality of chimpanzees and orang-utans. *Proc. Amer. Phil. Soc.* **55**, 281–90.

HAGGERTY, M. E. (1909). Imitation in monkeys. *J. Comp. Neurol.* **19**, 337–455.

HALL, K. R. L. (1962). Numerical data, maintenance activities and locomotion of the wild chacma baboon, *Papio ursinus. Proc. Zool. Soc. Lond.* **139**, 181–220.

HALL, K. R. L. (1963). Variations in the ecology of the Chacma baboon, *Papio ursinus. Symp. Zool. Soc. Lond.* **10**, 1–28.

HARRISSON, B. (1960). Orang-utan behaviour in semi-wild state. *Sarawak Musuem J.* **9**, 422–47.

HASLERUD, G. M. (1938). The effect of movement of stimulus objects upon avoidance reactions in chimpanzees. *J. Comp. Psychol.* **25**, 507–28.

HAYES, K. J., & HAYES, C. (1951). The intellectual development of a home-raised chimpanzee. *Proc. Amer. Phil. Soc.* **95**, 105–9.

HAYES, K. J., & HAYES, C. (1952). Imitation in a home-raised chimpanzee. *J. Comp. Physiol. Psychol.* **45**, 450–9.

HAYES, K. J., & HAYES, C. (1953). Picture perception in a home-raised chimpanzee. *J. Comp. Physiol. Psychol.* **46**, 470–4.

HEBB, D. O. (1960). The American Revolution. *Amer. Psychol.* **15**, 735–45.

HEDIGER, H. (1950). *Wild Animals in Captivity.* London: Butterworth.

HOBHOUSE, L. T. (1901). *Mind in Evolution.* London: Macmillan.

HUMPHREY, G. (1921). Imitation and the conditioned reflex. *Pedagog. Sem.* **28**, 1—21.

IMANISHI, K. (1957). Social behaviour in Japanese monkeys, *Macaca fuscata. Psychologia,* **1**, 47–54.

IMANISHI, K. (1960). Social organization of subhuman primates in their natural habitat. *Curr. Anthrop.* **1**, 393–407.

JACOBSEN, C. F., JACOBSEN, M. M., & YOSHIOKA, J. G. (1932). Development of an infant chimpanzee during her first year. *Comp. Psychol. Monogr.* **9**, no. 1.

KELLOGG, W. N., & KELLOGG, L. A. (1933). *The Ape and the Child.* New York: McGraw-Hill.

KEMPF, E. J. (1916). Two methods of subjective learning in the monkey *Macacus rhesus. J. Anim. Beh.* 6, 256–65.

KINNAMAN, A. J. (1902). Mental life of two *Macacus rhesus* monkeys in captivity. *Amer. J. Psychol.* 13, 98–148, 173–218.

KOFFKA, K. (1924). *The Growth of the Mind.* London: Kegan Paul.

KÖHLER, W. (1925). *The Mentality of Apes.* London: Kegan Paul.

KÖHLER, W. (1926). Intelligence in apes. In *Psychologies of 1925.* Worcester, Mass.: Clark University Press.

KOHTS, N. (1928). *Adaptive Motor Habits of the* Macacus rhesus *under Experimental Conditions.* Moscow. (Quoted by Zuckerman, 1932, p. 165.)

KOSHTOYANTS, K. S., ed. (1955). *Selected Works of I. P. Pavlov.* Moscow: Foreign languages publishing house.

LASHLEY, K. S., & WATSON, J. B. (1913). Notes on the development of a young monkey. *J. Anim. Beh.* 3, 114–39.

MASON, W. A. (1960). The effects of social restriction on the behaviour of rhesus monkeys. *J. Comp. Physiol. Psychol.* 53, 582–9.

MASON, W. A. (1961). The effects of social restriction on the behaviour of rhesus monkeys. II. Tests of gregariousness. *J. Comp. Physiol. Psychol.* 54, 287–90.

McDOUGALL, W. (1908, 23rd ed. 1936). *An Introduction to Social Psychology.* London: Methuen.

MILLER, N. E., & DOLLARD, J. (1941). *Social Learning and Imitation.* New Haven: Yale University Press.

MILLER, R. E., MURPHY, J. V., & MIRSKY, I. A. (1959). Non-verbal communication of affect. *J. Clin. Psychol.* 15, 155–8.

MILLS, W. (1899). The nature of animal intelligence and the methods of investigating it. *Psychol. Rev.* 6, 262–74.

MITCHELL, P. C. (1922). Monkeys and the fear of snakes. *Proc. Zool. Soc. Lond* 1922, pp. 347–8.

MORRIS-GOODALL, J. (in press). Feeding behaviour of wild chimpanzees.

MOWRER, O. H. (1960). *Learning Theory and the Symbolic Process.* New York: Wiley.

NISSEN, H. W. (1944). The ape colony in Florida. *Anim. Kingd.* 47, no. 6.

NISSEN, H. W., & CRAWFORD, M. P. (1936). A preliminary study of food sharing behaviour in young chimpanzees. *J. Comp. Psychol.* 22, 383–419.

PRESLEY, W. J., & RIOPELLE, A. J. (1959). Observational learning of an avoidance response. *J. Genet. Psychol.* 95, 251–4.

PRIMATES RESEARCH GROUP, KYOTO UNIVERSITY (1955). Field notes on the social behaviour of Japanese monkeys (*Macaca fuscata*). (Cyclostyled.)

RIOPELLE, A. J. (1960). Observational learning of a position habit by monkeys. *J. Comp. Physiol. Psychol.* 53, 426–8.

ROMANES, G. J. (1886). *Animal Intelligence.* New York: Appleton.

SCOTT, J. P. (1958). Critical periods in the development of social behaviour in puppies. *Psychosom. Med.* 20, 42–54.

SHEPHERD, W. T. (1915). Some observations on the intelligence of the chimpanzee. *J. Anim. Beh.* 5, 391–6.

SPENCE, K. W. (1937). Experimental studies of learning and the higher mental processes in infra-human primates. *Psychol. Bull.* 34, 806–50.

TARDE, G. (1904). *Les lois de l'imitation.* Paris: Alcan.

THOMPSON, W. R. (1958). Social behaviour. In *Behaviour and Evolution* (ed. Roe, A. & Simpson, G. G.). New Haven: Yale University Press.

THORNDIKE, E. L. (1898). Animal intelligence; an experimental study of the associative processes in animals. *Psychol. Rev. Monogr.* Suppl. 2, no. 4.

THORNDIKE, E. L. (1901). The mental life of the monkeys. *Psychol. Rev. Monogr.* Suppl. 3, no. 5.

THORPE, W. H. (1956). *Learning and Instinct in Animals.* London: Methuen.

TINKLEPAUGH, O. L., & HARTMAN, C. G. (1930). Behavioural aspects of parturition in the monkey, *Macacus rhesus. J. Comp. Psychol.* 1, 63–98.

VERPLANCK, W. S. (1957). A glossary of some terms used in the objective science of behaviour. *Psychol. Rev.* Suppl. 64, no. 6.

WARDEN, C. J., & JACKSON, T. A. (1935). Imitative behaviour in the Rhesus monkey. *Pedagog. Sem.* 46, 103–25.

WARDEN, C. J., FJELD, H. A. & KOCH, A. M. (1940). Imitative behaviour in Cebus and Rhesus monkeys. *J. Genet. Psychol.* 56, 311–22.

WASHBURN, M. F. (1908). *The Animal Mind.* New York: Macmillan.

WATSON, J. B. (1911). Literature for 1910 on the behaviour of vertebrates. *J. Anim. Beh.* 1, 430–47.

WATSON, J. B. (1914). Imitation in monkeys. *Psychol. Bull.* 5, 169–78.

WITMER, L. (1910). Intelligent imitation and curiosity in a monkey. *Psychol. Clin.* 3, 225–7.

YERKES, R. M. (1934). Suggestibility in chimpanzees. *J. Soc. Psychol.* 5, 271–82.

YERKES, R. M. (1943). *Chimpanzees.* New Haven: Yale University Press.

YERKES, R. M., & YERKES, A. W. (1929). *The Great Apes.* New Haven: Yale University Press.

ZUCKERMAN, S. (1932). *The Social Life of Monkeys and Apes.* London: Kegan Paul.

424

Further Reading

BEACH, F. A., 'Can animals reason?' *Nat. Hist.*, vol. 57 (1948), pp. 112–16.

BIRCH, H. G., 'The role of motivational factors in insightful problem solving', *J. comp. Psychol.*, vol. 38 (1945), pp. 295–317.

BOLWIG, N., 'An intelligent tool-using baboon', *South African J. Sci.*, vol. 57 (1961), pp. 147–52.

BROGDEN, W. J., 'Animal studies of learning', in Stevens, S. S. (ed.), *Handbook of experimental psychology*, Wiley, 1951, pp. 568–612.

BUTLER, R. A., 'Investigative behavior', in Schrier, A. M., Harlow, H. F., and Stollnitz, F., *Behavior of nonhuman primates*, Academic Press, 1965, pp. 463–94.

CRAWFORD, M. P., and SPENCE, K. W., 'Observational learning of discrimination problems by chimpanzees', *J. comp. Psychol.*, vol. 27 (1939), pp. 133–47.

FANTZ, R. L., 'Ontogeny of perception', in Schrier, A. M., Harlow, H. F., and Stollnitz, F., *Behavior of nonhuman primates*, Academic Press, 1965, pp. 365–404.

FERSTER, C. B., 'A complex concurrent schedule of reinforcement', *J. exp. animal Behav.*, vol. 2 (1959), pp. 65–80.

FLETCHER, H. J., 'The delayed response problem', in Schrier, A. M., Harlow, H. F., and Stollnitz, F., *Behavior of nonhuman primates*, Academic Press, 1965, pp. 129–66.

FRENCH, G. M., 'Associative problems', in Schrier, A. M., Harlow, H. F., and Stollnitz, F., *Behavior of nonhuman primates*, Academic Press, 1965, pp. 167–210.

HALL, K. R. L., 'Observational learning in monkeys and apes', *Brit. J. Psychol.*, vol. 54 (1963), pp. 201–26.

HALL, K. R. L., and GOSWELL, M. J., 'Aspects of social learning in captive patas monkeys', *Primates*, vol. 5 (1965), pp. 59–70.

HARLOW, H. F., 'Primate learning', in Stone, C. P. (ed.), *Comparative psychology*, Prentice-Hall, 1951, pp. 183–238.

HARLOW, H. F., 'Solution by rhesus monkeys of a problem involving the Weigl principle using the matching-from-sample method,' *J. comp. Psychol.*, vol. 36 (1943), pp. 217–27.

HERON, W. T., 'Complex learning processes', in Moss F. A. (ed.), *Comparative Psychology*, Prentice Hall, (rev. edn), 1942, pp. 248–79.

ITANI, J., 'On the acquisition and propagation of a new food habit in the natural group of the Japanese monkey at Takasakiyama', *Primates*, vol. 1 (1958), pp. 84–98.

KAWAMURA, S., 'The process of subculture propagation among Japanese macaques', in Southwick, C. H. (ed.), *Primate social behavior*, Van Nostrand, 1963, pp. 82–90.

KELLOGG, W. N., and KELLOGG, L. A., *The ape and the child*, McGraw-Hill, 1933.

KLOPFER, P. H., 'Observational learning in birds', *Behaviour*, vol. 17 (1961), pp. 71–80.

KLÜVER, H., *Behavior mechanisms in monkeys*, University of Chicago Press, 1933.

KÖHLER, W., *The mentality of apes*, Harcourt, Brace, 1925.

425

MAIER, N. R. F., and SCHNIERLA, T. C., 'Higher mental processes', in Maier, N. R. F., and Schnierla, T. C., *Principles of animal psychology*, McGraw-Hill, 1935, pp. 444–80.

MEYER, D. R., TREICHLER, F R., and MEYER, P. M., 'Discrete-trial training techniques and stimulus variables', in Schrier, A. M., Harlow, J. F., and Stollnitz, F., *Behavior of nonhuman primates*, Academic Press, 1965, pp. 1–50.

MILES, R. C., 'Discrimination-learning sets', in Schrier, A. M., Harlow, H. F., and Stollnitz, F., *Behavior of nonhuman primates*, Academic Press, 1965, pp. 51–96.

MILES, R. C., and MEYER, D. R., 'Learning sets in marmosets', *J. comp. physiol. Psychol.*, vol. 49 (1956), pp. 219–22.

NISSEN, H. W., 'Phylogenetic comparisons', in Stevens, S. S. (ed.), *Handbook of experimental psychology*, Wiley, 1951.

RIOPELLE, A. J., and ROGERS, C. M., 'Age changes in chimpanzees', in Schrier, A. M., Harlow, H. F., and Stollnitz, F., *Behavior of nonhuman primates*, Academic Press, 1965, pp. 449–62.

RIOPELLE, A. J., 'Complex processes', in Waters, R. H., Rethlingshafer, D. A., and Caldwell, W. E. (ed.), *Principles of comparative psychology*, McGraw-Hill, 1960, pp. 208–49.

SCHILLER, P. H , 'Innate motor action as a basis of learning', in Schiller, C. H. (ed.), *Instinctive behavior*, International University Press.

THORPE, W. H., *Learning and instinct in animals*, Methuen, 1962.

VEVERS, G. M., and WEINER, J. S., 'Use of a tool by a captive Capuchin monkey (*Cebus fatuellus*)', in Napier, J. R. (ed.), *Symposium on primate biology*, Zool. Soc. of London, 1963, pp. 115–17.

WARREN, J. M., 'Primate learning in comparative perspective', in Schrier, A. M., Harlow, H. F., and Stollnitz, F., *Behavior of nonhuman primates*, Academic Press, 1965, pp. 245–82.

WYCKOFF, L. B., Jr., 'The role of observing responses in discrimination learning. Part I', *Psychol. Rev.*, vol., 59 (1952), pp. 431–42.

ZIMMERMAN, R. R., and TORREY, C. C., 'Ontogeny of learning', in Schrier, A. M., Harlow, H. F., and Stollnitz, F., *Behavior of nonhuman primates*, Academic Press, 1965, pp. 405–48.

Acknowledgements

Acknowledgements are due to the following for permission to publish extracts in this volume:

AMERICAN JOURNAL OF PSYCHOLOGY

W. T. Shepherd, 'Some observations and experiments of the intelligence of the chimpanzee and ourang', vol. 34 (1923), pp. 590–1.

AMERICAN PSYCHOLOGICAL ASSOCIATION

J. Cole, 'A study of discrimination reversal learning in monkeys', *J. comp. physiol. Psychol.*, vol. 44 (1951), pp. 467–72.

M. Crawford, 'Further study of coöperative behaviour in chimpanzee', *Psych. Bull.*, vol. 33 (1936), p. 800.

C. L. Darby and A. J. Riopelle, 'Observational learning in the rhesus monkey', *J. comp. physiol. Psychol.*, vol. 52 (1949), pp. 94–8.

G. V. Hamilton, 'A study of trial and error reactions in mammals', *J. animal Behav.*, vol. 1 (1911), pp. 33–66.

H. F. Harlow, 'The formation of learning sets', *Psychol. Rev.*, vol. 56 (1949), pp. 51–65.

K. J. Hayes and C. Hayes, 'Imitation in a home-raised chimpanzee', *J. comp. physiol. Psychol.*, vol. 45 (1952), pp. 450–9.

K. J. Hayes, R. Thompson and C. Hayes, 'Concurrent discrimination learning in chimpanzees', *J. comp. physiol. Psychol.*, vol. 46 (1953), pp. 105–7.

M. Levine, 'A model of hypothesis behaviour in discrimination learning set', *Psychol. Rev.*, vol. 66 (1959), pp. 353–66.

N. R. F. Maier, 'Reasoning and learning', *Psychol. Rev.*, vol. 38 (1939), pp. 332–42.

H. W. Nissen, 'Analysis of a complex conditional reaction in chimpanzee', *J. comp. physiol. Psychol.*, vol. 44 (1951), pp. 9–16.

H. W. Nissen, J. S. Blum and R. A. Blum, 'Analysis of matching behavior in chimpanzee', *J. comp. physiol. Psychol.*, vol. 41 (1948), pp. 62–74.

P. H. Schiller, 'Innate constituents of complex responses in primates', *Psychol Rev.*, vol. 59 (1952), pp. 177–89.

E. L. Thorndike, 'Animal intelligence: an experimental study of associative process in animals', *Psychol. Rev., Monogr. Suppl.*, vol. 2 (1898), pp. 1–9 and 47–52.

BRITISH PSYCHOLOGICAL SOCIETY

K. R. L. Hall, 'Observational learning in monkeys and apes', *Brit. J. Psychol.*, vol. 54 (1963), pp. 201–26.

CHARLES SCRIBNER'S SONS

From *Introduction to comparative psychology* by C. Lloyd Morgan. Charles Scribner's Sons (1898).

CURRENT ANTHROPOLOGY AND MRS PAULINE S. HALL

K. R. L. Hall, 'Tool-using performances as indicators of behavioral adaptability', vol. 4 (1963), pp. 479–94.

ACKNOWLEDGEMENTS

EDWARD ARNOLD (PUBLISHERS) LIMITED
C. Lloyd Morgan, *Habit and instinct*, 1896.

MRS PAULINE S. HALL
K. R. L. Hall, 'Animals that use tools', *Animals*, vol. 7 (1965), pp. 16–21.

DAVID KRECH
I. Krechevsky, ' "Hypothesis" *versus* "chance" in the pre-solution period
in sensory discrimination-learning', *Univ. Calif. Publ. Psychol.*, vol. 6
(1932), pp. 27–44.

ROYAL ANTHROPOLOGICAL INSTITUTE OF GREAT BRITAIN AND
IRELAND
M. R. A. Chance, 'Köhler's chimpanzees – how did they perform', *Man*,
vol. 60 (1960), pp. 130–5.

SCIENTIFIC AMERICAN
M. Scheerer, 'Problem-solving', reprinted with permission. Copyright ©
1963 by Scientific American Inc. All rights reserved.

WAYNE STATE UNIVERSITY PRESS
H. W. Nissen, 'Problems of mental evolution in the primates', *Human
Biology*, vol. 26 (1954), pp. 277–87.

WILLIAM & WILKINS CO.
H. G. Birch, 'The relation of previous experience to insightful problem-
solving', *J. comp. Psychol.*, vol. 38 (1945), pp. 367–83.
K. W. Spence, 'Gradual *versus* sudden solution of discrimination problems
by chimpanzees', *J. comp. Psychol.*, vol. 25 (1938), pp. 213–24.
O. L. Tinklepaugh, 'An experimental study of representative factors in
monkeys', *J. comp. Psychol.*, vol. 8 (1928), pp. 197–202.
B. Weinstein, 'Matching-from-sample by rhesus monkeys and by children'
J. comp. Psychol., vol. 31 (1941), pp. 195–213.

Author Index

Ades, H. W., 228, 232
Adler, H. E., 399, 421
Agassiz, G. R., 285
Andrew, R. J., 155, 156, 172, 174
Aronowitsch, G., 406, 421

Bakay, E., 114
Baldwin, J. M., 285, 286
Baldwin, M., 354, 355, 357
Beach, F. A., 104, 114
Beatty, H., 149, 172
Beniuc, M., 305, 314
Bernstein, I. S., 410, 421
Berry, C. W., 264, 285
Bierens de Haan, J. A., 150, 172
Bingham, H. C., 96, 97, 102, 119, 136, 415, 421
Birch, H. G., 41, 97, 102, 104, 107, 114, 116, 136, 151, 173, 386, 388
Bishop, A., 155, 173
Bleuler, E., 277, 285
Blum, J. S., 22, 25, 303, 304, 334
Blum, R. A., 22, 25, 303, 304, 334
Bolwig, N., 150, 173
Boring, E. G., 31
Boulenger, E. G., 142, 173
Bowman, R. I., 146, 173
Breed, F. S., 103, 115
Brehm, A. E., 142, 173
Bromer, J. A., 319, 333
Brügger, M., 112, 115
Buytendijk, F. J. F., 79, 81

Carmichael, L., 103, 114

Carpenter, C. R., 140, 141, 142, 156, 171, 173, 412, 416, 422
Carreri, G., 52
Chance, M. R. A., 91, 161, 173
Chapman, F. M., 359
Child, C. M., 294, 296
Chisholm, A. H., 138, 173
Chotin, B., 406, 421
Church, R. M., 394, 422
Čiák, R., 158, 159, 170, 173
Cole, J., 297, 302, 304
Cooper, L. R., 144, 173
Corner, E. J. H., 416, 422
Cowan, E. A., 79, 81
Crawford, M. P., 179, 370, 377, 378, 387, 388, 394, 404, 406, 422

Dampier, W., 52
Darby, C. L., 370, 377, 404, 422
Dart, R. A., 164, 173
Darwin, C. R., 9, 15, 50, 51, 88, 285, 286, 391
Dashiell, J. F., 288, 289, 296
Descartes, R., 46
DeVore, I., 140, 151, 173, 175
Dodson, J. D., 260, 285
Dollard, J., 375, 377, 396, 423
Duerden, J. E., 140, 145, 173
Duncker, K., 29, 32, 33

Eibl-Eibesfeldt, I., 85
Elliot, J. M., 37

Feller, W., 239, 251
Finch, G., 338, 349

Fischel, W., 120, 136
Fisher, E. M., 86, 148, 173
Fjeld, N. A., 91, 102, 403, 424
Fogelsonger, H. M., 293, 296
Forster, A., 160, 173
Forster, M. C., 19, 25, 160, 173
Fowler, W., 360
Freud, S., 17, 277, 285
Frisch, J. E., 417, 418, 422
Furness, W. H., 319, 333, 397, 422

Galt, W. E., 305, 314
Gellermann, L. W., 235, 251
Gesell, A., 103, 114
Girden, E., 112, 115
Givens, R. D., 160, 173
Glees, P., 302, 304
Goldstein, K., 31, 301, 304
Goodall, J. M., 160, 161, 169
Goodnow, J. J., 233, 235, 251
Grether, W. F., 18, 25
Guthrie, E. R., 114, 115

Haggerty, H. E., 401, 422
Hall, K. R. L., 85, 137, 140, 141, 144, 148, 149, 150, 151, 156, 157, 159, 160, 161, 162, 163, 166, 167, 168, 169, 170, 173, 390, 416, 417, 422
Hamilton, G. V., 255, 285
Harington, C. R., 148, 174
Harlow, H. F., 20, 25, 99, 102, 144, 161, 173, 207, 228, 232, 233, 234, 235, 241, 242, 244, 245, 250, 251, 252, 298, 301, 302, 303, 304, 305, 312, 314, 319, 333, 334, 338, 347, 349, 350, 370, 376, 377, 387, 388
Harlow, M. K., 245, 251
Harrisson, B., 419, 422
Harsh, C. M., 376, 377

Hartman, C. G., 408, 424
Haslerud, G. M., 405, 422
Hayes, C., 227, 232, 376, 377, 378, 388, 411, 415, 422
Hayes, K. J., 227, 232, 376, 377, 378, 388, 411, 415, 422
Hebb, D. O., 396, 422
Hediger, H., 393, 422
Herbert, M. J., 376, 377
Herrick, C. J., 295, 296
Hess, W. R., 112, 113, 115
Hewes, G. W., 161, 162, 171, 174
Hicks, L. H., 250, 251
Hilgard, E. R., 346, 349
Hill, O., 170, 174
Hingston, R. W. G., 140, 142, 174
Hobhouse, L. T., 58, 59, 71, 83, 117, 136, 422
Hollingworth, H. L., 23, 25
Hornaday, W. T., 142, 174
Horton, G. P., 114, 115
Hough, W. R., 77
Hubbard, R. M., 187, 197
Huling, M., 33
Hull, C. L., 27, 225, 298, 304
Humphry, G., 396, 422
Hunter, W. S., 77, 78, 80, 81

Imanishi, K., 161, 174, 417, 418, 422
Itard, J. M. G., 317, 333

Jackson, T. A., 105, 115, 128, 136, 378, 389, 399, 402, 424
Jacobsen, C. F., 123, 136, 302, 304, 409, 422
Jacobsen, M. M., 123, 136, 409, 422
James, W., 23, 25, 41
Jarvik, M. E., 370, 377
Jenkins, W. O., 370, 377

Jennings, H. S., 10
Jerison, H. J., 165, 170, 172
Johnson, B., 49
Joleaud, L., 142, 174
Joule, J. P., 46
Jung, C. G., 277, 285

Kaufmann, J. H., 142, 143, 174
Kawamura, S., 161, 162, 174
Kellogg, L. A., 123, 136, 387, 388, 411, 423
Kellogg, W. N., 123, 136, 387, 388, 411, 423
Kempf, E. J., 401, 402, 423
Kenyon, K. W., 149, 174
Kinnaman, A. J., 118, 136, 142, 174, 400, 423
Klapper, Z. S., 33
Kleemeier, L., 382
Klüver, H., 119, 120, 136, 150, 174, 346, 349
Koch, A. M., 91, 102, 403, 424
Koffka, K., 208, 394, 395, 396, 423
Köhler, W., 27, 28, 80, 81, 83, 84, 91, 92, 94, 95, 96, 98, 101, 102, 105, 106, 107, 113, 115, 116, 117, 118, 120, 128, 130, 131, 134, 136, 159, 186, 197, 208, 394, 395, 396, 415, 416, 423
Kohts, N., 79, 81, 114, 315, 318, 326, 333, 349, 402, 423
Kooij, M., 144, 145, 174
Kortlandt, A., 144, 145, 174
Koshtoyants, K. S., 423
Kreschevsky, I., 181, 183, 197, 233, 251, 297, 301, 302, 304
Kuenne, M., 213
Kummer, H., 156, 174

Lack, D., 85, 146, 174

Ladd, G. T., 117, 136
Lashley, K. S., 183, 184, 187, 190, 196, 197, 298, 301, 302, 304, 305, 312, 314, 318, 333, 349, 408, 423
Learned, B., 387, 389
Levine, M., 181, 233, 241, 248, 252
Levinson, B., 241, 252
Lewin, K., 290, 293, 294, 296
Loeb, J., 10
Loomis, M., 359
Lorenz, K., 15, 25, 97
Lubin, A., 233, 252
Luchins, A., 41

Maier, N. R. F., 112, 115, 134, 136, 287, 290, 291, 292, 296, 376
Marshall, A. J., 139, 174
Mason, W. A., 99, 102, 242, 245, 251, 407, 423
Masserman, J. H., 153, 174
Marquis, D. G., 346, 349
McClearn, G. E., 370, 377
McCulloch, T. L., 346, 349
McDougall, W., 138, 174, 391, 423
Merfield, F. G., 140, 142, 149, 174
Meyer, A., 277, 285
Miller, H., 140, 142, 149, 174
Miller, N. E., 375, 377, 394, 396, 405, 423
Mills, W., 353, 398, 423
Mirsky, I. A., 394, 423
Mitchell, P. C., 408, 423
Morgan, C. L., 9, 13, 26, 28, 54, 78, 138, 174, 283, 286, 353, 366, 393
Morris, D., 162, 174
Morris-Goodall, J., 149, 174, 397, 415, 423

Moseley, D., 104, 115
Moseley, L., 53
Moss, E. M., 298, 304, 376, 377
Mowrer, O. H., 112, 115, 376, 377, 394, 395, 396, 423
Munn, N. L., 185, 197
Murie, O. J., 148, 174
Murphy, J. U., 394, 423

Napier, J. R., 155, 162, 163, 165, 174
Nellmann, H., 79, 81
Nissen, H. W., 15, 19, 20, 22, 25, 151, 175, 305, 314, 315, 326, 331, 333, 334, 338, 346, 349, 376, 377, 406, 409, 423
Noer, M. C., 20, 25, 305, 314
Nowlis, V., 334, 349

Oakley, K. P., 151, 158, 175
Ovsiankina, M., 291, 296

Pavlov, I. P., 27, 396
Pechtel, C., 153
Peckham, E. G., 138, 175
Peckham, G. W., 138, 175
Perkins, F. T., 198, 208
Pettigrew, T. F., 233, 235, 251
Pitman, C. R., 149, 175
Postman, L., 233, 251
Presley, W. J., 405, 423

Razran, G. H. S., 19, 25
Reed, H. B., 77
Restle, F., 250, 252
Riopelle, A. J., 167, 171, 228, 232, 250, 252, 370, 376, 377, 404, 405, 423
Robertson, C., 50
Romanes, G. J., 43, 170, 175, 285, 286, 366, 397, 423
Rubenstein, I., 233, 251

Rueping, R. R., 99, 102, 242, 245, 251
Rusin, H. H., 334, 338, 349

Schaller, G. B., 86, 142, 143, 148, 149, 162, 169, 175
Scheerer, M., 26
Schiller, P. H., 97, 98, 99, 100, 102, 103, 114, 115, 151, 153, 155, 175
Schneirla, T. C., 112, 115, 127, 134, 136
Schrier, A. M., 243, 244, 252
Scott, J. P., 168, 171, 392, 423
Settlage, P., 228, 232, 312, 314
Shanks, B., 233, 251
Shepard, J. F., 103, 115, 293, 296
Shepherd, W. T., 70, 118, 136, 397, 423
Sherrington, C. S., 117
Simpson, M. M., 334, 349
Simpson, G. G., 16, 17, 24, 25
Skinner, B. F., 114, 115
Spaet, T., 305, 314, 334, 350
Spalding, D., 103, 115
Spence, K. W., 18, 25, 198, 199, 208, 298, 301, 303, 304, 370, 374, 377, 378, 387, 401, 404, 406, 422, 423
Spencer, H., 285, 286, 288, 289
Spragg, S. D. S., 110, 115
Stone, C. P., 104, 115, 184, 185, 186, 189, 197

Tarde, G., 391, 424
Tellier, M., 318, 333
Thompson, R., 227, 232
Thompson, W. R., 394, 424
Thorndike, E. G., 26, 27, 28, 42, 116, 117, 118, 136, 167, 168, 175, 285, 351, 363, 398, 399, 400, 424

Thorpe, W. H., 137, 152, 175, 420, 424
Tinbergen, N., 152, 175
Tinklepaugh, D. L., 77, 408, 424
Tolman, E. C., 113, 115
Trendelenburg, W., 79, 81

Ulrich, S. L., 79, 81

Verlaine, L., 318, 333
Verplanck, W. S., 393, 424
Vivers, G. M., 170, 175

Wallace, A. R., 88, 140, 142, 143, 175, 360, 361
Walton, H. C., 79, 81
Warden, C. J., 91, 102, 378, 386, 389, 399, 402, 403, 424
Washburn, S. L., 151, 165, 169, 175, 393, 396, 424
Watson, J. B., 27, 71, 80, 81, 397, 399, 408, 424
Weimer, J. S., 170, 175
Weinstein, B., 317, 333, 334, 350
Wertheimer, M., 28, 29, 41

Wheeler, R. H., 198, 208
White, L., 161
Williams, J. H., 139, 147, 175
Williston, S. W., 138, 175
Witchell, C. A., 355, 360
Witkin, H., 33
Witmer, L., 397, 424
Woodworth, R. S., 117, 136

Yarbrough, J. V., 79, 81
Yerkes, A. W., 136, 319, 333, 378, 389, 412, 413, 414, 424
Yerkes, D. N., 80, 81
Yerkes, R. M., 80, 81, 83, 99, 105, 110, 115, 117, 118, 119, 123, 136, 260, 285, 319, 326, 331, 333, 376, 377, 378, 389, 399, 410, 412, 413, 414, 424
Yoshioka, J. G., 123, 136, 409, 422
Young, M. L., 334, 350

Zable, M., 298, 301, 303, 304, 312, 314
Zeigarnik, B., 293, 296
Zuckerman, S., 120, 136, 140, 175, 401, 402, 403, 418, 424

Subject Index

Abstract generalization
     mechanism, 346, 347
Acuity, visual, 18
Adaptability, 172
Adaptive actions, 45, 52, 157
Adaptive outcome, 16
Aggressive action, 141, 153
Agonistic behaviour, 139, 140
Alternation habit, 189–97
     see Hypothesis
          Position alternation
          preference
          responses
Anecdotal method, 64
Associative connections, 198
Associative processes, 363
Attempted solutions, 183, 190,
     196
Avoidance learning, 405
Axes of comparison, 18

Box stacking, 110

Categorizing, 334
Chance, 183
Chastisement, 53
Cognitive functions, 18, 23
Combination of experiences,
     287–96
     see Reorganization of ex-
          perience
Complexity of behaviour, 19
Complex responses, 103
Concepts, 21, 22
Concurrent discrimination
     learning, 227–31
Conditional reaction, 305–14,
     334
Conditioned response, 103

Conditioning, classical, 19
Consciousness, 17, 45, 119
Continuity, evolutionary, 16
Continuity theory, 297
     see Gradual solution
Co-operation, 53, 179, 406
Copying, 357
     see Following
          Imitation
Correction method, 298, 336
Cues, 20
Culture, 16
Curiosity, 351

Delayed reaction, 77–81
Delayed response, 75, 289, 334
     nonspatial, 376
     to objects, 317
Direction, 293
Discrimination reversal, 215–
     19, 297–303
     see Learning set
Displacement activity, 141,
     153

Emergent traits, 16
Empathy, 394
Ethology, 94
Excitatory,
     strength, 199–208
     tendency, 199–208
     see Continuity theory
Exploratory tendencies, 390

Field of strain, 293
Fixation, 29, 33, 36, 37, 39–42
Following, 404
     see Copying
          Imitation

Form, 21, 22
  see Gestalt
    'Good' configuration
Functional extension of arm,
    135, 137
Functional relations,
    awareness of, 119

Generalization, 150, 317
Gestalt, 27, 28, 30, 131
Gestures, 177, 179
'Good' configuration, 132
Gradual solution, 198
  see Continuity theory
Grooming, 22

Homology, 151, 158, 170
Hypothesis, 183, 297
Hypothesis behaviour, 233–51

Ideation, 71, 105
Identification, 390
Imitation, 21, 22, 71, 171, 351,
    353*ff*.
  delayed, 379
  intelligent, 402
Induction, 54
Inference, 49
Innate constituents, 99, 103–
    15
Insight, 28, 29, 105, 118, 119,
    131, 198–208, 287–96
Instinct, 20, 21, 49, 353–61
Intelligence, 18, 20, 24, 43, 45,
    49–52, 62–9, 363
  see Insight
Intent, 140
Introspective method, 9, 54
I.Q., 19

Judgement, 58

Language, 23

Learning
  mechanism, 342–4
  sets, 181, 209*ff*., 233*ff*.
  to learn, 209–26
Lose-stay, win-shift
    hypothesis, 235*ff*.

Matching, 22, 315, 334*ff*.
  from sample, 317*ff*.
Mating, 21
Maturation, 103, 151
Meaning, 92
Means, perception of, 60
Mechanical principle, 52
Mimesis, 393
Mind, 44–7
Morgan's canon, 9–10, 13, 26

Nest building, 409

Objects as weapons, 140
Observational learning, 167,
    351, 370–7, 390*ff*.
Oddity, 334
One trial learning, 209*ff*.

Patterns, 21
Perception, 20–2, 28, 45, 48,
    57
  mechanism, 344–5
Perceptual organization, 99
Perseverance, 189–97
  see Position preference
Perseverative interference, 312
Play, 20, 53, 108
  imitative, 379
Position
  alternation, 235*ff*.
    see Alternation habit
  preference, 235*ff*.
  responses, 189–97
    see Hypothesis
Potentialities, 21, 22

Pre-solution period, 183
  see Continuity theory
Primates, 16–18, 24
Primitive instrumental act,
  154
Problem solution behaviour,
  236ff.
Problem solving, 26, 29, 42,
  104, 387
Protista, 19
Punishment, 53
Purposive behaviour, 141

Random responding, 236ff.
Ratiocination, 49, 62
  see Ideation
Rational inference tendency,
  279
Reaction time, 18
Reason, 48–9, 57–8
Reasoning, 51, 70, 287ff.
Recentering, 32, 34
Recognition, 23
Reflex, 45–7, 49
Reinforcement, 199
  see Continuity theory
Relations, 56, 58
  means-end, 60
  parts-to-whole, 92
  perception of higher level,
    22, 59, 133
Reorganization of experience,
  134, 198
  see Combination of
    experience

Sagacity, 23
Sameness, 317
  see Similarity-difference
Scale phyletic, 18
Screw, 52

Serial discrimination, 228
Shift of behavioural set, 317
Similarity-difference, 334,
  341–7
Snakes, 53
Social facilitation, 390, 394
Stamped in, 27
  see Continuity theory
Stereotyped modes of
    searching, 280
Stimulus
  alternation, 235ff.
  enhancement, 374, 390
  preference, 235ff.
Stimulus-response, 20, 21,
  198–208
Stupidity, 64
Sudden solution, 198–208
  see Gestalt
    Insight
Sultan, 93–4

Teamwork, 179
Tenerife, 27
Tool making, 151, 158
Trial and error, 28, 255ff.
Tuition, 21, 22

Unadaptive behaviour, 281
Unlearned motor patterns,
  105
Unmodified searching
    tendency, 280

Values, 24
Vision, colour, 18
Volition, 48

Wild boy of Aveyron, 317
Win-stay, lose-shift
    hypothesis, 235ff.

Penguin Modern Psychology Readings

Titles available in this series are:

MOTIVATION ed. Dalbir Bindra and Jane Stewart
A collection of papers which deal most directly with the three
central problems of motivation: *drive* (what instigates an organism
to action); *goal direction* (what directs behaviour towards certain
ends); *reinforcement* (what precisely makes certain events
rewarding and others punishing). UPS 1

EXPERIMENTS IN VISUAL PERCEPTION
ed. M. D. Vernon
The volume reviews four central topics – the perception of form,
space and distance, 'constancy' phenomena and movement – and
then explains the variations in perception which occur within the
individual and between individuals. Four excerpts from Piaget on
perception in infancy complete the volume. UPS 2

ATTITUDES ed. Marie Jahoda and Neil Warren
Three sections of readings which cover studies and problems in
concepts, research, and theory and measurement. UPS 3

PERSONALITY ASSESSMENT ed. Boris Semeonoff
Readings on variations in normal personality, which include
Galton and the early writings on typology, and the applications of
psychometric methods and of controlled observations in selection
procedures. UPS 4

INTELLIGENCE AND ABILITY ed. Stephen Wiseman
'The slow emergence of a coherent theory of the structure of
human abilities' is both the subject and the object of this volume.
Professor Wiseman has chosen readings from philosophers and
psychologists, covering a century of speculation, hypothesis and
research on man's intellectual powers. The earlier papers provide
the student with a historical perspective from which he can
appraise the present position. In the last section of the book
Professor Wiseman presents some of the results of research into
learning theory and into human ability. The integration of these
two sectors of psychological enquiry will, he believes,
revolutionize the work of the educational and vocational
psychologists of the future. UPS 5

ABNORMAL PSYCHOLOGY ed. Max Hamilton
The papers are grouped into four categories; first, clinical
descriptions, second, the application of psychological methods to
abnormal psychology, third, experimental work on animals, and
fourth, psychodynamic theory. The first two sections include work
by theorists such as Kraepelin and Pavlov, and Freud and
Masserman. UPS 6

The next titles currently published in this series are:

DECISION MAKING ed. Ward Edwards and Amos Tversky
'Decision theory has a problem for every taste': to prove it, the
editors have included the writings of philosophers such as Adams,
Davidson, DeGroot and Suppes, of mathematical statisticians
such as Mosteller, Raiffa and Savage, of a mathematical
economist, Marschak, and of a variety of psychologists. The book
is divided into four parts. The first is a general introduction to the
subject, the second is about the notions of utility and subjective
probability, the third deals with riskless choice, and the fourth
with probabilistic theories of choice. UPS 8

PERSONALITY ed. Richard S. Lazarus and Edward M.
Opton, Jr
The topic of personality has provoked brilliant speculation,
careful observation and experimental research. Professor Lazarus
and Dr Opton have gathered into this volume twenty-two seminal
articles and excerpts on theoretical and experimental work. The
four sections deal with description of personality structure,
development of personality, dynamics of personality and
determinants of personality. Among the writers represented are
Gordon Allport, Raymond Cattell, Erik Erikson, Sigmund Freud,
Ernest Hilgard, Robert Holt and Carl Rogers. UPS 9

The Science of Animal Behaviour

P. L. Broadhurst

For generations men have employed dogs and hawks to hunt, cormorants to fish, and performing animals for entertainment. Modern research on scientific lines may greatly widen the use of animals in human society. In this brief and fascinating study the director of the animal psychology laboratory at London University's Institute of Psychiatry recounts how, with the use of test apparatus, monkeys can learn to work for wages paid in token coins; how white rats can be trained to thread their way through a maze or be taught specific drills in such devices as the 'shuttle box'. He describes, too, the scientific observations which have been made on the behaviour in the wild of – for instance – penguins or crabs, and the questions that these raise.

Such experimentation and observation, under approved conditions can be shown to advance the treatment of human mental disorders and to help in the study of such difficult problems as pre-natal influences. The study of animal behaviour may also, as the author suggests, lead to such extraordinary developments as the training of chimpanzees as engine-drivers or the employment of pigeons as production-line inspectors.

This authoritative book explains very clearly the meaning and purpose of modern research into animal behaviour.

The Mentality of Apes
Wolfgang Köhler

Professor Köhler studied the mentality of apes with two interests: to ascertain the degree of relationship between anthropoid apes and man in the field of intellectual capacity, and to gain knowledge of the nature of intelligent acts by studying them under the simplest conditions. By tests applied to his colony of nine apes, in the spheres of the use of implements, the handling of objects, building, the handling of forms, imitation, and detours with intermediate objectives, he concluded that chimpanzees manifest intelligent behaviour of the kind familiar in humans.

The Psychology of Interpersonal Behaviour
Michael Argyle

Looks, gestures, and tones of voice may be powerful factors when people meet. Moreover, these rapid and subtle messages are highly co-ordinated.

Experimental techniques have recently been developed for studying the minutiae of social behaviour scientifically: these are described here by a social psychologist. The study of social interaction demands a 'language' of its own, to which Michael Argyle supplies a clear key. But the reader will not be slow to grasp that 'the motivation of social interaction', 'the sychronization of styles of behaviour' between two or more people, and 'the presentation of a self-image' refer to things we encounter every day.

Certainly specific skills, such as interviewing, group leadership, public speaking, and even child-rearing, are discussed in the light of the latest research, and the author devotes a good deal of space to mental health and to training in social skill. His outline of what amounts to a break-through in psychological analysis makes this a book which the student of psychology may well find indispensable; and the relevance of his material to everyday life offers irresistible reading to the plain man.

New Horizons in Psychology
Edited by Brian M. Foss

Psychology as a science of observation and experiment is 100 years old. In the last decade it has expanded greatly, exploring new fields of human behaviour and using new techniques.

New Horizons in Psychology is both a progress report and a guide to the exciting developments in coming years. All of them will affect scientific thinking in many fields, and some of them will influence the way we live.

Visual illusions, information theory, creativity, genetics, motivation, drugs, operant conditioning, programmed learning, behaviour therapy, personal construct psychology, small groups, cross cultural studies – psychology is seething with new ideas and methods today. These, and many others, are explained here by a distinguished team of experimental psychologists. A linking commentary by the editor, Professor Foss, paints the conceptual background to each topic.

The Psychology of Perception
M. D. Vernon

When we look at the world with our eyes, do we see it *as it really is*? In this authoritative study the Professor of Psychology at the University of Reading shows how, behind the retina of the eye, many more fallible mental processes cause errors and inconsistencies to creep into our perceptions. Here is a non-technical outline of the psychological processes which have been shown to be involved in our visual perception of things about us. The perception of shape, colour, movement, and space develops gradually from infancy upwards. Finally this book, which is based on over thirty years of psychological research at Cambridge and elsewhere, shows how the perceptions of different people are not always alike: they vary with attention, interest, and individual personality factors.

Human Groups
W. J. H. Sprott

This book deals with 'face-to-face' relationships. These occur in
relatively permanent groups, such as the family, the village, and
the neighbourhood. Some of the studies which have been made of
such groups are described. There has also been a great deal of
experimental work done on the way in which people behave in
artificial groups set up in the psychological laboratory, and a
general review is given of such work and of the principal findings
in the study of 'group dynamics'. An account is also given of
groups of a more temporary nature, such as crowds, prison
communities, and brain-washing meetings. These studies are
relevant to the meaning of the expression 'Man is a social animal'.
The author shows that man derives his specifically human nature
from his social relationships, and discusses the present-day
problem of satisfying social needs in a world of impersonal
contacts. The dangers of over-socialization are also pointed out.

Freud and the Post-Freudians

J. A. C. Brown

Freud and the Post-Freudians explains the main concepts of Freudian psychology and goes on to review the theories of Adler, Jung, Rank and Stekel. Later developments in the orthodox Freudian school are discussed, as are those of the American Neo-Freudians and the Post-Freudians in England. This is the first book published in Britain to bring together all these psychological and sociological schools and criticize them, both from the Freudian standpoint and that of the scientific psychologists.